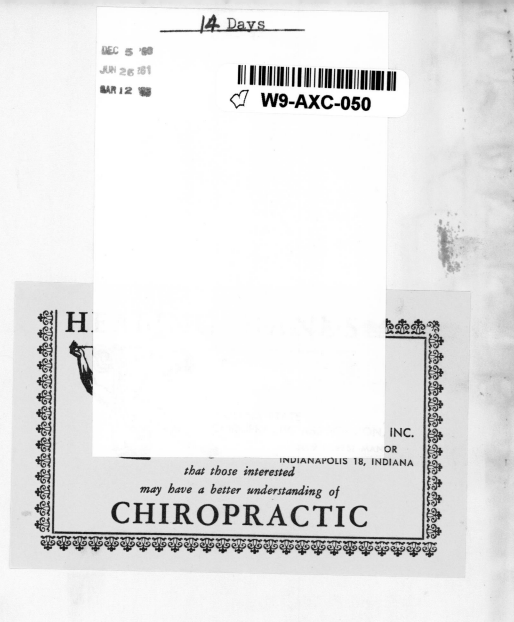

H INC.
OR
INDIANAPOLIS 18, INDIANA

that those interested
may have a better understanding of

CHIROPRACTIC

HEALING HANDS

by
Joseph E. Maynard D.C.

Here is the thrilling human drama that had to be told. It's the inside story of Chiropractic and the men responsible for it. It's the story of the struggle of Mankind for survival replayed in the lives of two men— Daniel David Palmer and Bartlett Joshua Palmer, father and son.

This biography is everything you can ask of the greatest in fiction...yet it's true. There's adventure, raw, human emotion, fighting courage, tragedy and the struggles of two soldiers fighting millions to win a battle of belief.

But the story is more than all this. It's the fight for recognition of a new, scientific method of healing. The story begins with the life of D. D. Palmer, an uninhibited individualist, an intellect whose mind sought out the "new" idea. Only such a man could discover Chiropractic—the science which cures by hand. It tells of his pioneering struggle to preserve and protect his science only to die—mentally and physically sick— before he knew that Chiropractic would not follow him to the grave.

But his life-long belief that the body can cure its own "dis-ease" did not die. The son, B. J. Palmer, picked up the seed and harvested a new professional field. It was not easy. He had to face hordes of scoffers; he had to fight the so-called scientists whose thinking couldn't reach beyond yesterday; he had to live through three trials on trumped up charges that he murdered his father.

He twice faced revolt among his Chiropractic students; he many times was the victim of outright hate.

But B. J. Palmer, the apostle of the new science, fought them all and placed Chiropractic in its rightful place amongst healing arts.

The story covers the evolution of Chiropractic and the revolution of two men.

DANIEL DAVID PALMER
DISCOVERER OF CHIROPRACTIC

HEALING HANDS

THE STORY OF THE PALMER FAMILY, DISCOVERERS AND DEVELOPERS OF CHIROPRACTIC

by

JOSEPH E. MAYNARD D. C.

President, Long Island Chiropractic Center Inc.
Managing Director of Precision X Ray Laboratories
President, Body Engineering Institute of America

"O God, give us serenity to accept what cannot be changed, courage to change what should be changed and wisdom to distinguish the one from the other."
Composed By Dr. Reinhold Niebuhr

JONORM PUBLISHING COMPANY

FREEPORT • LONG ISLAND • N.Y.

Edited By

B. J. Palmer, D.C., Ph.C.
Developer of Chiropractic
author-philosopher, scientist, artist, builder.

President, The Palmer School Of Chiropractic Inc.
Davenport, Iowa

President, Tri-City Broadcasting Co., Inc. Station WOC-AM-FM-TV
Davenport, Iowa

President, Central Broadcasting Co., Station WHO-AM-FM-TV
Des Moines, Iowa

President, International Chiropractors Association
Davenport, Iowa

President, The B. J. Palmer Associates, Inc.
Davenport, Iowa

President, Sterocolor, Inc.
Davenport, Iowa

Owner, Clear View Mental Sanitarium
Davenport, Iowa

Director, The B. J. Palmer Chiropractic Research Clinic
Davenport, Iowa

Director, Circus Hall of Fame
Sarasota, Florida

Member, Board, Circus Hall of Fame, Inc.
Sarasota, Florida

Dedicated to .....

The memory of my father

Dr. Leonard Edward Maynard

September 4, 1881 — July 24, 1959

IN APPRECIATION OF

UNIVERSAL INTELLIGENCE, who brought Mother Catherine and Father Leonard Maynard into wedlock, and who gave their first Son (the author), the influence and guidance for which he will be forever grateful. To my wife, Norma, for her continuing inspiration and influence.

To Daniel David Palmer who pioneered in the development of Chiropractic as a means of benefitting humanity, and to his son, B. J. Palmer, who harvested the seeds his Father had sown by developing the greatest method of drugless healing Man has ever known.

To Chiropractor Ralph Braids, Class of 1918, Palmer School of Chiropractic, who inspired the author to follow a career in Chiropractic.

And to Chiropractor Norman E. Starcke and his wife, Mary, (Apple) for the association which through the years has given the author a more extended meaning of the word "Love."

ACKNOWLEDGEMENT

I'D like to acknowledge my thanks to Martin Abramson, well-known author and magazine writer, for his valuable editorial advice and suggestions. . . .

CONTENTS

BOOK I

BOOK II

CONTENTS ix

PREFACE

THERE ARE MANY REASONS why a book is written. This author has been practicing Chiropractic for a number of years and has seen many cases which were given up as medical failures, but were able to regain their health through the values of chiropractic. The purpose of "Healing Hands" is to convey the knowledge of the value of Chiropractic and how and where to obtain its health benefits.

If even one person who needs the help of Chiropractic is stimulated to seek that help as a result of reading "Healing Hands," then we can call the book a huge success. When first bringing the idea for this book to B. J. Palmer several years ago, his reaction was: "Whether the book glorifies me or not, does not matter—its main purpose is to introduce Chiropractic to people who need it, but who because of suspicion, rumors and halftruths, will not seek the help it can give."

In writing the book, "Healing Hands," your author is deeply grateful for the assistance given him by Dr. B. J. Palmer. Dr. Palmer is the only authority who could verify the historical accuracy of the history of Chiropractic. Further, in no instance throughout the years did B.J., when checking the manuscript, suggest as to what the author should or should not write. His only insistence was that the material in the book confine itself strictly to the absolute historical facts. Were it not for the understanding cooperation of Dr. B. J. Palmer, "Healing Hands" could not have become a reality.

The author feels that each person, who has been benefitted by chiropractic methods, should then, as a humanitarian, spread the message of chiropractic values to their friends and relatives. It is further hoped that "Healing Hands" will stimulate organizations throughout the world toward understanding the great role Chiropractic plays in healing the sick. It is the author's dream to see this great nation of ours through a

xi

combine of health authorities in every field of science, contribute toward a disease free World.

Should such a sincere and realistic effort be considered by any reader of the book: "Healing Hands," and should any reader require further scientific appreciation of Chiropractic, the author suggests contacting Dr. B. J. Palmer at the B. J. Palmer Research Clinic, Davenport, Iowa.

JOSEPH E. MAYNARD D.C.

AUTHOR'S FOREWORD

THE NAME PALMER and the word Chiropractic belong together for they are as oxygen is to life.

Without Daniel David Palmer, the discoverer, this scientific method of correcting the cause of dis-ease by hand may never have been developed to save the lives of so many sick, medically-disappointed, people.

It took an uninhibited individualist, an intellect whose mind could accept a radical, "new" idea; it took a strong, determined man who could not be defeated by the scorn of his fellows, by the clogged, rusty thinking of so-called "scientists." It took a pioneer.

It took such a man as Daniel David Palmer to give the world Chiropractic . . . a principle based on the belief that the body can cure its own dis-ease.

And it took D. D. Palmer's son, Bartlett Joshua Palmer, the apostle of this new science, to take up where his father left off and fight those who sought to stop Man from benefiting from Chiropractic.

He fought and he won. Today, less than sixty-three years since the inception of the idea, Chiropractic is achieving its rightful place as a cure for man's ills.

In Davenport, Iowa, there stands a museum: a monument to the men, a testimonial to the science. That museum stands for the suffering, the humiliation the men had to bear to achieve their goal.

To understand this relatively new science, we must understand the men who gave birth to it and nursed through its crises.

To do that, we must start at the beginning. . . .

BOOK I

1

ONE OF EIGHT

IT WAS A FEW MINUTES before the dawn of March 7, 1845. Snow was packed solid against the wood-rotted log cabin. Smoke, which curled from the chimney, was the only evidence that life existed in this remote region, a few miles east of Toronto, Canada.

A wail broke the silence and a female voice shouted, "It's a boy. Thomas Palmer, you got yourself a handsome son."

Thomas Palmer picked up his ax and walked down the familiar back path to a clump of trees where he had spotted a tall hemlock out of which a cradle would be hewn for the new born—Daniel David Palmer. Chopping down a tree, skinning off the bark and carving a cradle was a family ritual. It was done for all eight Palmer children.

The father, a big, raw-boned frontier shoemaker of English and German extraction, had explained to his tiny wife Catherine, "Each of my children is going to start out in life owning something of his own. I am not a rich man. I live off the Earth and the Earth will give my children their first gift."

She had agreed then when she was only a bride. Their children would have something of their own to start out with, but they would have to work for whatever else they got.

The Palmers lived a rugged life. Their children learned early that

1

they must stand on their own two feet; their hands became calloused before many Winters had passed.

Catherine prided herself on the fact that she had eight strong normal children. They all looked much alike dressed in their hand-sewn clothing. Thomas was proud that they all resembled him in some way.

"They're all peas out of the same pod," he'd bellow as he patted one or the other on the head, "all eight of them."

And although Daniel was one of those eight, it became evident he wasn't like the other seven. The other seven were strong normal children; Dan too was strong, but he was well above normal in thinking capabilities, ambitions and dreams which could become reality. Dan was like the other seven insofar as he did daily chores with the others, but he was never too busy working to overlook the things about him. From his first awakening to Nature, Dan was fascinated by the wonder of it. He would hesitate during the working day to wonder why the birds made sounds which sounded like music, he would puzzle over the wetness of the grass when there had been no rain the night before. He listened and watched, made mental notes and wondered about Nature. One thing that caused him contemplation was why it snowed in Winter and not in Summer.

But Summer was the season he liked the best. The ground was uncovered and he could spend any free time, after his chores were done, looking for the skeletons of animals that had perished during the long coldness. While his sisters and brothers played with homemade toys on rainy days, Dan would take out his bone collection, tie the bones together in proper articulation and try to figure out how animals walked and why the spine always seemed to be the main support of their bodies.

"Why," the youth would think, "doesn't everybody in our house get sick when one of us does? We all eat the same things.

"What makes one animal strong and another sick?"

One night as he pondered these questions he heard his mother say, "I'm sorry, Tom; I just have a headache. It's been with me all day."

He went to her bed where she lay suffering and massaged her brow. After 15 minutes, the pain subsided.

"You have magic in your hands, son," his mother told him.

After that Dan comforted anyone who felt sick in the family; he never thought it strange that the family went to him for comfort.

If he found a bird or an animal with a broken bone, he made splints out of twigs and cloth and applied them to the creature; the bones always mended. His mother was even more positive that her son had magic in his hands. Dan knew that without his bone collection he would never have known how the framework was constructed.

Young Dan grew into a short stocky young man. He was not athletic and he wasted little time trying to develop muscles. His strongest belief was, "The body takes care of itself."

As a man, Daniel David Palmer did not drink, chew tobacco, smoke or swear, although in his later years, he developed the habit of sipping a little port with his evening meals.

He didn't play checkers, cards or dominoes, which were the parlor games of his era. He had no interest in sports or gambling.

While others "wasted" time, Dan devoted himself to reading books which would add to his knowledge of the human body. He was a voracious reader.

Dan might have spent more years with his parents, priming his mind with reading, but soon after his twentieth birthday, the Civil War broke out in the United States. Many American men of draft age slipped into Canada and flooded the Canadian labor market. The resulting employment problem drove Dan from home.

On April 3, 1865, Dan and his brother Tom decided to seek greener pastures. With the money they had saved, they packed their carpet bags and headed south on foot. Their first day brought them 18 miles to a town called Whitney. A month later they arrived in Buffalo, New York. There, they bought passage to Detroit, Michigan. That took their last bit of money.

It was dark when they reached Detroit. The boys slept on grain sacks on a nearby pier and breakfasted on a persimmon they found on the dock. They searched for transportation out of Detroit. At a railroad station they met the commander of a military train, and the boys talked themselves into a ride to Chicago with the Army troops.

Neither cared too much for Chicago; Tom wanted to go further west, Dan preferred Illinois. They parted promising to keep in touch with each other.

Dan's travels carried him to New Boston, Illinois, where he found a job, and later married his first wife. He bought his own home, a small farm with a forest of young locust trees and became a bee-keeper. Business prospered. Dan became one of the biggest honey raisers in the country. He was happy, his wife bore him a son and a daughter; he was successful. At the end of each year he took a load of honey to New York and came home $5,000 richer. Quite a fortune . . . then.

The world seemed to be his. Then tragedy struck; his beloved wife died. Dan could not be consoled for weeks. He lost interest in the business and the children and the things around him.

Dan's world rested in the grave beside the sweet face of his wife.

Slowly he became reaware of the world about him. He shook off the weight of grief, but he knew happiness was not to be found in New Boston with his wife gone. He could no longer live in the house he had built for her without her; he sold the farm and moved to What Cheer, Iowa—where his brother had settled.

Tom was the owner and publisher of "The What Cheer Patriot," a weekly newspaper. Soon after Tom came to What Cheer, he had sent for the rest of the family.

Dan found Tom going about business heedless of brother Bart, the town loafer; heedless of his sister Verne, who filled the house with the stink of the black cigars she smoked. But Dan, like Tom, was a man who could take care of himself and his family's idiosyncrasies didn't bother him.

After finding a place to live and someone to keep an eye on the children, Daniel set out to find a business of his own. Not knowing if he'd like What Cheer, he did not want to invest his capital in just anything.

He spent a few days walking around town and talking to people. He found there was an open market for selling fish. It was a food most people ate and there was little or no competition because it was scarce in this area. The distance to either of the United States' coasts made it difficult to obtain.

Dan procured a contract with a Mr. Barr who lived in Davenport, Iowa, right on the Mississippi River. Since this was a natural port and shipped merchandise landed here, Dan figured he had a pretty good thing, but he wasn't sure if people would take to his new venture. He did not want to risk his money to outfit and rent a store; he had to find another way to sell his goods.

He thought about it and finally came up with the idea of a special wheelbarrow, which he designed and built himself. This wheelbarrow had compartments to hold fish and ice. The fish would be transported in boxes of ice by Mr. Barr from Davenport to What Cheer, and Dan, with his wheelbarrow picked the fish up at the train depot. Never missing a trick, Dan made sure he got all the remaining ice along with his fish.

Now that he was in business, he knew he would need some sort of signal to announce to the people on his route that he was there. He purchased a horn. Its toot became known as the calling card of Dan, the fish man.

The first time he travelled one route in a better part of town, he came upon an especially nice-looking house. He stopped outside the gate and tooted his horn. Not long after an upstairs window opened and a beautiful woman, sleep in her eyes, peered out.

"What, my dear man," the woman asked, "are you tooting that horn for?"

"I am the fish man, ma'm. I have all kinds——."

"I happen not to be interested in what kinds of fish you have. I am, however, interested in getting my proper rest. You will do me a great service in the future by not blowing that horn and waking me."

This seemed strange. No one slept until noon. Everyone he knew was out of bed for hours unless they were sick.

"I am terribly sorry, ma'am, I——"

"Have I your promise that you'll refrain from blowing that thing under my window?" she asked.

"Yes ma'am," he said.

"Then I forgive you this time."

Dan suddenly became aware that she had a Southern accent.

"Do you come from the South?" he asked as she was about to close the window.

"Yes, I do. In the South people of culture sleep late. Just because I'm in Iowa doesn't mean I should discontinue the habit."

Dan tipped his hat, mumbled another apology and went on his way. He turned several times to stare at her window; she wasn't there, of course; she was back in bed, but he was intrigued by her. She popped into his head all day as he went along his route. Her beauty and culture were something to marvel at; Dan had never met people of her class before.

He found himself thinking more and more about her that week. The next week as he approached her house, his heart thumped loudly. He made it a point not to toot his horn unless he felt the distance was out of her hearing. He had hopes that she would call him one morning and buy fish from him, but she never did.

Not too long after his meeting with the beautiful Southern lady he got to see her more closely. He was sitting in Tom's newspaper shop when the woman walked in. She inquired of Tom about advertising rates. She wished to sell her home furnishings.

Dan stood and walked closer towards the two.

"Oh, this is Dan. This young lady, Dan, has graced our fair city with her presence for quite a while. This is my brother. He—"

"We have not met under too pleasant circumstances, I fear." She smiled a beautiful white smile. "I'm sorry for my behavior that morning, Mr. Palmer, a woman is never at her best when she first awakens."

She thanked Dan for discontinuing his tooting after she had told him it was disturbing to her.

"Quite all right, Miss." He hoped to get another smile from her.

She turned to Tom.

"Tom, do you know of a refined boarding house where I might find lodging? If I sell my furniture, I shall need a place to live."

"Is there room in your boarding house, Dan?"

"It just so happens that my housekeeper is leaving town. I might make arrangements to get you those quarters if you find them suitable."

"You're very kind."

She took the address and said she would call after her furnishings were sold.

She moved into adjoining quarters shortly thereafter. She and Dan, none to Dan's regret, became friendly. She immediately liked Dan's children.

"Who cares for them since your housekeeper left?" she asked.

Dan felt the selling of her furniture indicated that she was pressed for money. He had thought about asking her to watch the children, but he was fearful. Suppose she was insulted? He ventured to ask her anyway.

"I would love to," she said. She showered him with a smile. "Suppose we start now?"

She helped him put the children into bed and stayed for a cup of tea. As they sat and drank their tea, he told her something of himself and she told him of herself.

She told him of her home life in Louisiana on the large family plantation. Her early years were soft and wonderful; she and her family had love and fun.

"And then," she continued with that soft drawl, "the Civil War disrupted our lives. Daddy and my brother were killed fighting and it broke Mommy's heart. She died not too long after they did, but I guess I was lucky in one way. My plantation wasn't totally destroyed as so many were; I still got a pretty good price for the house and plantation when I sold them. Under other conditions I could have sold the 900 slaves, instead I had to free them.

"If my family was still alive, I might still be in Louisiana. It's hard to be on the losing side of the war without a family. I came up North and chose this town for no other reason the name, What Cheer. I've been here for a few years now and I have seen my money, the little I had from the sale of the plantation, dwindle. Time has a way of eating into your savings when your source of income is lost so the money didn't last, no matter how far I tried to stretch it."

Dan sat at the edge of his chair as she talked. He liked the way her "I"s sounded like "ah"s. She looked lovely in the lamplight.

She glanced at him and something in his face made her say, "I do not want you to feel disturbed about having asked me to watch your children and take care of your house. I am really quite grateful that I can do this for you. I was never trained for employment, I never thought I would have need of it. Being a woman, though, with natural maternal instinct and maternal tendencies, I know I will do a good job of watching the children for you."

As time passed, they became fond of one another. They often sat and talked most of the night and early morning hours away. Dan was still intrigued by her culture and charm. When he felt he knew her well enough and long enough, he summoned all his courage and asked her to marry him. She accepted without hesitating.

There was some talk about town that Dan was marrying her so he would have a housekeeper without wages. Dan denied these accusations whenever he heard them. He had always made enough money to take care of his children, a home and housekeepers.

As he told Tom after the wedding announcement, "I am lonely and I believe man was made for woman and woman for man. A man should have a wife and a home, and children should not be deprived of a mother."

The Palmers were all happy for Dan. At the sound of weddings and funerals, the Palmers always felt a surge in their veins; they weren't close but they did have the same inherent tendencies.

They were married. Everything seemed to be going well. Dan's home life was taken care of and business was going well.

"Dan, dear," his bride said one night as they sat before the fire, "I don't want to sound like a snob, but why don't you find another business?"

"What is wrong with the fish market?" he asked in a strained voice.

"Not a thing, Dan; it makes you a good honest living, but Dan, you aren't *any* man. Any man would be content with fish peddling; you are not suited to it."

Dan thought about it. He pondered the businesses he could go into. After all, now that he was married, he would settle down in What Cheer and he should find something more suitable.

Having decided upon going into the grocery store business, Dan made arrangements for a good store location. He rented a store and furnished it with proper provisions. Since the type of business he was in never bothered Dan as long as the business was successful, Dan soon made a success of his grocery business.

Not as successful as his business was his home life. His wife had borne him three children, two girls and a boy, but she did not live up to his conception of a dutiful wife. In her he had a lady of culture and breeding, but that did not get the housework done. Dan's love for any woman never overruled his judgment of her duties as a wife. One of the objections he had was that she could never break her habit of sleeping until noon. Another very strong objection was her insistence upon having toddies in bed before breakfast, a habit she had become accustomed to when in the South and which she continued in the North.

"They may be 'toddies' to you," he accused during one of their many arguments, "but to me, liquor is liquor, no matter what you call it or what you add to it."

To his insinuation of "drunkard," he soon added the words "lazy," "indolent" and "incompetent."

While Dan's second wife was doing her drinking, she was nursing their son Bartlett Joshua Palmer, who acquired a taste for liquor in his mother's milk. When he was weaned he still had a taste for it and his cries were loud and long until his mother began giving him a few drops from her bottle each morning.

It took Dan a while to realize what was going on. When he did, he was enraged. As Bart howled for his morning toddy one day, Dan's self-control left him. He grabbed a pint of whiskey and gave Bart his needs; then he poured the rest of the pint down the infant's throat. Being a small frontier town, everyone in What Cheer soon heard of the whiskey incident and loud voices proclaimed that if the eighteen-month-old boy died, Daniel Palmer's neck would be stretched so that he might share the infant's grave.

This was ironic for later, much later, Bartlett Joshua Palmer was tried three times in Grand Jury hearings on the charge of having murdered Daniel D. Palmer, his father.

2

THE MAGNETIC HEALER

WITH A BIOGRAPHER'S hind-sight, it may now be said the time is ripe for D. D. Palmer to mark his place in history.

His problems developed his character. His extensive reading opened his mind and made him prone to acceptance of "radical" ideas.

His second marriage ended with his wife's early death. His bitterness at her eccentricities subsided. His irritation toward her laziness faded. He gathered his family and fled to Letts, Iowa.

There he gained a job teaching school, calling upon his experience and informal education as a guide. For additional income he studied Phrenology, the science of the brain concerned with moral, intellectual and sensual dispositions of the individual which are supposed to be indicated by the undulations of the cranium. He toured the surrounding communities lecturing on the subject.

And here begins his destiny. While on one of his tours, he met Paul Caster, an internationally known magnetic healer. Dan's eager mind forced his inquiry into the subject. He talked to Caster and made an appointment to visit his office.

The office walls were adorned with crutches, canes and braces. The explanation: "I devised a method where, by rubbing and slapping the entire body of a sick patient, I imparted my magnetism. It cured the sick," Caster explained.

A scene flashed in Dan's mind. He was back in the log-cabin in Canada. His mother lay before him, her head throbbing with pain. Dan placed his hand on her head and the pain and throbbing was slowly erased. Was this magnetism? Did he have the ability within him to cure?

He did! He was convinced he did. He decided to study under Caster to learn the method of magnetic healing and to sublimate the frustration of a third romance.

Dan had been courting a pretty young lady, Molly Hudler. But his courting was with the caution of a man hurt by personal tragedy. He fought the impulse of asking her to marry him. He hesitated; he rationalized and he lost Molly to another man.

Beaten, bitter, depressed by loneliness, he packed and moved to Burlington, Iowa, where he became a student of Paul Caster.

He learned quickly and soon opened his own healing office in Burlington. Business was slow. He was in competition with his teacher; certainly not a good business policy. He decided to find a new location and open for business.

He wrote his friends explaining his idea. He heard from Mr. Barr, the man from whom he had bought his fish years earlier.

Barr suggested he set up in Davenport. Why not? Wasn't it one of the Tri-Cities of Davenport, Iowa, Rock Island and Moline, Illinois? The location appealed to Dan Palmer, the newly-learned magnetic healer.

Once again Dan packed up his family and moved to set up a new home . . . this one much different than the others. Barr showed Dan an office on the second floor of the Ryan Block, big enough for his practice and with rooms for living quarters. Dan liked it and rented it.

He set up the interior for his family and got ready for business. The first order of business was to have his name painted on the door. He hired a sign painter to paint "Dr. Palmer."*

When finished, Dan stepped back to gaze at it. He smiled. A day during his stay in Letts filled his memory. A spiritualist had visualized a similar door in Dan's future with the words "Dr. Palmer" painted on it. She said that he one day would lecture in a large hall telling an audience about a new, "revolutionary" method of healing the sick. Dan laughed . . . then. The vision had struck him as ridiculous. Now here it was—"Dr. Palmer"—painted on a door.

As for the second part of the prediction, it later proved to be true.

Dan, the independent thinker, the uninhibited man whose intellect was ready for new fields to conquer, expanded on magnetic healing. He had no preconceived opinions on healing. He figured out a method of treating the body. Instead of rubbing and slapping the body all over, treat the organ that is sick. Why bother with the whole body when the

* In those days a healer had the right to assume the title "Doctor."

problem may rest with the liver or stomach or lungs? Throw the magnetic strength in one organ.

With this in mind, Dan had his patients lie on their backs on a comfortable coach and then proceeded to place one hand over the sick organ and the other hand on the back under the organ involved. Holding both hands still he would then pour his personal magnetism from his positive right to his negative left hand. He would give 15 minute treatments of this type.

His office opened for business at 8 A.M. and he practiced till noon. He then took a two hour break; an hour for lunch and an hour for his siesta which he felt replenished his body with magnetism so he could continue his practice and appointments in the afternoon.

Dan would storm and rage if anyone dared to awaken him during his siesta. He justified awakening only in case of fire or death.

As his practice developed, his groping mind sought answers to questions:

· Why was one organ sick and the rest of the body well?
· Was this one organ weak? If so, why?
· Was it because one organ was not getting its normal strength? If so, why wasn't it?
· Was it because of a lack of nerve supply? If so, why?

He reasoned there was a reserve supply in the body but not in the sick organ. If so, why wasn't it getting its supply from the brain to the body? Somewhere between brain and body there must be a damming backward with a starving supply forward. If so, why?

Where was the stoppage? Eventually, in ten years of research and studying the spine and the nerves, Dan reasoned out Vertebral Subluxation.

But while figuring out answers to the many questions, he had a practice to take care of and a life to live. One of his patients was a woman, Villa Thomas, niece of General Thomas of Civil War fame at the Battle of Nashville, Tennessee.

Villa was paralytic in the lower limbs. She had to crawl up stairs on her hands and knees to visit Dan's office for treatment. In time, when she regained her ability to walk, Dan courted her. He asked, for a third time, a woman to become his wife. She accepted. And in spite of a growing business and his aging family, Dan married.

This marriage brought Dan to the brink of Hell. It was hurtful to Dan, harmful to his business and it scarred the minds of his children for life.

Villa Thomas, unknown to Dan when he married her, was a dope addict. Without the "junk" she was the devil's fury; with it, she was an angel's joy. She was the female counterpart of Dr. Jekyll and Mr. Hyde.

Dan's business at this time had so prospered that he had taken over the entire top floor of the Ryan Block, consisting of 42 rooms. He worked out a deal whereby he sent his patients across the street to eat. There they could get 21 meals for $3 a week. Because the food was of poor quality and often in Winter it was unpleasant for his patients to go across the street, Dan established a kitchen and dining room in what he now called his Magnetic Infirmary.

And while business prospered, his wife's inconsiderate behavior steadily grew worse. She made him set aside a private table for their meals.

(It was about this time that Dan acquired the habit of taking a bit of bread, rolling it between his fingers until it grew as small as a pea. He did this unconsciously, while he meditated.)

Dan's children were not permitted to eat at the same table as he and his wife. At his wife's insistence, they were forced to eat in the kitchen with the colored cooks and waiters. The help always sat down to eat, but limited space in the kitchen forced young Bart and his two sisters to stand.

By orders of Villa, the children were not permitted to eat dessert. The help, though, could eat all the ice cream, cake and pudding they wanted to.

Imagine the impression made on the minds of young children? The injustice of it? The young minds could not accept this unfair situation and devised ways to get around it.

And it wasn't hard. The children were well known by the town's people. And Bart, an energetic and bright youngster, was the leader whenever it came to pranks of mischief.

When everyone had gone to bed, Bart and his sisters would raid the icebox. Everything was fine until one night one of the colored help caught them and reported the incident to Villa. She told Dan and the children received one of the worst beatings of their lives.

Beatings were not uncommon to the children. In the years during their growth the beatings took place frequently and people who knew what was going on would periodically have Dan arrested and locked up for the night.

Bart, to this day, has a fractured lower vertebra and a curvature because of these beatings.

But to hold Dan responsible for inhuman conduct wouldn't be completely fair. Dan was deeply involved in reading, writing and researching his new theories. He had little time for the children. In addition, his wife's fury when without dope frayed his nerves and put a keen edge on his temper. And then, Bart was no angel. . . .

There was that one day when Bart came home from the grocery with a basket of ten dozen eggs . . . most of them broken. Bart's explanation to his father was, "That's the way the grocer gave 'em to me."

Dan took Bart and the eggs, stormed into John Eagle's store, and demanded to know why the grocer palmed off the eggs on Bart. The grocer denied the charge, saying the eggs were whole when Bart left the store.

The father looked at the son, hesitated, then left the store. Once home he asked for the true story.

Bart was trapped: "You know that long iron grating in front of the Western Union Building, the one worn smooth?" Bart said, "Well the snow made it nice and slippery, so I decided to try and slide over it.

"I fell and broke the eggs and I was afraid to tell 'cause I thought you'd give me a beating."

And Bart that night did feel the heavy hand of justice enforcing a law of his father's house: "I won't stand for my children lying," was Dan's edict.

Dan's uninhibited nature didn't know the meaning of embarrassment. One day Bart's sister Jessie had forgotten to empty one of the potties of a patient in the infirmary.

When her carelessness was reported to Dan, he immediately went to the high school where Jessie attended class, and marched boldly into the auditorium.

He asked the teacher for permission to address Jessie and the 400 other children in the auditorium.

His voice boomed out. "I want my daughter Jessie to come home and empty the pottie she forgot to empty this morning," and then he walked out, confident he had taught his daughter a lesson.

He had humiliated his daughter then and many more times before she was eighteen. Acts such as this drove each of his daughters out of the house to make a living any way they could.

But the peculiarities of Dan's nature weren't contained within the family. The neighbors also felt the brunt of it.

In those early days, Dan's magnetic cure and infirmary was on the corner of Brady and Second streets. The front room, which was used as a reception room, was at the street intersection. In those days in the Tenderloin District (skid row), the Salvation Army would regularly conduct parades, which would end up under his reception room.

Dan hated the racket. He complained to the police and the mayor but got no satisfaction. He took matters in his own hands. When the Salvation Army gathered below, he'd throw buckets of water on them. They, in turn, would forgive him and go on playing.

Dan was at his wit's end when the big idea hit. Bart had always wanted to play the piano. Why not get a piano, put it by the window, and let Bart practice and his wife screech? And that's what he did.

So Bart played "The Holy City" while his wife gargled out "Jesus Lover of My Soul" while the Salvation Army tooted their cornets, banged on their drums and sang their songs. And the crowds gathered to watch the "doings." If nothing else, the circus got Dan free advertising. The people wondered about who was trying to save who from what. Dan got nick-named "The Healer of the Discordant Ills of the Sick."

But more and more people discovered the wonder of magnetic healing.

3

THE PERSECUTION OF BART

WHILE BUILDING UP HIS PRACTICE, Dan searched for ways to make an extra dollar. He decided to buy and sell goldfish. He bought them by the thousands, but storage became a problem. So Dan took Bart's bedroom away from him, and put him into another room. Dan converted Bart's bedroom into a big aquarium. He designed two big cypress wood tanks, 12 feet long, 6 feet wide and one foot deep, putting one on top of the other. Dan made contacts to buy small fish from breeders in Iowa, Indiana and Maryland. Being an original and independent thinker, he arrived at a new idea for shipping of fish . . . an idea which is used by the fish industry to this day.

In those days shippers of live fish used deep milk cans in the belief that the fish need much water. Dan's thoughts were that live fish needed more oxygen with more water surface. He drew up a design for a type of low shipping can. The new cans increased the water surface by three times and reduced the quantity of water by two-thirds. This cut down express charges in shipping and also made it possible to ship twice as many fish with less fish dying en route. The can Dan designed is still in use today.

Dan put Bart in charge of what he called "the fish room." Bart had dip nets, glass bowls of various sizes and fish food for sale. Mornings when he was not going to school, it was his job to go downstairs and onto

15

the sidewalk in front of the entrance to their office building with colored chalks to work out signs and designs. One which Bart used a great deal was, "Two goldfish for 5¢ apiece." People would come up and ask for two goldfish for a nickel. When Bart tried to explain that they were a nickel apiece, they would often get mad and call him a liar. He would take them downstairs and prove they were 5¢ apiece. People usually bought the fish.

Dan had many peculiarities which he could not explain. One was that if he was in close proximity of a person in pain, regardless of what part of the body the pain was in, making no difference whether the pain was excruciating or dull, Dan would get the same kind and degree of pain in the same place the person had the pain.

Sometimes Dan would double up with a sudden attack. He found that if he told another person about the pain, it would leave him immediately. If he remained silent about the pain, it lingered until he did tell someone about it. Was this some sort of telepathy other than telepathy as we know and use the term? Was it sympathy between patient and doctor? Was it similar to the prospective father who has morning sickness? No one can tell, but the pains were real.

As amazing as Dan's sympathy pains, so was his ritual in the post office. Before going for the mail, he rose early and drank cream which enabled him to think; then, he walked to the post office to pick up his mail.

"There is a letter for me here from O. G. Adams, Dubuque, Iowa, that was mailed yesterday. It has your postmark as of 3:00 P.M.; would you get it for me?" Dan told the clerk.

The clerk stared at him. Sheer amazement registered in his face. He got the letter, handed the envelope to Dan who, holding the sealed letter flat against his forehead, read it. He read the entire letter, exactly as it was written, handed it back to the astonished postal clerk and had the clerk open it and verify the accuracy of his reading. On such occasions, Dan was always 100 percent correct down to the signature, and including misspelled words.

But even with such ability Dan could not foresee Bart's actions. Bart, attending high school, was still much the prankster. He decided to bring to school a few companions one day . . . three live mice, which he carried in a cigar box. The principal, J. R. Baldwin, immediately expelled him. (This same teacher, in later years, enrolled in the Palmer school and studied under Bart. And from a boy whom he had expelled, Baldwin learned a science which he placed above all his other learnings.)

There was no schooling in the immediate future for Bart after his expulsion from high school. He decided to get a job . . . not so much because he wanted to, but because he knew his father's feelings on the matter. His first job was as a delivery boy in a Davenport department store.

"Hi," Bart's boss, decided that one of Bart's special deliveries should be made to certain addresses in the Tenderloin District. This part of town, skid row, had many houses of prostitution in it. On this first delivery Bart had been appalled. After knocking on the door a raspy, throaty voice told him to come in. He opened the door to a stench which suffocated him. The room was filthy, clothes were strewn everywhere, partially full whiskey bottles were on the floor, dirty beer and whiskey glasses were thrown around the room.

Bart untied the packages as per the woman's instructions and tried to leave.

"Wait, sonny," she said, "I ain't paid you yet."

Before his young eyes she removed her dirty housecoat, under which she wore nothing, and tried on the merchandise. Bart felt slightly sick.

She made her selection. She picked up a pair of men's trousers and went through the pockets methodically. Bart realized the pants belonged to the naked, hung over form of a man on the bed.

She took his money and paid Bart the C.O.D. charges. Bart took the money and ran.

"Hi" always sent Bart to the houses of prostitution with special deliveries and the boy was filled with revulsion. He preferred not to go to those houses, but he was afraid to refuse. Later he was glad he had made deliveries there . . . the houses taught him many things. But in the beginning he saw the girls only as filthy dwellers in a dirty house. If he had seen them in the evening after their baths with their faces made up, he may have had a different impression.

They represented all the lewdness of the morning after the night before.

One of the madames, to whom Bart had occasional deliveries to make, was Lottie. Bart was No. 52, Special Delivery boy of the H. A. St. Onge & Co. Department store, who had all the business from this district.

Years later, when a professional man, on Top of Brady St. Hill, at 808 Brady St., the now B. J. Palmer, Chiropractor, received a call from Lottie.

"Doctor, my mother living on a farm out of Williamsburg, Iowa, had a stroke a few days ago. They don't expect her to live. Will you go out and see her and do what you can?"

Assuring her that he would, the only train he could take on the Rock Island Lines was at 4 P.M. which would take him to a station about 15 miles from the farm.

Lottie told B.J. she would have her brother drive in and pick him up at about 6 P.M.

Boarding the train at Davenport, the day-coach was full except for one double seat. To B.J.'s surprise who was there but Lottie. B.J. took the other seat.

The brother met Lottie and B.J., they went to the farm. B.J. studied her mother's case, gave her an adjustment. At retiring time, Lottie said: "I have only one other double bed here. You lie down and sleep until 4 A.M. when we will call you, you can check mother, brother will drive you to town so you can catch the 5 A.M. train back for Davenport."

Upon leaving, B.J. jokingly said to Lottie: "I have slept on ONE-HALF of that bed so-far, YOU can sleep on the other half the rest of the night."

Upon returning home B.J. jokingly told Mrs. Palmer, "Lottie and I slept in the SAME BED last night." Her answer was, Well, what of it!

However that wasn't all B.J. was to hear from that experience. Business men and other Davenport people on the train saw Lottie and B.J. seated and talking together. It wasn't long until he got smirks and smiles, backhanded several times.

It illustrates ONE lesson. Gossip is usually the destructive ONE-HALF of all the FACTS. If the OTHER HALF was known, it reverses bad into good.

Bart often wished other boys could see these creatures, he hesitated to call them women, as he did. He was sure they would not have patronized them. The girls were neither glamorous nor enticing.

What kind of girls were they?

After many deliveries Bart found he must revise his opinion about the girls who earned their living in these houses. He found most of them kind, thoughtful and generous. They were always willing to hand out money for any worthy cause; they were generally quiet and serious and, he found, they read a lot, trying to gain an education in the hopes of keeping others out of the racket they were in.

He never knew of them trying to drag anyone in. Bart found the gals different from the public's conception of them. Many of them were mothers of dearly loved children, others supported aged parents.

One person who stands out vividly in Bart's memory of those days is a man by the name of Ned Lee. He ran the mission in the Tenderloin District. Ned's financial support came from the houses of prostitution, not from respectable people and churches in the city.

Ned Lee rented a building and fixed it up for the kids of the district. The children met and played games here rather then searching for mischief on dark streets. He revolutionized the kids of the alleys. (In return for Ned's kindnesses Bart arranged for the Davenport department store to give unsold, odd-sized and damaged goods to Ned Lee's mission.)

Ned, Bart recalls, did more to clean up the district than all the churches and goody-goody people of Davenport who had tried to close the district for years. Ned did not preach religion; he lived a good life and helped others to be good if they wanted to be.

Ned Lee was the chief destroyer of sin in Davenport; he did not preach to the prostitutes, he talked common sense. He did not show people how bad they were and give them his ideals which might be too hard to live up to, he offered them a better life through temperance. Bart often thought that the Ned Lees of the world made the world a livable place.

Besides his job as a special delivery boy, Bart helped at Ned Lee's, helped around his father's infirmary, and still had time to maintain a hobby. Like all kids of his day, he had a craze for gathering stamps. On his way home he gained permission to go in the back of the Eagle grocery store and removed the stamps from all the envelopes in the waste basket. Then he returned the basket with all the envelopes and papers to its original place.

Diagonally across from John Eagle's grocery store was John Hageboeck's saddlery. On one of the days that Bart was making his stamp collection, John H. was standing in the rear door of his shop. The next day, John Eagle caught Bart going into the store and started to beat him.

Bart screamed and raised such a commotion that John Hageboeck came running towards them.

"Why are you hitting the boy, John?" he called.

"The thief has returned to the scene of his crime," Eagle said. "This culprit stole my apples yesterday." He continued to beat the boy who tried to wriggle away.

"Let him alone, John," Hageboeck said sternly. Eagle looked at him defiantly but released Bart. "I saw him yesterday; he stole no apples."

Bart stored this act of kindness in his memory file and hoped someday to repay Hageboeck. Many years later Bart came to Mr. Hageboeck's rescue. While he was practicing Chiropractic John H. became ill with typhoid fever and was given up to die. Bart broke all ethics and insisted upon seeing John. He adjusted him and saved his life.

Later, when he was walking around, he went to visit Dr. B. J. Palmer to pay his bill.

"You owe me nothing," B.J. told the man. "You paid me in advance many years ago by taking the trouble to stop me from getting an unwarranted licking."

That Christmas John sent Bart a large framed mirror for his adjusting room in his home. It is in B.J.'s Trophy Room today.

Still later it was through the good graces of John Hageboeck that Bart was accepted into the Masonic order in Davenport. Bart had fought for years to get into the Masons, but he was always rejected. Bart was pretty sure he was being black-balled by medical doctors who were in opposition to the work he was doing. John, a member of the order, fought long and hard to have Bart accepted and while he fought he managed to unravel the reason why Bart had been rejected so often before.

When Daniel Palmer was running the infirmary, he had a patient who was bedridden. Since the patient and her family lived far away, it was impossible for her husband to visit her often. He decided to contact a fellow Mason in Davenport and ask him to visit her. The brother Mason went to the infirmary armed with jokes to cheer the patient. When he entered the room, a stench filled his nostrils; he asked what it was. She told him she had had a bowel movement in the morning.

"Because there are so many patients here and such a lack of staff, I guess I was overlooked. I am sorry if the smell is offensive."

This Mason told his brothers about it at a lodge meeting. It was a story that was spat out and repeated many times, a story which gathered worse implications as time went on. It was the men who had heard this story who for years to come slipped the little black ball into the box when Bart was proposed for membership.

Bart had thought medical doctors who refused to recognize his father's and his learnings were the cause of his not being accepted into the Masons, but he found out that it wasn't any one group of men, it was just men who were ignorant of Chiropractic and needed some sort of excuse to keep him out of the brotherhood. That Bart was being persecuted for something his father had done didn't bother him. He was glad to finally be accepted as a Mason. Today he is a York Rite and Consistory Rite as well as Shriner and a Jester.

4

THE GREAT DISCOVERY

DAN BECAME a successful practitioner of magnetic healing. And he displayed his success in this radical field by becoming radical in appearance. He wore his coal black hair combed back and reaching down to his waist. He braided it at night before retiring. He wore no collar or necktie because his long flowing beard covered his throat and the long hair covered the back of his neck. He wore a big specially made Stetson cowboy hat. It was flat like the Mennonites wear, only much larger. He also had special soft leather boots. His appearance was his trade mark; it advertised him to Davenport. (The clothes are now in the Palmer Museum.)

He drove a pair of handsome, spotted Indian ponies. And finally, with his new success, he discontinued using his full name; instead he adopted his initials: D. D. Palmer.

During the 1800's medicine has been practiced in this country in varying forms. Only a few early medical practitioners had attended a medical college or a tax-supported university.

Long after the Civil War practitioners gained medical knowledge by serving a term of apprenticeship with some local M.D. Many gained knowledge of medicine while sweeping out offices, cleaning M.D.'s stalls, currying his horses or driving the M.D. around the countryside on his house calls.

In most academic institutions in these years attendance was required for a limited time. Only in rare instances was it longer than one year. It was not until the 80's that laws were written stating licensees of medicine must have graduated from a recognized medical college before obtaining admission to practice in a state. Many early medical doctors were of the itinerant type who traveled from town to town and peddled cure-alls or allegedly superior Indian herb cures as they went about the country. Some noted surgeons of the past were graduates of terms of a shorter duration than one year. One well-known surgeon actually attended a medical institution for a brief term of 6 months.

Few M.D.'s knew the internal structure of the human body; few could boast of the background, practice and study that went into D.D.'s education and few had the interest to search for new methods of curing the sick. D.D. was one of the few who attacked mysterious problems which perplexed others with a zest and zeal that knew no bounds.

Pills . . . potions . . . powders . . . blood-letting . . . prayers . . . herbs . . . symbols and signs . . . alcohol . . . fancy-named medicines: THIS they called medicine; this is how people were deluded.

"Well, the yellow stuff didn't help . . . neither did the green one; maybe the blue medicine will turn the trick . . ."

That was the prevailing situation amongst doctors in 1895 when D. D. Palmer embraced Destiny.

Business was slow one day. D.D. was meditating when Harvey Lillard, the Negro janitor, walked into the office to clean up.

"Excuse me, Doc, I thought you were in the examining room," Lillard said.

D.D. looked up, paused and then beckoned him closer.

"Sit down, Harvey, I have been meaning to talk to you." D.D. was curious to know what caused Lillard's deafness and what measures had been taken to restore his hearing.

Lillard sat down facing D.D., his eyes glued to the doctor's lips.

"How long have you been deaf, Harvey?"

"Well, Doc, I guess it was about 17 years ago that I stooped over trying to do something or other when I heard a snap in my neck. Then I noticed I got a bump, see it? Haven't been able to hear a darn thing since. I've been to all sorts of doctors, but what do they know? They even tried to tell me I had the bump since I was born."

"Do you mind if I examine it?" Harvey nodded and D.D.'s fingers pressed the bump as thoughts whirled in his head. "You say the bump came and you lost your hearing." D.D. wasn't questioning Lillard. His mind said that if the production of the bump meant the losing of this man's hearing, the reduction of the bump should restore it. He asked Lillard if he could work on him.

For three consecutive days D.D. gave the bump thrusts. On the third day Lillard jumped up. "Doc! Doc! I hear!"

Lillard was hearing the rumble of horse-drawn trolley cars riding over the cobblestones four stories below.

D.D. thought he had found a cause of deafness and began experimenting on deaf patients. He examined their spines and felt for other bumps and tender spots. Whenever he found one, he gave it a thrust. In the meantime he found other conditions clearing up within other parts of the body.

With his background and limited knowledge of anatomy, he went back to his books for further intensive study of the nervous system. He found that there were nerves emitting from vertebral openings going to every organ and tissue cell within the body. He discovered that the brain was like a human dynamo of the body like a generator to electricity.

He thought that maybe the brain generated nerve impulses and sent them down the spinal cord which might be like a telegraph system, comparable today to a switchboard in a telephone company. He thought if nerves were pinched, it was like an electrical short circuit and supplies needed to keep an organ normal were cut off.

D.D. had a big mirror on the side wall in his treating room.

"What are you doing?" a patient asked one day.

D.D. realized the patient was looking in the mirror and watching his motions. He took the mirror from the wall and smashed it.

If a man discovered something no one else knew, he could gather a fortune for himself. D.D. wasn't jeopardizing his secret by allowing anyone into it. Bone Setter Reese had gotten plenty for bone setting. He passed it down to his daughter, the next generation. He made a good living . . . and never went to a medical school.

D.D.'s new technique required a different table. He made one which was more than a flat one-piece type table, much like a workman's bench, only with shorter legs. This was made of plain pine wood with a leather covering tacked on over the wood.

D.D.'s patients lay on the long narrow table, face down, nose and chin pointed towards the table. When D.D. manipulated the spine, the patient's face and nose were pushed abruptly into the hard table. This occasionally caused nose bleeds and gained his table the title of nose breaker.

Patients complained to D.D. about the table. The popular attitude was that temporary pain from the table would be forgotten in the luxury of a less painful body.

D.D.'s interest was with the sick. He wouldn't hurt anyone if he could help it for he had devoted himself to relieving pain, but he would not coddle them. He believed patients came to him to be cured, not coddled. He was not the type of healer who attempted healing a sick body with an amiable bedside manner.

Dr. Palmer realized his table would need to be improved. He set about to devise a table more comfortable to patients which would allow better adaptability in rendering his manipulation.

He was a stickler for obtaining desired objects he felt necessary to patients with as few manipulations as possible. In early years, D.D. prided himself on his ability to accomplish cures in severe types of disease with one manipulation. If a patient came to him with a vertebra out of alignment, he interpreted that as the cause of the trouble. He gave the patient the feeling he was trying to make that vertebra go as far as possible towards its normal position on their first visit.

Patients were pleased with D.D.'s adjustments. He experimented with tables which were comfortable for the patient and doctor. In later years to come his son, Bart, perfected them.

One of D.D.'s early patients under the new type of healing was a Methodist Minister named Samuel H. Weed (they got this name because all the family, men and women, were over six feet tall and as straight as weeds). D.D. had treated the Rev. Weed a year before his healing discovery for spleen trouble which laid the Rev. up so he couldn't continue preaching. Mrs. Weed and her daughter were treated by the new healing methods and benefited greatly. Mr. Weed took adjustments for sciatica and obtained relief. Reverend Weed was a Greek scholar. D.D. asked him to find a name for his new science and art. The reverend was glad to help name the new method which had saved his family so much pain. From the Greek Rev. Weed originated the name "Chiropractic" meaning: done by hand.

Slowly D.D.'s business grew. He was now paying $175 a month for rent. His fee of $1. per adjustment at the time it was given wasn't raised, but he didn't tarry over patients.

He kept books which are in Bart's museum today. His income ranged from $30 to $50 per day. Multiplying that by roughly four dollars in this day's exchange, it was a good day's pay.

D.D. knew what he had discovered, he knew what a boon to mankind it was. He became boastful, domineering and overbearing. He became so dominant in manner that he talked, ate and dreamed Chiropractic to everyone until he became a bore, whether it be on the street or in his office.

Although Dr. Palmer stepped up professional value, he stepped down personal value. In due time his attitude caused business to fall off. Destiny swept D.D. from his feet; instead of taking the transformation from magnetic healing to Chiropractic calmly, he became violent. He was rude especially to those who could not and would not understand the simplicity of his new idea. He became cross and irritable; nice words came hard to him . . . and business fell off.

5

◆━●━◆

A DOCTOR SAVED FROM DISASTER

AT THE TIME of Chiropractic discovery, Bart was 14 years old. The subject fascinated him. He would sit for hours listening to talks between his father and his friends.

Bart cleaned out his father's waste paper basket at the end of each day to collect his father's thrown away notes. The fine penmanship and the thoughts expressed on these notes enraptured Bart. He kept the notes in a scrapbook (which is now in the Palmer Museum).

When Bart was 17 years old, he suggested to D.D. that a school of Chiropractic be started. His father at first was furious.

"It's a family secret," he said.

"You believe in your work and so do I," his son said. "But we cannot hope to adjust all the vertebral misalignments in all the sick people in all the world. There must be others to help us cure the sick."

D.D. finally agreed and started the first Chiropractic school. It was known as The Palmer Infirmary and Chiropractic School.

Four students graduated in the first class. One was Bart and another was a man named Heath. When he received his degree, Bart changed his name from Bartlett Joshua Palmer to the initials B. J. Palmer.

Because B.J. was only 17 and rather young looking, he grew a mustache and beard to appear older. He moved to Lake City, Iowa, to start his own practice. In time, he moved on to Manistee and Manistique, Mich., then to Kerens, Burlington and Elkins, West Virginia.

Elkins presented a stiff challenge to B.J. The town's doctors were determined to drive him out. Letters attacking him were published in the local paper, but the papers wouldn't sell B.J. space to answer the attacks. He was forced out of the house he rented. No one in town would rent him a room. Eventually he got rooms on a farm owned by one of his patients. His only equipment was a suitcase-type manipulation table that he designed before he left Davenport.

His landlords loaned him furniture for his office. But he could not rent a team of horses to bring his patients to the farm. He bought his own; hired one of his patients to drive it and bring other patients to the office.

Since newspapers wouldn't rent him advertising space, although they gave medical doctors free space, he wrote, edited and had printed his own little paper and distributed them, house-to-house, at night by himself for which he was arrested "for peddling without a permit." His practice slowly became successful.

Early on the morning of May 15th, Mrs. Thomas Storey, wife of Thomas Storey, a doctor of Chiropractic, hurried quickly into her husband's office in Duluth, Minnesota. "Tom, Tom," she called anxiously. There was no answer. The outer office was empty and the doctor's private office was empty too. Dr. Storey had not been home the night before. Occasionally, when he was working late, and was very tired, he'd forego the trip home, and slept instead on his office couch. Mrs. Storey always came in the office on Fridays to assist her husband, because most of his women patients had appointments on Friday, and they kept him busy from early morning until late at night. On this particular Friday Mrs. Storey got in at 8:00 A.M., expecting to wake her husband up and help him get ready for his first patient. When she found the office empty, she became alarmed and called her son, Thomas J. Storey, Jr.

"There's nothing to worry about, Mother," Thomas J. told her. "Dad probably woke up early and went to get some breakfast."

Mrs. Storey went out to a nearby cafeteria where the doctor usually ate. Nobody there had seen him. She went back to the office and began to search it. Underneath a few papers on top of the desk, she found an envelope addressed to her. She tore it open and read this note:

"Dear Sarah: I have been called away suddenly. Get along as best you can until I return."

—Thomas

Could the doctor have been called away on an emergency case? Mrs. Storey called her son again. This time, there was more than alarm in her voice—there was hysteria. "Thomas, come quick, I think something terrible has happened," she screamed.

When Thomas J. got to the office, he found his mother so overcome with panic, she could hardly make herself understood. He examined the note and assured her the doctor must have gone on an emergency call.

But as the morning hours fled by and the doctor failed to return, it became obvious he hadn't gone out on a call. Further, there was no sign the couch had been slept on and apparently, the doctor had been missing since the night before. Thomas J. took his hysterical mother home and put her under a doctor's care. He held off notifying the authorities for a few days, hoping against hope his father would turn up. Finally, in desperation, he called in the police.

"Who was the last person to see your father?" the police asked Thomas J.

"I guess I was," Thomas J. answered. "I saw him late yesterday after his last patient left. He seemed perfectly all right."

"Did he say anything about having to make a trip, or having to see somebody today?" the police wanted to know.

"Not a word," Thomas J. told them.

"Did he have any family troubles? Was he getting along with his wife? Is it possible he had another woman and wanted to desert your mother for this woman?" the police demanded.

"Why, that's ridiculous!" Thomas J. said angrily. "My parents have always been happily married."

"All right, don't get excited, son," a burly detective told Thomas J. "We have to check everything, you know. It's our job. Was your father a wealthy man? Could he have been kidnapped?"

Thomas J. was taken aback. "I never thought of that," he said. "Dad has a large practice and he's made a good deal of money. If a kidnapper took Dad, he knows we'd spend our last cent to get him back."

Thomas J. was told to go home, take care of his mother, and wait for further word from police headquarters. The Missing Persons Bureau flashed an alarm across the country giving Dr. Storey's description and asking that reports on his whereabouts be rushed to Duluth police headquarters. Meanwhile, Dr. Storey's patients, friends, business associates, and neighbors were called into police headquarters. All were questioned intensively, but none could offer a single clue or provide a lead. Railroad stations, bus lines, cab companies, and steamship companies were contacted and asked to check their records to see if they had taken Dr. Storey anywhere on the night of May 14th. This drew a blank.

From all the police were able to find, Dr. Storey had apparently been swallowed up— If he had been kidnapped, it was by men singularly adroit at covering up their tracks.

It was not until May 25th that anything new developed in the case. On that day, a letter arrived at the Storey home addressed to Mrs. Storey. It was postmarked Seattle, Washington, and was dated May 19th. The distraught woman tore it open and read this:

"Your husband is in good hands and is being taken care of by his fellow Masons. He was found wandering around the railroad station here in Seattle. From a ticket in his pocket, it was evident he had come here by through train from Duluth. He was acting strangely and couldn't seem to give an account of himself. His name and identity were learned from papers in his wallet and he was taken by Seattle police to the city hospital. The examining doctors reported he was suffering from a brain fever and was not coherent. His papers showed him to be a Mason and our local Masonic organization was contacted and asked to get in touch with Dr. Storey's family. We have taken him out of the hospital and arranged for him to rest in a suite at the Hotel Rainier Grand. The doctor seems to be improved, but he talks continually of Dr. Murray and Ida and says something about having to take Ida's baby where nobody can find it. I will write you again in a few days and let you know how Dr. Storey is getting along."

The letter was signed by a W. H. Watson and was written in lead pencil on Hotel Rainier Grand stationery.

Mrs. Storey went wild with joy. She had feared her husband was dead, and now she had tangible proof even though he was ill, he was much alive. She immediately put in a person-to-person call to her husband at the Hotel Rainier Grand. Then came the first shock. He wasn't registered —he had never been registered.

"What about Mr. Watson? Put me on with Mr. Watson," she demanded.

Now came the second blow. Mr. Watson had been registered all right . . . but he had checked out on May 20th, the day after he had written her, and left no forwarding address!

Sobbing fitfully, the grief-stricken woman notified the police in Duluth of this latest turn in events. Chief Troyer, the chief of police, took over personal command of the case and asked Seattle police to search for both Dr. Storey and Watson. The Seattle cops turned the town upside down without result. There was no trace of either Dr. Storey or the mysterious Watson. Storey had never been admitted to any hospital in Seattle nor did any hotel in town have a record of him.

Now the Duluth police began intensive questioning of the Storey family again. Did Dr. Storey ever have a friend named Watson? Did he know anybody in Seattle? Mrs. Storey and son Thomas J. could only answer "No." They'd never heard of anybody named Watson. Dr. Storey had never been in Seattle before, he didn't know anybody there. And yet this man Watson, or whatever his real name was, could not have made up his letter out of thin air. Dr. Storey and Mrs. Storey DID have a daughter named Ida who lived in the east. She had given birth to a baby a few weeks before, but the baby had died. The death of his grandchild had been a bitter blow to Dr. Storey, according to Mrs. Storey and son Thomas J.

The police began work on the theory that Watson was a kidnapper who had spirited Dr. Storey out of town and had him hidden somewhere. "But if he's a kidnapper, why didn't he ask for ransom money?" Thomas J. asked. The police had no immediate answer, but they surmised that a ransom letter would come soon.

Mrs. Storey and her son didn't hold with this theory. They were convinced that the missing doctor was ill, and he and his strange companion Watson were wandering around the country. Now they decided to bring D. D. Palmer into the case. They knew that Storey, a graduate of the Palmer School of Chiropractic, was deeply devoted to D.D. They thought he might turn up at Palmer's home in Davenport. So they wrote D.D. telling him the whole story.

On June 7th, only a few days after D.D. received this letter from Mrs. Storey and her son, he received another letter postmarked San Francisco. He tore it open. "My God," he said. "It's from Storey!"

The letter was brief and to the point. Dr. Storey said he was visiting in San Francisco and was going on to Los Angeles. He wanted D.D. to send him some chiropractic literature to show to friends in Los Angeles. D.D. knew Dr. Storey's handwriting. There was no doubt in the world that the letter was genuine.

D.D. called Mrs. Storey in Duluth to tell her her husband was alive and there was no evidence of his having been kidnapped or hurt in any way. "It may be he felt he had to get away for a while," he said. "Give him a few more days and I'm sure he'll come back."

A few days later, D.D. got another letter from Dr. Storey. This time it was postmarked San Diego. When D.D. and the Storey family tried contacting him in San Diego however, he had already left town. For the next few weeks, D.D. continued to receive mail from his former pupil sent from all parts of the west coast. Dr. Storey apparently was spending a day or two in each town, and then moving on.

On June 14th, D.D. decided to go to the west coast and try to solve the mystery of the missing doctor. He went to San Diego, the city where Dr. Storey had been living according to his last letter. After a search of rooming houses, D.D. found the place where the missing man had been staying. But the landlady told D.D. that her tenant had checked out, without saying where he was going.

D.D. traveled to various towns in California, trying to run down Dr. Storey. In each town, he notified fellow members of the Chiropractic profession to look for the missing man. While he was in California, Mrs. Storey received a rambling letter from her husband. This letter was sent from a rooming house in downtown Los Angeles. She notified D.D. who went to the rooming house. Dr. Storey wasn't around, so D.D. began looking in the nearby area. As he got ready to board a streetcar a few blocks from the boarding house, a man brushed by him to enter the car. The miracle had happened—it was Dr. Storey!

The doctor's face was bloated, his eyes had a strange look and his clothes looked wet and soiled. When D.D. went to him to introduce himself, he stared at him as if he didn't recognize him. Then he mumbled, "Your face looks familiar, but I'm not quite sure who you are."

Dr. Storey was accompanied by a young boy. The boy said the doctor had met him on the streets of Los Angeles and had hired him to guide him and take care of him because he realized he wasn't "quite right in the head."

"I'll take care of him now," D.D. told the boy. "He's an old friend of mine."

It was obvious to D.D. Dr. Storey had suffered a mental derangement. D.D. knew too, the cause of the mental block was a subluxation at cervical. He spoke frankly to Dr. Storey about his condition and the doctor nodded in understanding. "I'd like to take care of you now," D.D. told him.

D.D. led Dr. Storey to his hotel room and asked him to lie down on his portable adjusting table. Dr. Storey made no objection. D.D. adjusted the displaced cervical which had been pressing on the nerves that led to the right side of the patient's head. In less than a minute, Dr. Storey raised his hand to his head and said, "This side of my head has been gone for a long time. It is back now."

Dr. Storey got off the table, stared at D.D. and said, "D.D.! It's you . . . what are you doing here?"

The miracle had come to pass. Dr. Storey's mental condition had been cleared up completely. And now he unfolded the truth of his baffling disappearance.

"I don't remember leaving the office in Duluth, and I don't even remember going on a train to California," he said. "The first I knew that I had run out on my family was when I found myself walking the streets of San Francisco. I asked somebody where I was and when he said, "San Francisco," it suddenly dawned on me that I had run away and left my family behind. I wanted to go back immediately, but another intelligence had a hold of me. This other "fellow" controlled part of my mind and I couldn't shake him loose."

The movement of Dr. Storey from town to town and state to state had been at the direction of this other intelligence who had control of part of his mind. It was Dr. Storey himself who had written that letter to his family, and signed it "Watson." "Watson" was the name Dr. Storey adopted when this second intelligence was in control of him.

Dr. Storey told D.D. one day during this period of derangement, he had gone for a ride on a boat to Catalina Island. "When I was half way there, my second intelligence took over and told me to jump over-board and commit suicide," he said. "It was all I could do to fight off this second intelligence and hold on for dear life."

During this period of derangement, Dr. Storey apparently was treated in a hospital for a short period because he ran into a male nurse who told him he had treated him and that he had been under a doctor's care.

"This episode is blanked out of my mind," Dr. Storey told him. "All I know is that the hospital obviously didn't help me, because when I left there, I still wasn't in control of myself."

D.D.'s adjustment saved Dr. Storey from the tragedy of a commitment to an insane asylum. No sooner had Dr. Storey recovered, than he wired his family to come out west where he would set up a new practice of chiropractic and begin life anew. Thanks to D.D., this strange story had a happy ending.

6

THE FALL AND THE RISE

It was while B.J. was practicing in Manistique, Michigan, that his father wired him to come home. When he got back to Davenport, he found that business was poor. His father was six months behind in rent and had run up so much credit no one would extend any more. D.D. sold the equipment and borrowed so much from patients that he was $8,000 in debt.

B.J. arrived in the morning; his father turned over the bankrupt business to him and that night D.D. skipped town.

During a visit with an old woman who had befriended Bart in his childhood, Bart confided that he was confused as to what he should do.

"My son," she said, "do right, because it's right to do right."

His friend was right. If chiropractic was to ever amount to anything, he would have to make a stand in the town. The town would have to discover that he meant to do right. He begged the merchants to let him rebuild his father's business. Some, out of common decency, were willing . . . others were not. His father's landlord was one of those who was not forgiving.

"My father has left town . . . I'll pay you the back rent he owes, if you'll give me a chance."

"Hmph!" said the landlord. "What can I expect of you? You are all out of the same litter of pups."

B.J. was disappointed at this attitude. He was being persecuted for his father, but he had to beat it some way. He went to Joseph Schilling and R. H. St. Onge and pleaded his case.

"Well," St. Onge said as he scratched his chin, "I really don't know."

"As far as I can remember, Bart was a good boy. I will loan him enough to pay back his pressing debts. We'll see what happens."

Rufus St. Onge did loan him enough to pay the most pressing debts. With the loan he paid the landlord who allowed him to remain at the same location. At least people who knew of the infirmary could find it. Bart could tell that the landlord and many of the town's people were not too happy but he was remaining.

An odd coincidence happened when one of Davenport's merchants, years later, taken sick, traveled throughout the United States trying to locate a doctor who could help him. There was none to be found so he went abroad. Once abroad he went to an eminent specialist.

"As far as I can see, sir," the specialist said, "there is only one man who can help you . . . I cannot understand how you overlooked him; he, too, lives in Iowa."

"Guess I looked too far," the merchant said. "Who is he?"

"Here's his name and address. Make sure you see him."

The specialist had written, "B. J. Palmer of Davenport, Iowa."

B.J. got him well and to show that he forgave him for his distrust years ago, he charged him nothing.

At the age of twenty when most men are beginning to think of their future lives, B.J. decided to dedicate his life to the development and preservation of Chiropractic for humanity. He made a solemn vow and stuck to it. He became so obsessed with the idea that people often laughed and called Chiropractic his "child." In truth Bart felt that it was his child, a child deserted by its father.

D. D. Palmer did much in discovering Chiropractic, but this only scratched the surface. It was B.J. who weaned and watched Chiropractic crawl. It was B.J. who picked Chiropractic up, stood it on its feet and taught it to walk. It was B.J. who led Chiropractic along the future right path.

B.J. had a strange affection for his father; D.D. had been the only parent ever known to Bart and he inherited some of his characteristics. Bart realized he had some of his father's qualities, some good, some bad. He also realized he had inherited some soft, cultured qualities from his mother. If he was to be a success, if he was to help people and make people want to be helped, he must overrule the bad qualities picked up from D.D. and replace them with those genteel qualities of his mother.

B.J. spent the next twenty years of his life doing just this.

It was no easy task to control himself in every action. It took much self-control and will power to think twice about everything he did. But each time he chose the way his mother would have done something and yet follow in his father's professional footsteps. He learned to discriminate between necessary qualities of his father to develop, detect and defend Chiropractic while he fought methods which destroyed his effectiveness in dealing with people. B.J. learned to follow the path of hardest resistance, but it was no easy task.

After B.J. paid the landlord's back rent and other debts, he started building a practice of his own. He started the Chiropractic School again. He contacted one of the graduates of his own class, and appointed him Dean of the Palmer Infirmary and Chiropractic School.

Upon making a weekly visit to "Daddy's" class, Bart was surprised to see a woman patient. B.J. sat quietly in the back of the room, listening and watching the girl. She was lovely.

"B.J., this is Mabel, meet the director of this fair institution."

"How do you do," she said. She kept staring at him.

"I am glad to meet you," he said. His eyes did not meet hers.

B.J. discussed a few things while Mabel kept staring at Bart. She knew he was young. She could not understand why he wore a beard; she wondered why he wore his hair long. She made a mental note to get to know him better in the future.

As time progressed the two got to know each other better. B.J. was impressed with her human understanding and intelligence in Chiropractic. That she was a woman struck him as strange, but uppermost was the feeling that she was a woman such as he'd never known. Uppermost was the feeling that she was worth knowing.

"Why did you decide to be my patient, Mabel?" he asked her one day.

"For several reasons," she answered. "One was that I could be close to you; another that I have always liked anatomy . . . it fascinates me. Ever since I learned how to read, I've read books which dealt with the subject. Chiropractic is a way to put my knowledge and studies to use."

Mabel aroused Bart's interests and he started to call on her. Their courting was not like others of their generation. They didn't admire the moon and spoon, they discussed the science that was much a part of both of them.

"Mabel, I have to prove Chiropractic to the scientific world. It must be accepted . . . I need a philosophy."

"You will find one, B.J., you'll find one."

They would walk to the top of Brady street hill, the section of town where most millionaires lived. The view was breathtaking; for miles the Mississippi River twinkled with boats and lights, the lights of Davenport.

On their way home, they would peek into windows of the wealthy and look at people serving their guests and planning. B.J. and Mabel had plans, too, not about riches, but of Chiropractic. B.J.'s love of the science rubbed off onto Mabel.

Later Mabel went to Chicago to further her studies of anatomy enabling her to be of greater help to B.J. Her work at B.J.'s side as a teacher helped him develop the philosophy which was to be Chiropractic's strongest link. She became one of the foremost anatomists in the U.S.; her lectures on anatomy had been published in a book and are widespread.

In the days before all this, Mabel and B.J. dreamed about Chiropractic as a recognized science; they dreamed of money to buy one of the Brady street houses . . . to make a modern school. They dreamed of working together.

Mabel and B.J. were married. They had much in common. With little fanfare, they set up housekeeping in one room of the Infirmary.

The Infirmary staff was at the wedding. B.J. considered them part of the family. He never left all the decisions to himself; he realized the shortcomings of Man and accepted them. He surrounded himself with people who loved Chiropractic as much as he. He consulted them, used their suggestions and congratulated them when they did a job well.

If someone made a suggestion and it turned out as not expected, B.J. placed blame on himself. He felt it was for him to hold the family together and they all respected and loved him. They knew his feelings on his father's squandering and helped him to stay away from the straits his father traveled.

B.J. incorporated the Palmer School of Chiropractic (a name he decided upon in 1904), in 1905 it was incorporated under the laws of Iowa as an educational institution. Uppermost in his mind was the protection of Chiropractic by giving it a solid foundation, the backbone of its growth. This school is now known the world over as the Chiropractic Fountainhead.

The Palmer School barely resembled D.D.'s infirmary, for B.J. made many changes when he took over his father's defunct business. He installed crockery and toilets convenient to patients.

B.J. inherited his father's feeling of compassion for the sick, but it went further. B.J. did not agree with D.D. that temporary pain was necessary to remove more permanent pain; he perfected the Chiropractor's couch. He installed toilets so he need not be humiliated by showing a patient to a junk-like room, but he wasn't satisfied. He felt Chiropractic was a far reaching discovery and he wanted all things associated with the science to be the best.

7

D.D.'S TRIAL

WHEN D.D. LEFT DAVENPORT he was despondent and lonely. He went to Letts, Iowa, where he had once lived, hoping to renew old friendships and gain companionship. He knew his old friends might cheer him and help him climb out of the black depression which seemed to travel with him in those days. He decided he needed friends badly.

D.D. had few friends left in Davenport. He felt he could renew friendships and rebuild his practice . . . All he needed was a rest; B.J. had said that, too.

Bart amused D.D. with a 20-year-old's impatience and optimism he intended to build a practice far greater than his father's. D.D. had no such illusions. No, the kid couldn't do it without D.D. D.D. would see a few people, stay in Letts for a while and then go back to Davenport and straighten things out.

One of the first people D.D. met was Molly Hudler, the old girlfriend of long ago, the girl he had lost to another because he had been too slow to speak.

"Dan! Daniel David Palmer!" she screeched when she saw him. "I thought for sure my eyes were deceiving me . . . Dan, you look wonderful."

"Molly, you haven't changed a bit; you're still a beauty. I take it marriage has treated you well?"

"I'm a widow, Dan."

"Oh, I am sorry," he murmured. He realized that expressions of sympathy were sometimes false; he knew he wasn't sincere in his sympathy.

"It happened long enough ago for me not to be bothered about it anymore . . . Dan, you must come home with me. I'll make supper and we'll talk about old times."

She dragged him home with her and they spent a quiet evening talking. She kept looking at him and wondering what was bothering him, but she wouldn't ask. Long ago, even though she loved Dan, she married another because Dan didn't ask her to marry him. She still loved Dan and she wanted to help him, but she knew she could not unless he wanted her to. She hoped he would tell her about his problem, whatever it was.

He sulked for weeks, but he didn't mention anything to her.

"I was hoping you would ask me to get married this time, Dan. I'd be honored to be your wife. I love you very much, Dan. I love you more now than I did when we dated years ago; I guess added maturity does something for people."

Dan and Molly played the role of newly-weds. Both were very happy. A source of constant amazement to both was that they felt they had never been married before.

Being newly wed to Molly took Dan's mind off of circumstances in Davenport for a while, but soon his mind travelled back to Davenport and he again began to brood.

"Dan, you haven't said a word to me since supper," Molly accused one night.

"I was just thinking of how to tell you, Molly. I guess I should have told you a long time ago."

"What is it?" Molly feared he didn't love her.

"Well, I don't know how to begin . . ." He began from the beginning and told her of the affairs in Davenport.

"Dan, I can hardly believe it of you. If any other man did what you did, I doubt if I'd speak to him again, but I love you and I'm glad you told me about it. You did a cowardly and selfish thing by running away and leaving your son to face accusations. I'm ashamed for you."

"The only way you can make amends to your son and your beloved Chiropractic is to go back to Davenport. If you would have stayed, things wouldn't be too bad; now, I'm afraid, you will probably be prosecuted for the things you did. Either way, Dan, we must go back and face this thing. If we don't, things will never be right for us; this will hang over our heads for the rest of our lives."

Dan told Molly he knew she was right. The reason for his many sleepless nights was that all these things whirled around and bothered him. He didn't want to involve Molly and ruin her happiness.

"I am your wife and I love you. I am involved so let's go get it over with."

They went back to Davenport. Molly thought they were going back so Dan could repay his debts and help his son. What she didn't know was that D.D. had heard that Bart was doing well with the practice. This bothered him more than anything else, more even than the idea of facing a term in prison . . . more than anything at all.

D.D. found the practice growing and standing on its feet. He was enraged, but he kept the anger to himself. He found that he need not fear being tried for skipping town with other people's funds; B.J. had cleared the debts up. Instead of being happy about this, D.D. resented his son even more.

"Well, Bart," D.D. said after a few days, "I'm ready to take the business over again, if it's all right with you."

Bart knew the practice had belonged to his father in the beginning. By rights, it now belonged to B.J., but he said nothing. He rather liked the idea of getting D.D. back into the business; he didn't know how others would feel about it.

"I cannot turn the business over to you, I must speak to Mabel first, since marriage is a 50-50 proposition. I must speak to St. Onge and Schilling, too. They loaned me money to get the school on its feet."

D.D. was angered still more, but he said nothing. He wanted to be the boss again and he didn't care who his son spoke to as long as he was given control of the business.

R. H. St. Onge and Joe Schilling were against accepting D.D. back as head of the school . . . or in any other capacity for that matter. B.J. tried to convince them it would be for the good of the school. They agreed only because they knew it was what B.J. wanted, but they feared what might happen.

Mabel listened to B.J. and realized Bart wanted his father back. She thought about it and told him it might be a good idea.

"After all, dear, he did discover Chiropractic. I feel we should give him another chance. The Good Book says we should honor our mother and father."

"I'm glad you see it that way, Mabel," her husband said. "We all make mistakes; I think Dad benefited by his."

B.J.'s next step was to get all to okay D.D.'s return. None felt that D.D. should be allowed to take over, but they were convinced, over their better judgment, to allow D.D. to become a partner.

D.D. was allowed to have voice in the school. He found that his word was not law, however. He resented this. Still more, he resented Bart for commanding the respect of students and patients.

D.D. thought if anyone should command respect it should be him. It was he who discovered Chiropractic. His son was just practicing what the father had found. D.D. started to become bitter to B.J. and all connected with him. The bitterness and resentment showed in his practice and actions. A financial mess much like the one D.D. had left the school in was again encountered.

In the early part of 1906 D.D. and B.J. were indicted by the Grand Jury of Scott County, Davenport, for practicing medicine without a license. At their arraignment, D.D. and B.J. posted bond, and early in April D.D. were summoned to court to stand trial. For reasons known only to himself, the prosecuting attorney saw fit to bring D.D. to trial first.

The courtroom was crowded during the trial. The judge often rapped his gavel and threatened to clear the court if silence did not prevail. The onlookers remained silent for a while and then new chatterings broke out.

The jury went out to reach a verdict. They were out quite awhile. Daniel Palmer sat stern-faced and silent as the people about him buzzed with excitement. The jury entered the room and the judge asked the foreman of the jury if they had reached a decision.

"We have your Honor," the foreman answered. The judge nodded and the foreman continued. "We, the jury, find the defendant, Daniel D. Palmer, guilty as charged."

The court buzzed and the judge again rapped his gavel. "Has the defendant anything to say in his behalf?"

"May I be allowed to address the court?" D.D. asked. The judge consented. D.D. walked slowly to where the jury sat and looked at each person slowly. Many of them lowered their eyes. "You may have judged me, gentlemen, having in mind some of my actions that have taken place while I lived in Davenport for the past 30 years. This would not be fair, as you were told I was being tried for practicing medicine without a license. I cannot change your verdict, but I would like it known to you and all who sit in this courtroom, that the only thing I have done wrong was in getting sick people well where medicine failed. If sick people had been able to get well under medicine, they would not have tried the method which I have discovered. If they had not gotten well under my care, these same people would not have to come back.

"I am not guilty," he shouted, making people in court jump. "Medicine is guilty . . . for not getting these sick people well.

"Our ancestors came to this country and fought for freedom." He continued in a soft, passionate voice. "I believe freedom also constitutes a patient having his choice in a doctor and to select the type of healing his intelligence finds best to regain his health. Because medicine has failed in these cases, do these poor souls have to spend the rest of their lives suffering?"

D.D. raised both his hands, fingers outstretched, palms towards the jury. With a look on his face of strong conviction, his long hair hanging loosely, Dan said, "As long as I have these two hands and there are sick people to get well, I will use them."

To emphasize the main points in his lecture and make them descriptive, D.D. placed a skeleton on an upright supporting platform. He used this to explain what he did to the backbone to make sick people well. The skeleton, having been introduced in evidence, was marked "Defense Exhibit #1."

The Court House in which this trial took place had a small river running diagonally underneath its foundation. This caused parts of the building to sink, it caused plaster to fall, and cracks to develop. On top of this Court House, characteristic of such buildings in those early days, was a high, large tower. Many years later, this tower proved too heavy and was removed. In so doing, the custodian had to go into the large garret. In there he found the skeleton, "Defense Exhibit #1." He phoned B.J., who took it and placed it in his Osteological Laboratory. It remains there today.

The court was filled with silence. D.D. turned slowly to the judge and said, "Your Honor, I am ready to be sentenced now."

The judge, not entirely untouched himself, realized Dan had made an effect on the courtroom with his speech. He hesitated and then gave him a $500 fine.

"I respect the law, but there is a principle involved here and I have the right to serve time in jail in lieu of paying the fine."

The courtroom tittered; the judge stared at D.D.

"I hereby sentence you, Daniel D. Palmer, to jail where you shall remain until this sum shall be paid."

With the passing of sentence, D.D. was taken to jail. While there, he thought it would be good business as well as educational to adjust other prisoners that were in jail with him. This was continued for 17 days and the townspeople were talking about it. D.D. was getting restless in jail, though.

He called the guard and summoned the jailer to ask when he would be released. D.D. was sure he had paid the fine with the 17 days in jail.

"I have no orders on when you're to get out, Palmer. There is no date entered in my books for your release. I'll find out from the court if you'd like."

The jailer inquired in court and found that D.D. would not be released until after the fine had been paid. B.J. was summoned.

"What is going on?" Dan asked. "I was under the impression that I would work out the jail fine and when it was paid, I would be released."

B.J. who had been under the same impression told his father he would find out. He contacted their lawyer.

The lawyer reread the judge's decision and found the words "until this sum shall be paid." B.J. was told that with this interpretation of the law somebody would have to pay D.D.'s fine or he would remain in jail indefinitely. B.J. immediately made arrangements to pay D.D.'s fine and have him released.

For reasons known only to the local merchants of Davenport, B.J.'s trial was never brought to court and eventually was dismissed. This episode added salt to D.D.'s wounds and bitterness toward his son.

D.D., while in jail, had a private room with the usual facilities. He was permitted to have his typewriter where he concentrated on his writings. To keep active, he used to kick on one wall to see how high his foot could go. He kicked first with the right, then with the left leg. He drew lines endeavoring to increase the height of his kicks. One day, he kicked beyond his balance. He toppled back and hit his head on the hard cement floor. From then on, he gradually began to change. His brain apparently had been affected by the blow and his mind began to deteriorate.

While D.D. was in jail, he had lots of time to think. His mind became sour on the law. He began to dislike public officials, his dearest and closest friends and their thoughts. He thought everyone was in cahoots against him. When D.D. got back to the school he allowed his attitude to spread to include students and patients. Instead of things getting better as time passed, things became progressively worse. The school was losing patients.

From past experience, B.J. knew that this could not go on. He realized D.D. was hurting the development of Chiropractic, and B.J. tried to carry the burden of undoing wrongs on his shoulders. But as Emerson said, "Things refuse to be mismanaged for too long."

8

---·◆·---

GROWING PAINS

B.J. WAS VERY UNHAPPY with the way things were turning out. All were raising a fuss and patients and students were staying away. B.J. tried to talk to his father, but it was an impossibility. D.D.'s resentment and bitterness made him deaf to any appeal from his son.

Then one day D.D. went to his son and asked that their business be dissolved.

"Dissolve the business?" Bart repeated, thinking his hearing was defective. "I wouldn't dream of dissolving the business."

"Well, then I think you should buy me or I buy you out."

Bart knew he would have to buy his father out because he could not consider giving up the practice and the school. He was amazed that his father could even suggest giving up everything they had worked so hard to build. The two Palmers attempted to reach a financial settlement, but D.D.'s demands were sky-high. An arbitration committee was formed consisting of Joe Schilling and R. H. St. Onge. All property, titles and monies were deposited and controlled by the committee during this period of arbitration.

At one of the meetings, Schilling asked D.D. to state his terms for the record.

"I will take $2,000 for my interest in the bones we bought jointly

42

and those which I added out of my collection. I want $650 for my half interest in all furnishings including the office, bedroom, kitchen, dining room, etc., plus half the cash on hand, being $850. There will be nothing charged for the good will of the business, nor literature on hand which has already been written on. I will reserve the spinal column which is at my residence and also one abnormal one, the one I had in prison, and 6 individual vertebrae which I shall pick. I also want my pick of the books at the school library." St. Onge and Schilling were staring at D.D. He quickly added, "My pick of the books at the library . . . not to exceed twelve books."

Both of the arbitrators thought that D.D.'s demands were far too high. St. Onge and Schilling advised B.J. to hold out. If the old man wanted to leave town, he would have to come down on his terms.

B.J. thought his father was being unfair, but he wanted to do what was best. As long as they arbitrated about terms, the practice and the school would be neglected. He consented to his father's second terms.

A receipt was issued to B.J. which read as follows: "Received of Bart J. Palmer, $2,196.79 (two thousand one hundred and ninety-six dollars and seventy-nine cents) in payment for my interest in the Palmer School of Chiropractic as according to agreement with committee selected by myself and Bart Palmer for that purpose, signed Dr. D. D. Palmer and Mrs. D. D. Palmer."

With the money D.D. had gotten from Bart, Dr. and Mrs. D. D. Palmer left town. Molly figured they would get along very well because she had managed to save $400 besides.

B.J. was saddened that things had not worked out with his father, but he was glad it was over with. Now was the time for him to get to the heart of things and make Chiropractic what it should be. There were many things for him, Mabel and the students to do.

One of the first things Bart decided he must do was to establish his honesty and sincerity. He and Mabel thought that if he bought property and established something permanent he could build his credit, prove his business abilities and finally prove himself to the people in Davenport. He wanted very much to rebuild the name of Palmer and he wanted to prove that he had no intentions of pulling stakes and running as his father had.

The younger Drs. Palmer went searching for real estate. Like a dream becoming real they found one of the homes they had passed on Brady Hill was for sale. If they could obtain it, they would be on the inside looking out, not the outside looking in as had been the case in their courting days. Also, Mabel discovered she was pregnant and the house on Brady Street represented security for the unborn Palmer child.

They tried to make a deal with the owner of the house. No matter how hard they tried the owner demanded more cash than Mabel and Bart knew they could scrape up for years to come. Finally, the old owner decided to let them sign a mortgage. It was a mortgage which would hang around their necks, much like the albatross clung to the ancient mariner's neck, for years, if not paid off in future monthly payments.

As Con Murphy, B.J.'s attorney said: "It was a cut-throat mortgage. If you fail to pay any one month's rent, you forfeit everything you have paid."

Mabel and Bart packed their few belongings and moved up to the top of the 828 Brady Street hill. Since they had so few things, they put everything into one room. It seemed strange to have a big house all to oneself. That first night, they were very uneasy and slept very little.

"It will be better when we buy more furniture and fill the house," Mabel said.

"I am sure it will be, dear; now try to sleep. We have much to do."

But this house was never utilized exclusively as the Palmers' living quarters. They were not able to fill the rooms with furniture and enjoy the luxury of having an entire house to themselves. Times were very difficult for Mabel, B.J. and D. D. Palmer, Jr. (They named their son after his grandfather, but called him Dave not to confuse the child with the elder D.D.) The new house on Brady Street was partitioned so as to room and board students and patients of the clinic.

They also found it necessary to make room for classrooms, extra offices, a kitchen, dining room and other things. From time to time, B.J. tore out partitions, built lean-tos, shifted things from here to there trying to make more room. A week didn't go by when he was not making some improvements. He spent as much money as he could to build several lean-to frame structures. He was fortunate that he could not look forward and see what was in store for himself and his family as he went about his daily tasks. If he could have foreseen the future, he probably would not have believed that such physical discomfort, financial hardships, mental humiliation and fierce legal struggles could exist for one person.

B.J. built a classroom in the basement of the Brady Street house. Whenever it rained this classroom became flooded. He put boards on bricks to keep students' feet dry. He used to go down into the classroom through a trap door in the floor of his clinic room. But he never minded the difficulties which arose if his students were learning.

B.J. had one showcase with skeletons in the basement classroom. The talk of the town soon became that B. J. Palmer killed people upstairs where he adjusted them and then took them through the trap door and hung their skeletons in the classroom.

B.J. would wash dishes one hour and then teach a class in Chiropractic another, fire a furnace, direct his clinic, adjust his patients, wash and scrub floors, clean windows and lecture in the classroom, his first public lecture hall. And even though he was kept on the go every moment of the day, he still had time to dream great dreams for himself and his beloved science.

It made no difference to B.J. that he was surrounded by adverse boarding house conditions. He worked like a beaver, knowing that some day he and Mabel would have a house, a home; he worked like a beaver to make his dreams come true. He was also writing his first book.

Sunday was supposed to be a day of rest, but for the Palmers there were no Sundays. B.J. and Mabel cared nothing for society. Social activities were replaced by the Palmer School of Chiropractic. They belonged to no social clubs. They were workers not wasters. They had no social ladder to climb.

Mabel shared all of B.J.'s trials, bore with him and shared his burdens. B.J. knew Mabel was always there to turn to. When his spirits wavered, her faith would make him go on. Together they burned the midnight oil. People passing in the early hours saw two heads bending over a lamp studying.

Mabel and B.J. toiled together trying to master the knowledge that Fate had placed in their safekeeping. Together they worked, teaching classes, developing the science and philosophy of Chiropractic through research and experiments. Each helped the other toward their common goal. B.J. in these days referred to his wife as his "better ⅞ths."

Many things happened during this segment of their lives. For one thing a student came down with a communicable disease. They felt they could keep it under control and cure it with Chiropractic adjustments. Always keeping within the law, they notified the Health Department in Davenport of the existing condition. The Health Department sent a health officer, not a physician to examine the patient. After his examination, he told B.J. that the premises would have to be put under quarantine. B.J. went to a closet, got a loaded shot gun and pointed it at the health officer.

"Don't expect to leave this house then, sir. If all within this house are quarantined, so are you."

This layman looked at B.J. and thought he must be kidding. Upon closer examination, the man saw something in B.J.'s eyes. This strange-looking man was not joking.

"I don't understand you, Mr. Palmer," the officer said feebly.

"The name is Dr. Palmer; and I think you do understand what I mean: I am a doctor, but you say I must be quarantined because some of the germs might be carried out by me or our students. You're not a doctor but you examined him; therefore, some of the germs are on you. If I am not allowed to continue on my way because I might spread the disease, you must stay also."

The officer said that it was not within his power to consent in giving permission for B.J. not to be restricted to rules of quarantine, but he would take it up with the Health Department. In the meantime, B.J. was to go about business as per usual. B.J. never heard from the department again concerning the matter.

Another day, B.J. had occasion to go to his back door. Upon doing so, he found a man sitting on the back door step.

"Are you all right, sir?" B.J. asked.

"I have been ailing recently," was the reply. "I stopped to take a rest; I hope you don't mind."

"Certainly not. In fact, why don't you come in and have a bit of supper with us? We have nothing fancy, but the food is nourishing."

The man had dinner with them and B.J. discovered that he had a fine and agile mind.

"Tell me," B.J. said, "are you familiar with Chiropractic?"

The gentleman admitted he was not.

"Would you care to undergo adjustments under my care?"

The man said he would try anything if it would bring him some sort of relief. B.J. nursed him back to health.

"What will you be doing now that you feel like a new man?" B.J. asked him.

"I do not know . . . There is something I wish I could afford to do."

"And what is that?"

"I would like to study under you."

B.J. allowed the man to attend school tuition-free. Not too long afterwards, he graduated and started a practice of his own. He was unsuccessful and, soon, B.J. found the man again sitting on his doorstep. B.J. gave him a job of teaching on the faculty. The man knew his stuff, but he was too dependent on others to make a go of it himself.

Kindness is not always repaid in kind; such was the case with the stranger B.J. found on his doorstep, nursed to health, educated and befriended. This man and a few other members of the faculty rebelled and took 32 students from B.J.'s school, marched down the hill and started their own school.

This new school was called The Universal Chiropractic College. The faculty members who started it, the students who went with it and the people who supported it were those who did not agree with B.J.'s innate philosophy. The members of the new school knew that the Palmer School had a distinct advantage—it was the fountainhead of the science; Chiropractic had been discovered and developed by the Palmer family. The originators of the UCC also knew the Palmer School was looked upon much as Johns Hopkins was looked upon for medicine and Harvard for law, but they were not content with the simple procedure in the practical phases of Chiropractic, the palpation, feeling down the spine for misalignments, the Palmer recoil adjustment. The men who learned from the Palmers took some of the things they had learned and added others which detracted from the science.

Unlike D.D., B.J. liked the idea of competition. He felt that competition proved a healthy attitude in developing Chiropractic. As long as new-found schools stuck to straight Chiropractic principles, it was all right with him.

Time passed and soon B.J. was dubbed "Czar Palmer" by a few fellow Chiropractors. He would not support the new found schools that were practicing everything but Chiropractic.

As he told a few members of the faculty when asked about the new schools:

"These schools are infringing on the medical field as well as other types of healing . . . What they teach is not Chiropractic. When a Chiropractor, or one who goes under the name, has not been taught the philosophy, science and art that goes with his course of study to help sick people get well, he finds he is not able to benefit his patients with his hands. He is not being honest with himself nor with our science, and he will soon branch off into other modalities trying to make his patients feel good . . . not for love, but for money."

B.J. went on to say that the untrue Chiropractors were representing themselves falsely to the public. They were offering medicine under the name of Chiropractic to people who were going to Chiropractors because medicines had done them no good.

B.J. knew that for Chiropractic to succeed in the eyes of the scientific world, Chiropractors would have to confine themselves to the spine—the premise—and by using their hands as the word implied. A Chiropractor to B.J. was a man who applied the philosophy, science and art of Chiropractic to an ailing body. He also knew that one of the branches of healing that became separate and distinct from medicine was dentistry.

Sticking to the human spine was the thing that made Chiropractic a separate and distinct science and, to B.J., anyone who strayed from this path was not a Chiropractor.

9

◆━━◆◆◆━━◆

AN EDITOR WITH A CONSCIENCE

DURING THE EARLY DAYS of B.J.'s career, when B.J. was striving to get out from under his father's debts and recover lost standing in his community, he was arrested for "practicing medicine without a license." At this particular time, a man named E. P. Adler was owner and editor of the Davenport Daily Times. Adler wrote a scorching editorial attacking B.J. The editorial was an unjust personal attack. He was beset by many problems, but this one was maliciously unfair. He decided that the editor of the paper had a personal hatred and wanted to and could ruin him.

B.J. hurried to the office of the Times and demanded to see Mr. Adler. The minute Adler allowed him inside, B.J. vented his disgust. "The editorial you wrote was vicious slander," he shouted at Adler. "All those rotten things you said about me being arrested can smear me in this community, and apparently that's what you want. You're putting personal hatred in your columns and that isn't what a newspaper is for."

Adler listened attentively. When B.J. finally finished, the editor said briefly, "What you want to get into this newspaper is an advertisement; what you want to keep out of it is news. B.J., I'd also like to give you a bit of advice: If you're in the right, you can afford to hold your temper. If you're in the wrong, you can't afford to lose it."

This didn't placate or reassure B.J. He was so wrought up he couldn't see Adler's point of view. "I'll never speak to you again as long as you live," he stormed at Adler. Then he hurried out of the office.

For twenty years, B.J. lived up to the promise he made. He never saw Adler socially. When Adler walked into a meeting he was attending, he would walk out. When he passed Adler in the street, he would fix the editor with a baleful look of contempt and pass him by without a word of greeting.

When Kiwanis International was organized in Davenport, B.J. became a charter member. He attended regularly for many years. During this period the secretary of the Kiwanis chapter was Al O'Hern. O'Hern, a devout Catholic, was city editor of the Davenport Daily Times, and worked under E. P. Adler.

O'Hern suffered from tuberculosis and from time to time, was hospitalized for long periods. Finally, his condition got so bad he was told he would have to move to Arizona if he wanted to stay alive. O'Hern hated to leave his home community and his old friends, but when the doctors kept stressing the fact that it was a life or death matter, he decided he had no choice. He had to resign his job with the Times, give up membership in Kiwanis and other community groups, leave his wife, son and daughter (who were going to school in Iowa and didn't want to leave) behind when he moved west.

O'Hern remained in Arizona for about five or six years, and then died. His body was brought home to Davenport for burial and his friends of Kiwanis held a memorial service for him.

As O'Hern's long-time employer, Adler was invited to the memorial service. This was embarrassing to B.J., but there was no way he could avoid meeting his enemy. As Adler and his son Phil stepped up to the mezzanine of the Hotel Blackhawk, where the service was held, B.J. coincidentally passed by. He had always admired Phil, and though he still wouldn't talk to E.P., he stopped for a moment to chat with the son. Suddenly he said bitterly, "There is one advantage your father has over you; he has a better son than you have a father."

Phil was too embarrassed to say anything, but E.P. spoke up. "You may be right about that," he said. "At least, I won't bother to argue with you."

During the course of the memorial service, the president of the Kiwanis group announced that he had a story to tell and a tribute to pay. "I had been sworn to secrecy during O'Hern's lifetime," he said. "But now that our friend has passed on, I think the time has come to reveal something about Mr. O'Hern's devoted friend and employer, Mr. E. P. Adler."

The president said it had been Mr. Adler, an orthodox Jew, who paid transportation fare to Arizona for his Catholic employee and also paid for all of O'Hern's living expenses out west. On top of that, Adler arranged for O'Hern's wife and two children to visit O'Hern twice a year, and had footed their traveling expenses. He even paid for O'Hern's funeral. His modesty was such that he had sworn to secrecy those who knew about his generosity. As the president explained it, "Mr. Adler insisted he didn't want to be praised merely for helping a friend!"

When the president finished his tribute, B.J. felt ashamed. As he himself recalls, "If there'd been a hole in the floor, I'd have gone through it."

When the meeting ended, B.J. went over to E.P. and held out his hand. "I've been in the wrong, terribly in the wrong, E.P.," he said. "I should never have made that remark to you before the meeting and I should never have nursed a hatred toward you all these years. Will you accept my apology?"

Adler immediately showed B.J. what a big man he was. He accepted B.J.'s handshake and told him he would be delighted to forget the past and bury whatever hard feelings had existed.

"From now on, E.P., I'm going to be the best friend you've ever had," B.J. assured the editor.

During all the years that followed, until Adler's death in 1949, B.J. and the editor maintained a friendship that was as strong as their bitterness toward one another had once been. The two Davenport papers which Adler owned gave generous coverage to B.J.'s activities and to the advances he made in the science of Chiropractic. In turn, B.J. proved in various ways his respect and admiration for Adler. When competitors or business rivals of Adler called B.J. and asked him to work with them against the editor, he angrily turned them down. News of this would eventually get back to Adler and he would invariably call B.J. on the phone to thank him. At Adler's funeral, nobody mourned the distinguished editor more than the man who had once sworn to him, "I'll never talk to you again."

10

SURVIVAL

THE X-RAY WAS DISCOVERED by Dr. William Conrad Roentgen, professor of physics at the University of Wurzburg, Germany, in June of 1895, three months before Daniel David Palmer discovered Chiropractic.

In its early years, the x-ray proved dangerous to both technician and patient. Many technicians suffered fatal burns in the early use of the machine.

In spite of this, B. J. Palmer kept abreast with the x-ray's development. He felt it was one of the answers to his problem: proving to the world that vertebral subluxation caused nerve impingements.

Early in the evolution of Chiropractic, B.J. studied a spine taken from a dead body. He studied not only malformations of the spinal segments and the column as a whole, but he also studied the construction of the various processes and articulate facets of the individual vertebrae.

From the beginning of Chiropractic, B.J. had started to build one of the largest osteology and spine collections in the world. He did this so the faculty and students at the Palmer School of Chiropractic could get a thorough analysis of the construction of various segments of each individual spine. He hoped that through their studies they might discover a means where the principle of Chiropractic could gain greater use in society.

Before the x-ray, the only means of discovering misalignments or subluxations, was through training the finger tips of the Chiropractor to a high degree of sensitivity to detect misalignments when fingers were passed skillfully over the vertebrae. It was also the only way to make a skillful comparison of each spinous process with the processes of the contiguous superior and inferior vertebrae to determine laterality, and their superiority or their inferiority in relation to one another.

For the most casual observation of any spinal column, it is readily noted that the spinous processes may be enlarged, elongated or shortened.

Also, if twisted to the right or left, up or down, the spinal processes are in fact subjected to a multitude of malformations or accidental fractures that could cause one dependent solely on their palpation to believe what he had discovered was a subluxation when it was only a malformation.

The result of this was that many patients were adjusted for subluxations where none existed and many may have been adjusted in wrong direction so the subluxation or misalignment was exaggerated.

What happened in such cases was: instead of recovering health, some patients went away with no improvement or even in a worse condition than they were before.

B.J. realized this. He was very rigid in teaching the early pioneers of Chiropractic the fundamentals of the construction of the spine so his graduates were more often correct than wrong in their analysis of a subluxated or misaligned vertebra.

Because of B.J.'s standards, many patients regained their health after being adjusted by a competent Chiropractor.

The pioneers of this science did not altogether rely on their palpation in making their analysis. They frequently resorted to nerve tracing and other sources which helped in the making of a spinal analysis.

B.J., aware of these numerous possible malformations of the spinal vertebrae, felt he would have to buy and experiment with an x-ray machine if he was to put Chiropractic on a scientific level with other forms of instruction. He made every effort to secure an x-ray machine for his research.

But he met with almost insurmountable obstacles. He finally secured the first Scheidel-Ivestern x-ray ever used in Chiropractic.

The scientists who were developing the x-ray had realized its value to medical and surgical professions and attempted to prevent other types of healing from using it. They didn't want it used in drugless branches of the healing arts.

In 1909, B.J. acquired the first x-ray used in the Chiropractic profession, and in 1910 he built an x-ray laboratory with a library of several hundred glass negatives showing various spinal conditions.

B.J.'s farsightedness was unpopular with some of the members of the faculty at the school. They could not grasp the possibilities of the x-ray over palpation. They threatened to quit the school if B.J. introduced the x-ray into the curriculum.

B.J.'s decision was: bow to the whim of men who cannot adapt the new idea, or do what he thought best for the profession and risk losing some of his friends. He did not hesitate; he went ahead with his plans. The men, as they had threatened, left and started a school of their own, a school which was not going to use x-ray in its curriculum.

B.J. introduced the x-ray and set up a new department in the school, called the Spinographic Department. (The spinograph, the word B.J. coined for x-ray, is now considered one of the most important phases of training *in all* reputable Chiropractic schools.)

At first when spinographs were taken, patients would recline on the table, face up. The views were taken from front to back because it was thought this was the only position in which spinographs could be accurately made. Later on, B.J. developed the idea of taking spinographs with the patient sitting up.

Supports were provided to allow the patient to sit naturally. The change in spinograph technique came about after B.J. discovered taking spinographs in the reclining position would allow a possible straightening of the spine and in so doing, a true picture of the spine's condition did not come through.

All B.J.'s modifications in x-ray brought about new problems. He designed and drew his own plans and submitted them to manufacturers. They were reluctant to follow B.J.'s orders at first and had to be fought with until the work was finally done.

B.J. had another barrier to overcome: People were afraid of the new idea and didn't want to be used in experiments. Patients became guinea pigs for experiments. Each time B.J. undertook a new search for better scientific methods to insure the future of the profession.

And as if he didn't have enough problems, he constantly had to find ways of bringing in income to finance his research. Once, in order to raise money, he accepted the invitation of one of his early graduates to give a series of lectures in Portland, Oregon.

His financial condition forced B.J. to travel second class tourist on the Northern Pacific Rail Road. He and Mabel were forced to crowd their bodies, magic lantern case, slides and baggage in an upper pullman berth. For four nights they slept with knees hugging chin and baggage at the foot of the berth.

They didn't have money for food, and although Mabel made sandwiches, they turned stale before the trip was over.

He arrived in Portland with twenty cents which he spent for a sandwich and a cup of coffee. He was too proud to ask his host for a loan. Without a cent in his pocket, he started his lecture tour.

He received $25 per person for these lectures and pocketed $200 before the day's end.

That night he was invited to dinner at a private club. This he looked forward to for it promised him his first good meal in six days.

Before dinner he tasted anchovies for the first time, got sick, and couldn't eat.

The irony of that situation capped B.J.'s early struggles to nurse the infant science to a full-grown profession.

There was no sacrifice too great; no task too menial for B.J. He was a pioneer and had to suffer the hardships of a pioneer. And he did.

He fought scoffers, unmasked phonies, and educated the interested. He was fighting to prove what most disbelieved—that here was a new scientific way to get sick people well.

11

---❖---

SOMEONE OLD, SOMETHING NEW

WHEN D. D. PALMER and Molly left Davenport they went to Oklahoma where his brother Tom was living. Tom told them about the wonderful opportunities in this new territory and persuaded him to stay on instead of continuing to the West Coast.

In time, D.D. told his brother about his discovery of Chiropractic. He said his son robbed him of his money, of his school and library, and of his osteology collection.

Tom sympathized and suggested D.D. forget the past and start anew in a different field. He convinced his brother to go back to the grocery store business. D.D. followed the advice.

He opened a store in Medford, not far from Oklahoma City. The store prospered, but D.D. could not bend his efforts into this relatively unimportant work. He was not finished with Chiropractic. He was moving back into the field almost along the same steps he had traveled once before.

By chance he became friendly with Alvin Gregory an M.D. Gregory took an immediate interest in the science. He worked along with D.D.

He saw what could be done with Chiropractic and got D.D. interested in opening a new school. So it was that Alvin Gregory, M.D., and Daniel David Palmer opened a Chiropractic College known as the Palmer-Gregory Chiropractic School.

The partnership didn't last long. D.D.'s peculiarities made him too difficult to work with. D.D. left Oklahoma and moved to Portland, Oregon. While there he gathered together his earlier out-of-date notes on Chiropractic and put them into a book called "The Chiropractor's Adjuster."

D.D. continued moving around the country, setting up new schools and getting patients, then becoming fed up with his location, he moved on to a new one.

It was while in Los Angeles, California, that he met Frank Elliott, who lived next door in an apartment. Frank was related to Mabel Palmer. He came to Los Angeles to set up practice after graduating from the PSC.

Coincidentally, D. D. Palmer moved in next door and set a sign out on his lawn that read "Old Dad Chiropractor, Discoverer and Developer of Chiropractic, D. D. Palmer."

Frank and D.D. became friendly. They had an interest in common: Chiropractic. It became a topic of conversation and heated argument.

D.D., upon finding that Frank was a graduate of the school he first opened in Davenport, bitterly launched into attacking his son for a raw deal. His attacks became so treacherous and his reason so overworked by the heat of his excitement that he started making up ideas to support his attacks.

Frank took just so much, then, one day, he gave D.D. a double-barrel shot of truth. D.D.'s wife sided with Frank. There was no containing D.D. He became irrational. He cursed his son and everyone who had anything to do with him.

It was because of D.D.'s state of mind that Frank didn't let father and son meet when B.J. visited Los Angeles. Frank, in fact, had little to do with D.D. after his violent attacks on the accomplishments of his son.

While in Los Angeles, B.J. asked Frank to come back to PSC as a member of the staff. Frank consented. He mentioned this to D.D. who countered with a statement that caused Frank concern.

"I'm going to Davenport," said D.D. It was shocking news. Frank visualized the problems B.J. might have with his erratic father. And worst of all, Frank feared danger to the profession; D.D. was determined to get back at his son for what he thought was unjust treatment.

But there was nothing that could be done. The future would have to dig its own grave and bury problems as they came up.

B.J. was unaware of what problems the future might hold. He was too busy working for his science. His energies and attention were being poured into a mold out of which he hoped to see emerge a strong and accepted method of healing.

It was while in New York that good fortune teamed up with chance to work for B.J. He was at the theatre this particular night, and taking a between-the-acts-smoke, he met a Davenport neighbor, 3 doors away from the school.

Willy Peterson was the owner of one of the biggest department stores in Davenport. He had wealth, society standing and influence in Davenport. Heretofore, he never bothered talking to B.J. although he was a next door neighbor. He felt that B.J. had no money, no influence in town, and nothing in common with him, the pillar of society.

But when he met B.J. at the theatre he walked over and said hello. He seemed delighted to see his Davenport neighbor, and invited him out to supper.

While dining, Peterson suggested B.J. buy his home.

"It's yours for $25,000, $5,000 as a down payment and $1,000 a year," he said to B.J.

B.J. was interested, and became even more interested when Peterson said he would grant any reasonable time on the annual payments. But the purchase price was a fortune to B.J. and he had no money.

When he arrived back in Davenport, B.J. and Mabel decided they would buy the house if the bank would lend them the $5,000. It did.

It did so because, as the banker explained, B.J. had regularly met and paid all installments on two other pieces of heavily mortgaged properties that B.J. owned. The banker said that B.J. proved responsible, which in turn showed character.

A check was turned over to B.J. in return for merely his signature on a note.

The house on this new piece of property was built by a man who owned a lumber mill. He picked the construction lumber carefully. The entire house was made of solid butternut. The partition walls in the basement were eighteen inches thick and the outer walls were two feet thick.

When Willy Peterson bought the house, he made a special trip to Italy to bring back three carrara marble white fireplaces to replace the brick fireplaces in the house. He later installed electric lights and a boiler in the basement to heat the building.

Mr. Peterson also installed a first floor music room, a parlor and dining room. He painted and frescoed the rooms at the expense of $1,800 a room. He laid two inch tongue and groove solid walnut floors in three rooms, eventually grew tired of the floors and had parquet floors laid on top of them.

When B.J. and his wife moved from their one room at 828 Brady to this 22-room house at 800 Brady, they were lost in a great expanse. It was much like a pea rattling around in a big boiler. They stored all their furniture in one room, and locked the doors for the night in fear . . . of what they didn't know.

B.J. got busy and fixed the house up to fit his needs. Behind the house was a two-story frame stable. On its second floor was the haymow with bins for corn, oats and other horse feed. Downstairs were stalls for four horses and two carriages.

B.J. tore out bins and stalls, tore up the wood floor and laid a new cement one. He boarded up the upstairs and painted, and made new floors into two classrooms. The barn became a school.

It was months, though, before the barn rid itself of the odor of horse's urine. Many of B.J.'s older students remember the uncomfortable heat of those classrooms, but B.J. was struggling to prove a science and they struggled with him.

B.J. also did some remodeling outside the house at 834 Brady. On the north side there was a long narrow strip of land. With wood and nails he saved in the interior remodeling work, B.J. built a long narrow building from sidewalk to alley. It was about 20 feet wide and 120 feet deep. In here, B.J. started a printing plant. He brought in paper from the rear, stored it in odd corners and worked it forward through a series of mimeograph machines. He slowly progressed to a hand fed press, then to another and now he has one of the most modern and complete printing plants in the Middle West.

It was here he printed his Chiropractic magazine and the many other types of literature for the field in the 27 years he occupied that house. He spent well over three million educating and keeping Chiropractors informed of developments in Chiropractic.

It was a grind . . . getting Chiropractic accepted. It was problems, rebuffs, rejections . . . and successes. That too came. It took time. It took courage. But there was success. And the success came from many sides . . . from the printing plant, from the trials . . .

The chief thorn in the side of the new science was the occasional arrest of Chiropractors on the charge of practicing medicine without a license. The earliest case was the arrest of a Japanese practicing in La Cross, Wisconsin. He got in touch with B.J. when jailed and explained his position. B.J. took action. He got in touch with students practicing in the field and raised a small amount of money to employ counsel.

This was to be a test case to determine if Chiropractic came under the penal code in Wisconsin's medical laws. B.J. and a number of students went to La Cross.

There they consulted with the law firm of Morris and Hartwell and retained the firm to defend the local Chiropractor.

Thomas Morris, who had been lieutenant governor of the state when Bob LaFollett was governor, and upon LaFollett's election to the senate, became acting governor for a few months, was one of the lawyers. Tom Morris was a political power in both his state and community.

Fred Hartwell, the other member of the firm, was an able trial lawyer. He was prosecuting attorney of his county and was also a political power in Wisconsin.

Both men realized the significance of this case: If the Chiropractor was not acquitted, the decision would bar practice of Chiropractic in the state, and possibly spread throughout the rest of the country. This was not merely a criminal case, it was the life of Chiropractic.

The lawyers knew the importance and bent their talents to win a just verdict. They put up a battle. They argued, fought and knocked down all the myths and untrue statements medicine men made about the new science.

They won. The jury brought in a unanimous verdict for acquittal. Chiropractic had won its first battle against medical opposition in a court of law. The case set a precedent for hundreds of similar cases in years to come.

When B.J. came back to Davenport, he and the others discussed the feasibility of uniting all Chiropractors into a national association for the protection of Chiropractic's future in United States and Canadian Courts.

B.J. and his associates saw the danger of other instances where Chiropractors would be taken to court without able counsel and perhaps be convicted. It could exterminate the individual Chiropractors. It would wipe out Chiropractic. Years of struggle would be defeated by prejudice and ignorance.

To prevent this from happening, B.J. organized the Universal Chiropractors Association which became a hallmark in the development and evolution of the science of Chiropractic.

B.J. was the secretary-treasurer of the new organization. Morris and Hartwell became the organization's national counsel.

The association was independent of the Palmer School of Chiropractic. Its board of directors consisted of five members, all Chiropractors, who were practicing in various sections of the country. In later years, the constitution was amended so that not more than two members of the board came from the same Chiropractic school.

Membership in the UCA was highly desirable. The membership was highly selective, not open to any Chiropractor not practicing straight Chiropractic. This was to protect the reputation of the association and in turn the reputation of the profession.

It was due to this organization that the firm of Morris and Hartwell made it possible for Chiropractors in 44 states in this U.S., and in parts of Canada, Europe and the rest of the world, to practice legally.

B.J., for many years, travelled thousands of miles to act as an expert witness on Chiropractic and its philosophy while Morris and Hartwell fought for the profession's legal recognition.

Many Chiropractors were arrested on the charge of "practicing medicine without a license." Among them were Jo and Esther Strand of Forsythe, Mo. B.J. was at the trial with Tom Morris, senior national counsel for the Universal Chiropractors Association. B.J. was the president of the Association and was called to act as expert witness for the defense.

At the time of the trial, two evangelists, Curry and Meyers, were holding meetings in a tent nearby. They preached love of Christ and implored the people who listened to them to "sacrifice of yourself and give your heart to Jesus."

On the night before the trial, B.J., along with the Strands and attorney Morris was invited to dinner at the home of Mr. and Mrs. Shores, two of the most prominent citizens in Forsythe. When they arrived at the house, they found the two evangelists had also been invited over.

During the course of the dinner, evangelist Curry suddenly snapped at the Strands, "I don't have any sympathy for people like you. You've broken the law and you'll have to pay the penalty." The other evangelist also insulted Jo and Esther. "People like you are a disgrace to our society," he said. "You should be locked in jail and made to suffer for your crime."

The insults continued through dinner and finally, B.J. was no longer able to restrain himself. "Mr. Curry," he said, "I haven't said anything up till now and my two friends here have endured your slanders in silence, because they do not wish to create a scene at the home of our host. But I can't sit still anymore. You and your associate here are evangelists. Night after night, you hold meetings in your tent. At your meetings, you urge your listeners to come up and give their hearts to Jesus. You talk about love and charity and the fellowship of man, don't you?"

"Why yes," said Curry, "we do that."

"Have you men who preach the love of Jesus ever stopped to think that Jesus was a lawbreaker?" B.J. said. "He broke the official laws established by both Romans and rulers of the Hebrews. You men, of all people, should know there are occasionally laws made by men which are morally and ethically indecent and which a man of honor and goodwill has to break? You preach love of Jesus, who broke certain laws, yet you slander and attack these people here who have similarly broken laws that are immoral and unfair. How dare you disparage these people? How do you know but what they too are making history? You are narrow in your concepts, limited in your horizon and prejudiced in your views. You should be ashamed of yourselves!"

After this outburst, the two evangelists sat still and stared at the floor. Governor Morris then congratulated B.J. for having the courage to rebuke Curry and Meyers.

"I think they've learned their lesson now," he said. "I think they'll be better Christians from this time on."

Did Curry and Meyers really learn their lessons? Nobody can tell for sure. They may have—but we have our doubts!

It wasn't easy. People are basically afraid of a new idea. They don't readily accept the new, the unique, the unusual. They fear first. They protect this fear by ridicule. The few who seek and explore original ideas are in the minority. But fortunately, they do exist.

B.J.'s ready acceptance of something new was not just confined to Chiropractic. His mind was always keen and alert. He proved this many times and in many ways. He proved it by his acceptance of the horseless carriage.

B.J. bought the first gasoline horseless carriage that came to Davenport. It was the Knoxmobile, with its low front dashboard which opened up and came down to become a front seat for two.

B.J. sat up on the rear seat wearing his goggles, leather hat and duster. He steered the car by a handle that worked back and forth. The car had no brakes. It was stopped by use of the chain drive connecting within the engine.

The car had a crank on the side to wind it up to get it started. If the spark was advanced too far, the crank would kick back, the car would backfire, and B.J. would get an awful kick. (Fortunately, he never broke a wrist . . . for his hands were his livelihood.)

B.J., to make sure the townspeople knew who owned the first car, painted his name and address on the side.

He had a few near narrow escapes with his horseless carriage. Once when he was driving down Brady Street hill, the chain broke and he had no way of stopping the car. As the car moved down the hill it picked up speed; the further it went, the more speed it gained. Finally, B.J. whipped around the corner of Third Street and managed to jam the car into the high curb.

B.J. liked to show off his car to friends. His favorite destination for these trips was the Rock Island Arsenal. To drive there, he had to get a special letter pass. (The first pass the arsenal issued for a car was to B.J.)

One day, he came roaring down its Main Avenue, engine wide open, tires spinning in mad fury. He had that car way up to *15 miles per hour*. He passed a buggy, upset the horses, and forced the driver to lose control.

The buggy was operated by the Commandant of the arsenal. That was the end of B.J.'s pass.

His adventures in the car were many. He took trips of more than 15 or 20 miles in one direction.

Every time he went out for a drive, he took proper precautions, like calling the livery stable, telling them where he was going so they would have a team of horses ready to come and get him if he phoned for assistance.

He was constantly involved in court cases because of complaints against the car. He never had to pay damages, but it cost to defend himself, and he got bad publicity from the newspapers.

His car was a Knoxmobile, all right . . . and if it did nothing else, it knocked him for a financial loop—and proved to people that B.J. didn't fear a new idea.

B.J. at all times, in all ways, was a fearless youngster, never afraid to do the unusual.

When he was a student at old No. 2 stone school at the top of Perry Street hill, B.J. used to ride a bicycle down the hill to get home for lunch. He had two steps put on the hub of the rear wheel and he would coast down the hill, both feet on these steps, arms out, steering the bicycle with the sway of his body. At the foot of the hill, the Rock Island Line had its tracks. If he had ever run into a passenger or freight train, his life would have been snuffed out.

In those early years, the Mississippi River used to freeze over with ice five and six feet thick. Passengers were hauled across to Rock Island on sleighs and sleds. In the early fall, when ice was beginning to form, there was what was called "rubber" ice, where it was thin and gave under the weight of people on it. This necessitated fast movement to prevent falling in. One winter B.J. was THE FIRST to go to Rock Island on this "rubber" ice. It was risky, of course, but B.J. loved risks.

Later, when the kids were removed from No. 2 school to No. 8 at Ripley and 4th streets, several of them got together and built a bob-sled. B.J. used the steep Gaines Street hill to go for bob-sled rides. Knowing the Rock Island trains passed on the crossing street level, he posted one boy to watch for coming trains. Once, he wasn't there and a freight came along. B.J. had taken off from the top of the hill. Realizing he couldn't stop the sled in time he took the chance of laying flat down on the sled passing underneath the train. Miraculously, he was able to pass under the train at a spot between the front and rear wheels, and got through safely. If he had lifted his head while crossing under the train, it would have been torn off.

12

FATHER AGAINST SON

CHIROPRACTIC, LIKE TOPSY, GREW. But it didn't "Just grow"; it grew through work, it survived by conviction. Much of work involved in hypoing the profession's growth involved constant scientific restudy of what had been accomplished, and it involved a pooling of ideas by the practitioner.

This pooling of ideas was accomplished once a year at the annual home-coming. From the day B.J. formed his first school, an annual lyceum was held each year when Chiropractors from all parts of the U.S. and abroad came back to Davenport.

They would take a refresher course, studying the latest innovation, recharging their batteries. This new knowledge would be applied to patients, raising the percentage of results in getting the sick well.

The men and women who came to these conferences were the pioneers who were interested in the true development of the profession.

The convention served as a graduate course . . . and a vacation. The Chiropractors brought their families to Davenport . . . a home away from home.

The convention had its lighter moments. The first week was set aside for studies of new developments and the second week was for play, highlighted by a big parade. There were picnics, boating and a Grand Ball during this week. Nurseries for children were set up.

The Chiropractors looked forward to the home-coming. It was the chance to learn the new; the chance to see old friends. It was the Palmer School of Chiropractic family gathering.

This was of course known to the heads of the Universal Chiropractic College located at the bottom of Brady Street, PSC's competition. They were also aware of D.D.'s bitterness toward his son and the school.

So they invited D.D. to lecture at UCC during the week of the home-coming. This, they thought, was good business.

They wired D.D. who was living in Los Angeles, and he accepted. They hoped to win over PSC's graduates by having the founder of the science as a guest speaker. They figured Chiropractors would send patients and friends to UCC. Any school's matriculation is governed by the men in the field who recommend a school to friends.

When D.D. arrived in Davenport he looked up a family friend, Con Murphy, a prominent attorney. Frank Elliott, who when in Los Angeles feared the problems that might arise if D.D. came to Davenport, asked Con to bring about a reconciliation between father and son.

Con Murphy at first met resistance from D.D. but finally got him to agree to stay with B.J. D.D. promised not to start any trouble. All D.D. asked was that his son be a kind and courteous host.

D.D. couldn't understand that his son's affection never lessened. D.D. was bitter, and his bitterness warped his outlook.

So D.D. came to his son's home and there met for the first time his grandson David.

The day came for the big parade. Everybody spruced in preparation. It was a glorious occasion. The day was clear and sun was bright. It was as though fate decreed nothing should prevent a successful parade, a wonderful day. But this was not to be.

D.D. brooded all morning because while he was invited to lead the parade, it would be in a special automobile.

"I'm the founder of Chiropractic. This parade is in celebration of something that I discovered. It's my right to lead the parade, by walking at its head."

It was his right, B.J. agreed. But the weather was hot and D.D. was no longer a young man.

"I want you to ride in the special car along with me and other members of the faculty," he said to his father.

What would the people of Davenport think, seeing this old man, walking at the head of the parade, in the hot broiling sun, while the young son rode in an automobile behind the flags and the band? There was no way they could be told that this was being done at D.D.'s request and insistence. B.J. feared wholesale condemnation by the people of Davenport and therefore he insisted that D.D. ride with him in the car.

But D.D. didn't hear a word his son spoke. He was determined to lead the parade and, in his irrational mind, his son's offer was an attempt at preventing him from achieving this honor.

He walked away, hesitated a moment, then walked ahead to lead the parade. He pushed through the crowds, but before he could break in, Frank Elliott took him by the arm and walked him back towards the sidewalk. D.D. broke the grip, and ran down the street.

Frank ran back to inform B.J. who, in an attempt to save his father from humiliation, gave instructions to the police to stand by and keep D.D. from breaking into and leading the parade on foot.

D.D. ran well ahead of the marches. Just as the parade drew abreast, he again tried to break in, this time being prevented by the chief police officer of the parade.

The officer tried to explain that he wasn't being rude, just following instructions. D.D. was infuriated.

He left the scene of the march and headed back to his rooming house on Harrison Street. (He moved out of B.J.'s house at the insistence of the UCC faculty. They felt it wasn't good business to have D.D. live with his son at the same time he was to lecture at their school.)

He stormed into his room. His mind was afire with anger. Bitterness, hate and revenge squeezed his reason with the hold of an octopus. He was no longer in control of his faculties.

He called a friend: "My son just drove his car into me. He attempted to kill his own father," he said. The lie didn't matter to him, his motive was to degrade his son. He didn't care that something like this could prove dangerous to Chiropractic. He never realized that this lie, in time, almost did ruin the science. The strongest of men, when they store up bitterness and hatred, become mentally unbalanced. That's because vicious emotions are poison to the mind of the victim.

D.D. gave his UCC lectures, and he and his wife later went back to California. (Coincidentally, while he was lecturing, his thoughts reached into his past and came up with the memory of a certain spiritualist, in Letts, Iowa, who told Daniel David Palmer, "Someday you will lecture to a large audience on a new discovery and people from far and wide will give acclaim to you." Here he was, lecturing as predicted, but not "from far and wide" at the UCC.)

For the next several months D.D. thought more and more about what had come to pass. He thought not with the keen mind he once possessed. He thought with the demented mind of the mentally ill. And the poison in his mind spread through his body.

He became physically sick, and his body rapidly aged. Molly became increasingly concerned about his health and called a doctor, who said he had typhoid fever.

And in 1913, in his sixty-eighth year, Daniel David Palmer died in Los Angeles, California.

13

———◆———

CHARGE OF MURDER

DANIEL DAVID PALMER WAS GONE; his scientific discovery will never be forgotten.

The discoverer was old, tired and sick when he died. But his Chiropractic, his science which got the sick well by hand was young, energetic and healthy. It would live on giving its father immortality.

D. D. Palmer's bright star in the profession shone because it was constantly polished by B.J. The son took up where the father left off. He was truly the apostle of this art.

D.D. could never see this. He died bitterly hating his son. On his deathbed he told Molly that under no circumstances was B.J. to view his remains or attend his funeral.

This was a tough command to follow. Molly recognized that D.D.'s attitude was caused by a sick mind. She knew that D.D. was wrong in his hatred. She knew B.J. did all he could to constantly remind Chiropractors that his father was primarily responsible for the science they practiced.

D.D. held his son responsible for letting out his secret science to the world thereby taking away a sure fortune. Molly knew he was wrong, but she loved her husband in life and stuck by him; she loved him in death and felt it her duty to do what was right by him.

She knew that under the law she had the right to dispose of the body any way she saw fit. She wired B.J. asking for advice.

B.J. answered with a request that D.D. be cremated and the ashes sent to him. He placed the ashes in a monument erected by the Chiropractic profession on the PSC Campus, in honor of the discoverer. He had Molly send him D.D.'s personal belongings so they could be preserved in the Palmer Museum.

With D.D.'s death, the problems the sick father caused for his own science didn't end. That telephone call, that false charge that his son hit him with a car, now made itself felt.

A few days after the profession received the news of D.D.'s death, the members of the Universal Chiropractic College and others collected money to prosecute B.J. "for running into his father during the lyceum parade." They collected affidavits from people who claimed to have seen B.J. deliberately drive his car into his father, knock him down and then run over him. Evidence was conflicting but it was sufficient so when presented to the prosecuting attorney of Scott County, Iowa, he charged B.J. with murder and summoned the Grand Jury.

Three times B.J. went to court. Three times the Grand Jury refused to indict. B.J. each time collected evidence to prove he was innocent and that some of the affidavits were forgeries.

Three events helped B.J. prove his innocence:

The doctor who attended D.D. while he was sick testified that the cause of death was typhoid fever and that D.D.'s physical condition showed no evidence of any such accident as was charged.

Then there was the damaging affidavit signed by D.D.'s nurse which said death "was the result of an accident from an automobile driven by B.J. during a parade in Davenport." The affidavit mentioned date, time and place.

B.J. knew it must be a forgery for the nurse had never been to Davenport, much less seen the accident. When she was brought to substantiate the affidavit, she charged it was a forgery.

She said the only affidavit she ever signed was one attributing death to typhoid fever. She said the false part of the affidavit was typed in afterward to her original. She issued another statement, giving correct facts related to the death and charging that D.D. had no accident as far as she knew.

The third event that helped B.J. was a lucky break.

All the original affidavits held by the attorneys for the members of UCC were in an envelope which was on a desk in the offices of their prosecuting attorneys. It was found on the floor on one night, and was swept up by the janitor.

The janitor at the time attended PSC's evening clinic, which was taking care of over a thousand patients a day free of charge.

That evening the janitor told B.J. that he had spotted a batch of papers pertaining to a murder charge against him and asked if B.J. wanted to see them. He brought the original affidavits, and B.J. then was able to track down the forgeries.

B.J. had in his clinic then a patient who was a charge on county welfare. Upon hearing of this, the prosecuting attorney called B.J. and told him it would be better if he sent this case home. The attorney also asked B.J. to reimburse the county for the money paid for the patient's keep. B.J. turned a check for the amount over to the attorney.

The passing of the check was spotted by the attorney for the UCC who was in the anteroom of the prosecuting attorney. He immediately thought B.J. had been buying off the prosecutor and that's why the case was going against UCC.

UCC's attorney had a newsletter printed immediately which related the scene. B.J. sent a copy to the prosecutor, who upon seeing it, dropped his interest in the case.

B.J. later was completely exonerated. The trial had cost a total of $15,000, money wasted by both sides. Practically every one of the traitors to Chiropractic, the men who had tried to ruin B.J., are dead. Chiropractic lives on.

The court fight was necessary to save the reputation of the new science. If the traitors had smeared the Palmer name, the dirt would have rubbed off on the profession.

(Later, B.J. gathered all the evidence presented by prosecution and defense, including all affidavits on both sides, which were presented to the Grand Juries and to the Prosecuting Attorney. He had them published in one of his books, titled "With Malice Aforethought." Up until the day of the book's publication, many chiropractors bitterly condemned B.J. and B.J.'s standing in the profession suffered. Many dissidents shouted far and wide that B.J. had been disgraced. This publication stilled the criticism and for all time settled the issue.)

It is unfortunate that men, such as those traitors to Chiropractic, live only with emotions, passions and prejudices. Few men direct their lives with logic, reason and facts.

B.J. won the case because he let his innate or inborn intelligence direct his thinking. The innate always uses logic and reason. It has no emotions, passions or prejudices.

Shortly after B.J. had been exonerated, he took Mabel and young Dave on a trip around the world. One of the places visited was Udaipur, which is one of the central states in India, ruled by an independent Maharajah.

They stayed in a hotel which was a crude stone structure located in the middle of a Mohammedan cemetery. One morning while the family was sun-bathing in front of the hotel, a coach approached with two men dressed in red, signifying they were in the service of royalty. They asked the inn keeper for the famous American doctor.

B.J., who was watching the activity, had no idea they were referring to him until the two made their way across the lawn toward him.

The men told B.J. that his Royal Highness, the Maharajah Singh of Udaipur, commanded the American doctor to appear before him.

B.J. asked for an explanation of the command. The men said nothing. B.J. was about to refuse, when the inn keeper advised him to go with the men.

"No harm shall befall you. But if you refuse the invitation, you'll insult his Royal Highness," the inn keeper explained.

B.J. left his family behind, climbed aboard the handsomely decorated coach, and when he arrived at the palace, was escorted to the audience chamber where he was presented to the Maharajah.

Maharajah Singh of Udaipur was a sick cripple. He had commanded B.J. to appear because he sought the advice of such a famous American doctor.

B.J. went over the case, and when his study was completed, he realized he could not stay in Udaipur long enough to care for His Majesty. He, therefore, spent the next few days advising the court physicians how to best take care of the case.

The Maharajah asked B.J. his fee. B.J. explained he was on vacation, not making a professional tour, and for that reason, there was no charge.

The Maharajah, in turn, asked if there were some favor he could grant B.J. and B.J. replied:

"There are two things I wish: an autographed picture of Your Majesty and a guide to take my family on a tour of the palace and grounds." The requests were immediately granted.

B.J. was first taken to the family palace. It housed hundreds of rooms . . . but few were open to inspection because it was here that the Maharajah kept his royal harem.

B.J. was taken to a second palace, one reserved for the exclusive use of foreign guests. It had 400 rooms. In one room alone all the furnishings were of pure crystal . . . beds, chairs, table, mirrors . . . everything was pure crystal. The contents of the room were valued at a half-million dollars.

They were shown the money vaults and jewelry rooms in the basement. Room after room was loaded with jewels and many kinds of precious stones stacked on shelves. The contents of these rooms were estimated at a billion dollars.

The stables consisted of more than 200 elephants, 400 full blooded white Arabian horses with pink eyes, and 150 camels.

In front of the castles, on an island on a large artificial lake, was a

smaller palace carved of marble. It was here that the Maharajah took
rest from the affairs of state. It is said that it was in this castle **Muntuz
Mahal** and Akbar the Great rested.

On the opposite side of the lake there stood an arena where fights between wild boars and tigers were put on for His Majesty's entertainment,
and on this occasion, for B.J.'s pleasure.

Coincidentally, when B.J. left Udaipur, he visited its surrounding prin-
cipality . . . it was the most poverty-stricken area B.J. observed while
in India.

After completing the world tour, B.J. came back to Davenport. The
murder case was just a memory. He bent his energies toward building
up the school still further.

He gathered all students together and told them: "Soon we're going
into the construction business . . . temporarily."

And so the men students were issued hammers and crow bars and got
got to work tearing down the duplex building where now is the D. D.
Palmer Memorial Building. The women students organized a hot dog and
coffee brigade.

They started at 7 A.M. and by 6 P.M. the entire building was down,
lumber assorted, nails pulled out and the basement filled in.

The day wasn't all work. An incident gave B.J. and the students comic
relief from the destruction.

While the hammers were flying and B.J. was directing the work from
the sidewalk, a stranger drove up in a buggy, gave B.J. the reins to hold
and walked over to and into the school building next door.

"Where can I find a Dr. Palmer?" asked the stranger.

The man gave the stranger directions to the offices of PSC. There the
stranger asked Jerry Green for Dr. Palmer.

Jerry took the stranger by the arm, led him back onto the street and
pointed:

"See that fellow over there, the one with the handkerchief over his
head, holding your horse, that's Dr. Palmer."

The stranger was mortified. He had travelled over 2,000 miles to consult B.J. and on meeting him, had asked B.J. to hold his horses.

Jerry walked the stranger over to B.J., explained why the stranger
looked so red and flustered and all three doubled up with laughter, with
B.J. starting it off and laughing loudest.

Some time after the building was completed, B.J. decided he was entitled to a vacation. A student group and himself went to the Mardi Gras
in New Orleans. The Mardi Gras was gay and colorful. For the men
from Davenport it was a happy time, and eventful.

That year Bernarr McFadden, the physical Culturist, was exhibiting
his powers of physical perfection. B.J. introduced himself to Bernarr.

McFadden had heard of B.J.'s work and of his struggle in trying to help mankind. Bernarr was also having trouble putting his ideas over. His publishing business was just struggling along.

B.J. suggested McFadden quit traveling as a one man show and put all his time into the publishing business. B.J. felt this was the only way for McFadden to tell people about his work.

Bernarr McFadden took B.J.'s advice and closed his show. He went back to New York and began publishing one magazine after another. He amassed a fortune.

Bernarr and B.J. over the years met on various occasions. Once, when B.J. was invited to dinner at Bernarr's penthouse, opposite Central Park in New York, the Chiropractor witnessed an unusual dance. Bernarr's three daughters, who were at the dinner, did a dance in the nude. They were not ashamed, nor was Bernarr or B.J. All considered the dance art.

On another occasion, B.J. had an athletic float in the lyceum parade which featured Bernarr.

Although B.J.'s method of getting the sick healthy and Bernarr's method were miles apart, they both shared one thing in common; they were both great fighters in proving their methods to the man-in-the-street.

14

———◆———

THE GIANT

THE QUINT-CITIES CONSIST of Moline, Rock Island, Illinois on the one side of the Mississippi and Davenport on the other. Between the state of Illinois and Iowa is the River and on an island of 1,000 acres lies the Rock Island Arsenal. During World War I the Arsenal employed thousands of people. The neighboring factories were stripped of employees, the merchants and institutions lost their skilled and trained help; private industry and businesses were destitute. It was impossible to hold on to help since Uncle Sam paid several times more than businessmen could afford to pay each week.

The businessmen realized Uncle Sam paid more and decided this was the trend. Prices on all commodities were boosted to the extent of 5 to 15 times their regular prices. An example of this: suites were raised from $25 to $150, boarding houses, hotels, eateries skyrocketed in costs. Merchants justified their actions with the premise that it helped to go along with increased incomes. They felt they should not lose out on any boom.

People in Davenport could not afford to pay these outrageous prices. They drove as far as Chicago, 186 miles away, or to outlying towns not affected by the unseasonal and extraordinary high cost of living. Stores in Davenport were commercially and financially facing bankruptcy. The Chamber of Commerce was helpless to solve this problem.

Because of these increased prices, Davenport had the reputation for being the highest priced city in the United States; students refused to come to or stay with the PSC in Davenport. They felt they could enter some other kind of school and save this outrageous high cost of living. The merchants' business and PSC took a sharp swing downward. Drastic action of some sort was necessary, but no one was willing to take steps to stop the vicious crisis. There seemed to be no one to reconstruct; no one who had the courage to face the issue with a clean cut solution and it was time to halt Davenport merchants in their robbery.

Because the government managed to raise their income bracket, there was no reason for prices to rise. Davenport and Tri City people refused to buy from the local merchants even though travelling out of town was an inconvenience.

B.J. at this time invited 400 Davenport businessmen to an evening meal in his cafeteria, at a cost of $5 per plate, even then. (This had been built in the basement of the new Administration Building. He served more than 2,000 daily at nominal cost.) Most of the men came out of curiosity.

B.J. could ill afford to feed 400 businessmen, but he figured it was worth it if he could somehow stop the crisis to Chiropractic caused by the high prices to his students.

One of the things he suggested was that PSC students act as substitute clerks after school hours during their enrollment. This gave students, strapped by the high cost of living in Davenport, additional spending money. These students were quick to verify the fact that Davenport's merchants were cheating the population. They had often told B.J. about things they saw pulled.

"Yeah," said one of the students one night, "I know what sort of funny business is going on in the store. I saw the Old Man receive cans of peas, peas mind you that he only paid 7 cents for, and mark them with black crayon. He wanted 50 cents for that can of peas when other places out of Davenport charge 10 to 12 cents. It's highway robbery, that's what."

"I need the money," said another, "but I hate to stand by and go along with what they are doing. . . . There are lots of people in Davenport who aren't able to afford the prices."

"Someone should do something," a third student said.

"I thought I might try my hand at stopping it," B.J. said.

"Say," said the first student, "I'll bet you could do it."

"I'll help," said the second student.

"I will need all of you to help," B.J. said. "Now, here is my plan . . ."

B.J. asked the boys to keep track of everything step by step raising in prices that went on in all stores. He told them to keep track of what merchants paid for items, what they should have sold them for, and what they did charge. These students were to collect any and all data of specific items, including incidents, stores, names, addresses, dates and prices that were raised further. It was after B.J.'s hundreds of students had collected more than 5,000 affidavits that he called the businessmen together for this dinner.

After a slow and leisurely dinner, B.J. invited the 400 men to his roof garden auditorium on top of the Administration Building. The men seated themselves and talked nervously for a few minutes. B.J. got onto the platform and talked for two hours. During that two hours he recalled the things people in Davenport were doing and saying about the local businessmen. Then he started to read some of the affidavits.

The businessmen wondered what manner of creature was up on the stage before them. They could not understand why he had taken it upon himself to crusade.

"What's he trying to prove?" one asked the other. "Everyone knows that the people in Davenport don't think too much of him and his damned 'science.' "

"Who does he think he is? . . . And what does he expect us to do?" some whispered.

They soon found out.

"I am under no obligation to Davenport for anything, as you men know. My main obligation is to help make the sick well; my second obligation is to teach others how to use my science and make people whole again.

"Davenport is under an obligation to me. By my starting a school and clinic here, even though you opposed it, I have brought people from all over the country to your doorsteps to buy something or other that you couldn't possibly have sold to the inhabitants and natives of Davenport. We are now drawing over two million dollars of foreign money a year and leaving it here with you. But let's forget your obligation to me.

"You people have an obligation towards the community. Unless you want Davenport to become a town that never was, you must stop this silly price-raising nonsense. The people of Davenport are spending almost their all in other cities. Why? Is there any reason why they should have to?"

"They spend thousands of dollars here, too!" one of the men shouted.

"Of course they do, but the thousands they are spending here amount to nothing in comparison to what they spend in sister cities. Let us remember the hundreds of thousands of dollars spent in other cities is lost local income. Davenport has suffered a severe financial blow and it will continue to do so. In the meantime, you men will go broke."

"They earn more money, why shouldn't we?" another businessman bellowed.

"No one would have said anything if you had raised your prices on items a nickel. No one would have cared too much if rents had risen $5, but prices you ask are an outrage."

"You lie!" one of the men said, rising to his feet and shaking his fist.

Soon most of the men in the auditorium were on their feet. They were throwing accusations at him and B.J. realized a minor riot was occurring. Somehow he managed to quiet them down. He read more damaging affidavits that had been delivered into his hands by his students. B.J. took off the kid gloves and appalled the businessmen at the mass of signed and sworn to affidavits he read them.

The businessmen, on the whole, had intertwined motives and interests. They had been dismayed at losing their help to the government. They had been angry and hurt like children. They raised their prices. The government paid well. Merchants kept raising their prices still further. They figured they were entitled to extreme profits. They hadn't expected what they had done to sound so outrageous. In black and white, what the businessmen had done was close to disastrous.

Like children, they became rebellious. What could this character do to stop them, even if what they were doing was unethical? Who did he think he was?

"If you force me to," B.J. said, "I shall go to the newspapers and buy space in them. I will reprint these affidavits, one by one. The people of Davenport will never patronize you. The newspapers know about this already. . . . The people have an idea, but they don't realize how serious it really is."

There were representatives of two local newspapers present. They made it known that space for this purpose would never be sold to B.J.

"All right, then, I will forget the newspapers."

The sighs of relief were clearly audible. They had shown that Palmer couldn't be a one man ruler in a town and take it over. They had shown him that he could not dictate to them.

"Instead, I will have to use radio. Radio reaches more people anyway."

"Some of you are aware I have owned and do now own a radio station. My radio station reaches all homes right now. No one can stop me from using my own radio station for days, weeks or months for this purpose. I broadcast anyway so there is no additional cost involved."

B.J. stopped talking and studied the faces of the men before him. There were all sorts of expressions, but mainly there were two: bewilderment and that of being beaten.

"Now, gentlemen, I suggest that you start coming down in your prices. If you don't, I will start a radio campaign tomorrow. . . . I mean it, gentlemen, so go on home and sleep on it."

The merchants went home. They argued, they fussed, they fumed, but they realized they were licked. After the anger wore away, they managed to see that "that Palmer fellow's idea is sound."

The next day the two local papers added 8 additional pages of advertising. Everyone in Davenport was lowering prices. Prices were being lowered on furniture, clothing, food, shelter . . . everything. . . . In two weeks things were down to practically normal prices and business was booming.

B.J. feared the merchants would resent him for having found a solution where there seemed to be none. Most of all he knew that they would hate him for forcing them to do something . . . even if it was for the best. He used his radio station to encourage Davenport to buy Davenport merchandise. B.J. saved Davenport from financial ruin and helped to support and preserve the future of his student enrollment and Chiropractic.

Soon the reforms which took place in Davenport stretched across the river to Moline and Rock Island because the same radio campaign served them also. These two cities were suffering from the same financial crisis which had gripped Davenport.

As B.J. had foreseen, the businessmen were sullen and bitter for months to come. B.J. was a social, commercial, professional and financial outcast in Davenport, but they soon began to see the power of one man who was independent. They gradually realized the power of a man who knew he had nothing to lose and everything to gain, a man who was bold enough to fight for what he knew to be right.

The Tri-Cities had, for years, hurt B.J.'s enrollments whenever they could. If a prospect wrote the Chamber of Commerce about B.J., he received a derogatory reply. If a sick person came to town, he was told not to waste his money on B.J. The townspeople were opposed to B.J., Chiropractic, or The PSC but they were always glad to take B.J.'s money. For these reasons, B.J. was, in those days, under no obligation to the town. Every dollar the townspeople received made *them* under obligation to him. But he wanted to save the merchants of the town, nonetheless, and he used his radio station to help them.

Being an outcast in the town wasn't all B.J. had to contend with. His faculty was sullen. They said that they had stayed with him for years, helping him build things, but his inviting the 400 to dinner that night and what he said was enough to kill and destroy everything. They told him they were leaving, quitting, resigning.

In the morning most of the faculty had cooled down. Many of them saw what a great idea it was, others realized he was right when they saw the newspapers. No one left, some apologized.

Years later, B.J. was approached and thanked for being a saviour of Davenport. The businessmen who hated him, resented him and wanted nothing to do with him, thanked him for saving their businesses.

Many businessmen have in their possession to this day a little souvenir of those days. It was a gift from B.J. to each of the 400. The souvenir was a little eight inch wooden coffin. Inside the coffin was a little hammer.

The souvenir was a reminder. It meant that the merchants should "stop knocking" Chiropractic and the men associated with Chiropractic.

The coffin was given because for years the businessmen were organized, dedicated to knocking B. J. Palmer, his work, his science and his accomplishments.

On the cover of this model coffin were inscribed the words "Requiescat in Pace." The words suggested that Chiropractic had its place in the world and that the merchants should wake up and see what the science has and will accomplish.

Translated, the words bore the simple but thoughtful suggestion . . . "Rest in Peace."

A strong message to all men can be drawn from what one man, B.J., did against tremendous odds.

Today B.J. is Davenport's best known and most respected person. . . . He belongs to all local clubs and organizations. His credit standing is ace high. He is known as a man of integrity and of deep sincerity and thousands of local people who have taken adjustments through the years, swear by and not at Chiropractic. There's no doubt that an amazing change has taken place in the community's attitude towards him.

There are few men who are willing to face the masses and fight for the right. People find it easier to bow to the mass because they are afraid to stand for what they believe in, if what they believe in doesn't suit everybody.

How many men would pit their common grade school opinion against 165,000 organized, educated opinions lined up solidly against him? B.J. did!

B.J. is not a superman. He is not physically "different" from other men. But he is perhaps more practical because he let Innate direct him along what line of action to pursue.

He knew he was right and he had the courage to say so. He knew he was fighting for justice and he had the strength to overcome the odds.

He had on his side righteousness, justice and the power of the universe. He listened to Innate Intelligence.

Innate led him to the right action; Innate gave him the right words to say when others could not find them. The single power of Innate Intelligence, even though working through one person, was greater and more powerful than the combined educations of 165,000 weaker people. Education in one or education in 165,000 people could be wrong.

But not Innate Intelligence.

B.J.'s Innate was forceful enough to lead him to directing 165,000 people and helping them help themselves.

It was the case of one tremendous giant, one man using his Innate, against many educated pygmies.

15

ALONG CAME PETE

B.J. HAD DONE MUCH research in the field of radio before it was known to the general public. His son, Dave, had a receiving set in his pigeon roost which was located on top of their home. Dave spent nights listening to boats on the ocean. He spent nights listening to weather talk and weather conditions or just general sea talk.

About this time a student named Stanley W. Barnett enrolled in PSC. While talking, B.J. discovered that Barnett had been an amateur radio "Ham" before he became interested in Chiropractic.

"It's a great thing," Barnett used to say. "Any man who has a chance to get in on the ground floor, and doesn't, is a fool."

"If you are so sure it is a great thing, I will get in on the ground floor. Would you run it for me, Stanley?"

Stanley thought about it. Radio was a new field. Who knew if it would ever succeed? That was one of the reasons he had gotten out of it, really. If it didn't catch on, then what?

"Chiropractic was once an unheard of thing," Barnett said. "You are doing a great job with it. If you are willing to take the chance, I'll manage it for you. I'd love to, as a matter of fact."

A fellow who lived in Rock Island had a radio broadcasting set that he used as a hobby. Stanley got in touch with him and tried to buy it. He decided to sell. His hobby was too expensive to keep up. Stanley became the first radio announcer. In later years he reversed his initials to BWS to avoid similarity between his name and another announcer's. "SWB," incidentally, became famous.

B.J. built a room about six feet wide and twelve feet deep over the top of the stairway of his administration building to serve as a studio and to hold all equipment. The motor was under a rustic seat in the hallway adjoining. Shortly thereafter, he built a room on top of the roof garden on the east side and later added a reception room.

In time to come he built a control room and little by little he added all the things which made an up-to-date efficient radio station.

People told B.J. that a fool and his money are soon parted. He sank $420,000 into his new venture, before he was permitted to earn his first dollars selling time. The newspaper editors he went to for advice laughed at him. It was a plaything for boys not businessmen or men with money, or money itself. B.J.'s banker told him the same thing. They did not discourage him because he saw something far beyond the capabilities of the average mind of his day.

In these days anybody could build and operate a radio station. There were no regulations. B.J. gradually expanded from a 5 watt set to a 100 watt, 500 watt to 5,000 watt, which was the first to use that much power. All this time he put money out and there was none coming in. He kept on. His main idea was to be able to broadcast Chiropractic within the range of his transmitters. He spent years building bigger stations.

One day, in a talk B.J. delivered over radio at his station, he made this prophecy: "The day will come when radio will bring the voice and pictures of the world, even in color, into all your homes." That vision of service has come true.

In those early days, WOC was on 400 watts. It was one of only 12 stations in America and it was heard all over the world. Letters would come from people in Australia, New Zealand, South Africa, Russia, and many other countries. Broadcasts were even repeated after midnight and were heard so far that letters were received from the families of men stationed at the North Pole.

At one time B.J. asked for higher power than 5,000 watts. It was granted providing WOC (Davenport) would amalgamate with WHO (Des Moines). This was done and WHO was raised to 50,000 watts. Later, B.J. bought "K-I-C-K" from Council Bluffs and took back the WOC of WHO-WOC, Des Moines. Today, B.J. has two radio stations, both of which are AM-FM-TV.

About the time that radio station WOC came into existence, Harry Lauder, a Scotch comedian, was playing in Davenport. Lauder had come in President Theodore Roosevelt's private pullman and B.J. met him. Later B.J. was invited to have after theatre supper with the Lauders.

"I have heard you are involved in radio, Dr. Palmer," Harry Lauder said as Mrs. Lauder, Pete MacArthur and his wife listened.

"You have heard correctly. I figure that radio is an important development in not only publicizing Chiropractic, it is also a vastly important development in a service known and recognized by the world."

"There are many scoffers, you know. People think of radio as a crazyman's dream."

"People laughed at Edison and thought he was crazy and his invention still crazier."

"You may think I am crazy, too, Harry, but I have an interest in radio myself," Pete said.

"He has been talking about it for centuries," said his wife. "If he isn't crazy, he's sure to drive me crazy."

Again everyone laughed.

"I'm looking for a program director," B.J. said laughingly.

Just as laughingly, Pete said, "When shall I report to work?"

"Tomorrow?"

"Tomorrow," Pete said, still laughing.

The group moved on to other discussions, including Chiropractic and vaudeville. B.J. left early because he had a busy day the next day.

The next day B.J. was up early to check patients, speak to the faculty and students and visit his radio studio. Pete MacArthur was waiting for B.J. when he got to his studio at 8 o'clock.

Pete helped to build B.J.'s radio station and often dubbed in as a singer, program manager, all-around man, crew. (Harry Lauder was a heavy drinker. He was wined and dined by everyone of importance in the world and he was often so badly in his cups that he could not put on his show. Pete MacArthur had been his understudy for 20 years. The audience never knew the difference between them because Pete sang Scotch songs and told jokes as well as Harry did.) Every man of the radio crew found himself working at all the jobs in the early days. But later when B.J. annexed radio station WHO, Des Moines, which he bought since it was another 5,000 watt clear channel station, Pete was given complete charge of building WHO's Barn Dance Show. WHO grew into a large organization.

One of B.J.'s pleasant memories which he tells as a joke on Pete concerns the time when he saw Pete in Dr. A. B. Hender's office. (Hender was Dean of the PSC until 1943 when he died. He was a prominent medical doctor who associated himself with B.J. in the early days of Chiropractic.) Dr. Hender was using tweezers in taking slivers out of Pete's tongue.

"What is going on?" B.J. asked when he stopped in.

"Oh," came the reply, "someone dropped a bottle of Scotch."

Pete stayed with WHO and B.J. for 20 years. It was due to Pete, B.J. often says, that the station was one of the 5 outstanding and successful radio stations in the United States. But Pete became sick. He came down with Rheumatoid Arthritis. Eventually his entire body became solid bone from head to toe, even his jawbone. All bones were completely ossified and ankylosed. But sickness didn't get Pete down; he still belonged to a quartet in Davenport that sang at noon Kiwanis meetings. So freely did Pete give of his Scotch singing ability and his talent at directing shows that the Kiwanis sent Pete, at their expense, to Florida for a winter vacation.

While Pete was in Palm Beach, Florida, he became worse, but at least he was not alone. Before leaving Davenport, he met a Miss Hupp who married him and nursed him. She worshipped him; she never left his side for more than an hour in the 14 years he was bedridden.

"Pete is the most wonderful thing that ever happened to me," she told B.J. "My life was just one dull humdrum thing behind the counter in that department store. A wonderful guy like Pete made me feel that life is worth living."

If someone said, "He looks terrible," she said, "He looks bad because he is sick, but if he would be turned inside out, he would be a beautiful man. . . . Anyway, look what I look like . . . and I am not sick."

Pete was often visited in Florida by B.J. who went there to be cheered up. During his frequent visits he would try to get Pete's wife, Hupp as they called her, to tear herself away from the house. She would leave for an hour, but no longer.

Pete became blind in both eyes, but he was still cheerful. He would laugh and say, "I have everything to live for. . . . Look at all the friends I have."

Pete never groaned or gave utterance to the pain B.J. knew he must have. All B.J. could say about Pete was, "He was one of the greatest inspirations I ever had the pleasure of being associated with. As for Hupp, she was one in a million."

One day at Stuart, Florida, B.J. went fishing. He took Pete, put him into his wheelchair and rolled him through the streets to the wharf. There he put him into his deck chair aboard his boat, lashed it and took Pete out for a day of fishing. Pete enjoyed that day. At times he laughed with sheer delight.

Whenever people came to see Pete, he would say, "Hey, did I tell you that I went fishing with B.J.? Boy, did we have fun . . . more fun than I ever had. . . . Funny thing is, though, I didn't catch too many fish. . . . I was too busy laughing and enjoying myself."

Pete had no outside income. His wife's only income was that earned by taking in boarders in their home in Palm Beach. Sometimes when the season was short or visitors few, times were pretty tough for the two.

B.J. kept him on the payroll of the station from the day he left to the day he passed away, 14 years later.

"I am paying him a regular monthly salary," B.J. said. "I like to feel that he is still running things; he gave us the best 20 years of his life."

Pete told Mabel, "Your husband keeps saying that I gave him and the station the 20 best years of my life. Do you know why they were the best?"

"No," Mabel said.

"They were the best years because I associated with B.J. and radio. Both of them are unbeatable. B.J. is an example for all to follow. I always wished I had his tireless energy."

Mabel smiled thinking of Bart, with a serious, sorrowful look upon his face, saying, "Pete had so much energy. He gave so much. He is the only guy I can think of who is always ready to go anywhere or do anything for anybody with never a thought of gain for himself."

Such loyalty, B.J. felt, was entitled to every consideration. Besides keeping up his salary, he kept him on his employees group insurance payroll. When Pete departed to Heaven, "probably to rebuild and reorganize communications," Hupp received $7,000 insurance.

Hupp knew she was marrying a helpless cripple, but it did not deter her. She knew her life would be one of sacrifice, but she never considered it as such.

"I'm not too sure that caring for Pete was so much work, but if it was it was a labor of love. It happens only once in a million years to two people out of a million. My only great sorrow is that it was so short a time. But I have his memory as so many do, and I thank God for letting me have him for 14 years."

Pete is no longer in the flesh, but the kind memories, the laughter, the accomplishments still linger with B.J. Pete and Hupp are two people who linger with him always . . . and will as long as he lives.

16

DIAL WHO AND WOC

WHEN B.J. FORMED THE Central Broadcasting Company in amalgamating WOC, Davenport, 5,000 watts and WHO, Des Moines, 5,000 to convert WHO to a 50,000 watt station, he lacked $35,000 to make the necessary arrangements. The bankers of Davenport loaned him the money but they exercised two options to insure WHO as an outlet for the purchase of power the bankers owned. In turn, NBC bought the $35,000 option from the Davenport bank, to insure WHO as an outlet for the National Broadcasting Company.

In reality B.J. was under no obligation to buy this option from NBC; he felt it was an obligation. The legal counsels of NBC were amazed. It was unheard of to think of an affiliated station wanting to buy an option where there was no obligation.

This action on B.J.'s part proved to NBC a sense of B.J.'s fairness and justice, as well as moral responsibility in its attitude towards B.J. To this day, whenever B.J. is in New York, he never bothers the president unless there is business needing his attention. If the president knows B.J. is in town, he calls and insists that they have lunch together. The president of NBC, a very busy man, feels he is being done a favor if B.J. accepts.

By paying off the option, B.J. received dividends in years to come. During Lyceum, years later, the president granted B.J. a fifteen minute net schedule coast-to-coast talk. This was something B.J. had dreamed about.

When asked once why he bought the option from NBC, he said, "Innate told me it was the right thing to do; therefore, I did. What else could I do?"

As years passed, B.J. found himself becoming a great lover of music. He broadcast music on WOC Davenport. To further his interests in broadcasting music, he built a porch around his home and installed an Aeolian pipe organ which consisted of a grand, swell and echo organ. He installed it in two organ chambers, one in front for the grand and swell and the echo organ at the other end. The housing alone cost B.J. $10,000 for he had it heat-proofed, cold-proofed, rat and vermin-proofed. It is heated in the winter, thermostatically controlled.

This organ is a one thousand pipe-twin manual organ, containing various orchestration stops; this includes harp and Deagan chimes. He has frequently broadcast various instrumental combinations from his home over WOC. Everything from a full symphony orchestra to pipe organ and piano, cellists and singers have been broadcast. This organ cost B.J. $75,000. He plays it for his own enjoyment and visiting friends, and at the request of his vast radio audience, for the public.

Besides his love for his organ, B.J. had a great deal of love for Big Ben, a St. Bernard dog that weighed 185 pounds. The dog was devoted to its master and B.J. treated him accordingly.

Whenever B.J. went away on a trip, he left him in capable hands. Before B.J. went on one of his many trips to the Orient, he left word that if Big Ben died, his remains were to be shipped east to be mounted as he always slept. Big Ben died and B.J. placed him under the piano in the music room, since this had been the dog's favorite resting spot.

One day Grace Huber, now Grace Lohmiller, was singing over station WOC. She was being accompanied by the Chickering piano and organ. She looked down and saw Big Ben lying there.

Grace thought the dog might bark during her performance, but it didn't. She smiled at it and was glad it didn't bark. Then, it dawned upon her . . . he was dead. "He's dead!" she said, into the "mike" between stanzas.

The next few days B.J. received thousands of letters asking who died. He answered each letter with a printed explanation.

When B.J. got into radio he met many interesting people. He made many friends and he helped to make stars out of people. One of the radio announcers who worked for B.J., whom some of you might recognize, was a young man named Ronald Reagan.

In those early days, radio was a novelty. Everybody wanted "to get into the act." WOC had the honor of presenting many firsts, such as Rudy Vallee, Little Jack Little, (Here 'Tis), Ruth St. Denis, Ted Shawn, and many others who later demanded big fees for commercials on radio.

Soon after the start of radio, selling of advertising and space on the air was found to be difficult. The public was not ready to accept this new idea until it was proved, and the people who could advertise were waiting for the public to say, "We like this. . . . Go ahead, it's worthwhile for you to use this form of media." Eventually the public woke up and accepted radio, but while it slept the radio owners faced ruination. Most of the radio stations had very little capital to fall back on since radio was so expensive to keep up. Without advertising money, it was lost.

Some radio owners stopped putting money into the new field; they either sold or just shut down. Others looked for some way to remedy the situation but none seemed to be apparent.

B.J. also was having the same trouble. He didn't know what to do. Then he listened to his friend who is always with him . . . Innate Intelligence. It did not fail. It helped him write a book on radio salesmanship. The book became a standard text for 128 schools, colleges and universities of the radio stations in the world.

B.J. never traveled without his typewriter. No matter what time of the day or night it was, no matter in what part of the world he was, when his Innate dictated B.J. sat and typed. He has to date written 36 volumes. Almost all are the result of the inspiration given him by his Innate Intelligence . . . that inborn intelligence which knows what to do and how to do it when something must be done.

Among radio men, B.J. is credited with having saved the industry from going bankrupt.

The governor of the state bestowed the title of Colonel upon B.J. to honor him for his accomplishments.

Thus, again, as in so many cases, Innate helped B.J. to help others. This time it prevented bankruptcy and destruction from taking hold in the radio industry because it dictated a book which helped others sell air space.

17

B.J. AND ELBERT HUBBARD

ONE OF B.J.'S FRIENDS was Elbert Hubbard, a natural. He lived, loved, thought and wrote without inhibitions. What he thought, he said. If he found no words to express a thought, he coined them. His works on Journeys to the Homes of the Great and Near Great are masterpieces of modern thinking. He wrote about B.J. and Chiropractic. Elbert Hubbard admired hand-made arts and he enjoyed B.J.'s bedroom which is all Roycroft hand made furniture. In his cafeteria are many epigrammatic carved slabs; in his private clinic, there are hand made chairs; in his library, now, are handtooled leather bindings of Hubbard's autographed writings.

In the Palm Court of the B. J. Palmer Chiropractic Research Clinic, is the first piece of furniture made by The Roycrofters—a grandfather clock which strikes the quarters and the hours. After the passing of Elbert and Alice, B.J. wrote their son, Bert, and asked for it. Bert gave it to him gladly.

Hubbard made hand hammered metal ware of various kinds. B.J. has many lamps Hubbard made for him.

B.J. and Hubbard were intimate friends; B.J. admired the man. They were both national speakers of note and they met often on lecture tours.

Hubbard maintained a great hand set printing plant which used hobo type. It was Hubbard's idea to form the Roycrofters. Elbert's desire was to build a village of craftsmen who would work with their hands rather than stamp their products by machinery. He maintained shops in which all this was done, even to the hotel in which he entertained his guests. His buildings were built of cobblestone rather than bricks and the bedrooms were named after authors of note. It was a distinctively different institution for that day and there has been nothing to equal it to the present.

Whenever Hubbard was lecturing in the west, he cut off his journey to spend a few days with B.J. Hubbard never believed in knocking at the doors of his friends; he always walked in expecting to be welcomed, and he always was.

Elbert Hubbard always travelled with a secretary whom he called Percy. Hubbard thought of Percy as being the personification of nothing. One morning B.J. found Hubbard at his front door. He looked like a tramp who had ridden a freight train all night. He was dirty, his clothes and linen were unkempt and wrinkled. B.J. took one look at the full page advertisement and picture of Hubbard in an immaculate Royal tailored suit. This was on the cover of the current issue of *The Fra,* by Hubbard.

B.J. didn't say hello or greet Hubbard. Noting Hubbard's dilapidated appearance, he said:

"Behold the Royal Tailored man."

Hubbard smiled. "That was only an advertisement," he said.

Hubbard was followed into the house by Percy who was lugging a big Underwood typewriter. B.J. busily turned through the pages of *The Fra* again and read, "I wouldn't travel without my trusty Corona."

Hubbard laughed. "That is another advertisement. . . . I guess we're on to each other."

Of course while Hubbard visited with B.J. he lectured to the PSC student body. Hubbard enjoyed it and B.J. considered it a pleasure. The students loved it.

Shortly after, B.J. lectured in the East. He broke his journey to spend a few days with Hubbard at the Roycrofters Inn, in East Aurora, N.Y. In these days anyone of prominence could be met there. Here B.J. met Nazimova, Carrie Jacobs Bond and many others.

He met Carrie Jacobs Bond after luncheon one day.

"I am glad to meet you," she said. She disappeared shortly afterwards.

B.J. continued to talk to a few people and then he, too, wandered away. He heard music coming from the musical salon and he wanted to find out where it came from.

Sitting in the music salon with her back to the great hall, sat Carrie Jacobs Bond, strumming her tunes and singing to herself. B.J. entered quietly and listened for three hours. The famous woman was unaware that he was there. Shortly afterwards, Hubbard crept in. He saw what was taking place, closed the shops down and invited all of his helpmates to sneak in quietly and enjoy the performance.

As though the sun had just come above the horizon, Mrs. Bond became aware of the fact that crowds had gathered. She smiled and thanked them for listening.

"It was truly our pleasure," B.J. said. "Your tunes are beautiful."

"Why, thank you," she said, complimented.

"Tell me, how did you compose some of your famous numbers?"

"Which one in particular, Dr. Palmer?"

"I was thinking of 'The End of A Perfect Day.' "

"I composed that one after the death of my husband."

"What about 'Little Pink Rosebud?' "

"I composed that after the death of my little daughter."

B.J. marvelled. Out of her tragedies, she had created beauty for millions to enjoy. Truly, this was the way to get the better of tragedy and stand up taller and better than before.

Soon after B.J.'s visit with Hubbard, Elbert decided he would like to settle down. His little colony of Roycrofters gave him a lot to do and he derived much satisfaction from the group. He had a log cabin across the Nazimova creek which he called Pigeon Roost. It was here he came to rest away from the world and write about his journeys to the Great and Near Great of his time. He decided that to do this, he would have to become a semi-hermit. He never invited guests to visit him.

There was one exception to this rule, though. This exception was B.J. Palmer whom he frequently invited. Between weiner roasts and twilight the two settled many world problems.

The most publicized article ever written by Hubbard was *The Message to Garcia*. This piece sold millions of copies and was translated into almost every language. Part of B.J.'s ideas with him were incorporated in this piece.

One night while seated around the big fireplace in the big room of the Inn, Hubbard told B.J. how he happened to write this story. He had never told anyone how he happened to do anything, but he told B.J. because B.J. was more than a friend.

Hubbard was married to a woman whom he loved very much. When he built Roycroft Inn to house his friends who came and stayed, she did not mind. When he decided to become a semi-hermit, she let him. He decided to raise fruits, vegetables, poultry and make dairy products, she still agreed. He served these products at the Inn and charged so much per day.

Hubbard knew that there were rich men's sons and daughters who were useless except as social butterflies. Hubbard offered to take these boys and girls, at a fee of $500 per vacation periods from their parents.

He put the boys to work on the farms picking fruit, lugging slop to the pigs, feeding the cows and horses and churning butter. These boys did all the daily chores on the farm.

It was up to Alice Hubbard (the White Hyacinth) to teach the girls to can fruit and wait on tables.

"I will not serve your *guests,*" one sulking debutante told Alice. "I am no waitress."

Alice looked at the girl and smiled. "You are right, dear. You have not developed enough personality, yet. You will be a hostess."

Hubbard and his wife made useful people out of rich men's offspring. He was paid for what he did. He also reaped a rich harvest on hotel fees and other fees charged his guests.

On one occasion when Hubbard visited B.J. he took him into his Osteology studio where he showed him a spinal column of 18 vertebrae and another of 30. Twenty-four vertebrae are normal. One had 6 less than normal; the other had 6 more than usual. Hubbard wanted to know why.

"Man is still in the process. He has not yet arrived."

Hubbard was delighted with this explanation. He later wrote a story around B.J.'s idea and had it published in the *Philistine*. At dinner that night, Hubbard told B.J. what he had given him to think about.

B.J. was flattered. They continued with dinner chatter. After dinner, they got onto the topic of words.

"Now," said Hubbard, "I will give you something to think about. What are the two greatest words in the English language?"

B.J. thought about it for a moment and said, "I have my two words; what are yours?"

"Survival value."

"Survival value? I don't think much of them."

"I didn't think you would. The more you think about it, the more it will grow in your ideas."

And the more B.J. thought about the two words, the better they seemed to him, as Hubbard had prophesied. The words became valuable to him and he enlarged upon them. He later came up with these words: "Accumulative constructive survival value, and accumulative destructive survival value."

B.J.'s thoughts were that everything some men do is constructive or destructive. The longer they live, the more destructive value accumulates and survives after them. Napoleon, Mussolini and Hitler were men in that class. They leave behind a persistent trail of evil and suffering. Everything some other men do is constructive. The longer they live, the more that constructive value accumulates and survives after them. Examples: Abraham Lincoln, Thomas Edison, Henry Ford, D. D. Palmer and others. They leave behind a persistent trail of good helpfulness to mankind. The analysis of these actions is that the destructive type leave only the results of their educated emotions, passions and prejudices to follow. The constructive type leave the good of their Innates to follow them through life which exists long after they have gone.

B.J. always thought about Hubbard whenever he reviewed his philosophy. He remembered the way the Hubbards had worked together for things that would live on. Elbert Hubbard and his wife died the way they lived. When they were aboard the *Lusitania,* and it was sinking, there were no more life boats to get into.

"It's been a great life, hasn't it?" Elbert said to Alice.

She nodded and smiled. They took one another by the hand and calmly went into their stateroom. They went down with the ship.

18

---◆---

THIS WILL FRACTURE YOU

THE GROWTH OF CHIROPRACTIC is mute testimony to the men who fought to protect its principles. The fight wasn't easy. The enemy was too willing to grab a straw and turn it into a sword.

But Bartlett Joshua Palmer and the faculty of the Palmer School of Chiropractic defended the right and in this defense was their strength.

Their science wasn't based on mysticism or superstition; it was based on what now seems an elementary principle: The power Man has to help himself rests within Man.

This principle, revealed by D. D. Palmer and relayed to the world by his son, caught on. Chiropractic grew. Although there were temporary set backs, B. J. Palmer championed the cause. And he won.

B. J. Palmer is responsible for placing the second largest healing art on its solid feet and leading it from oblivion to success.

The Chiropractic profession has helped 40 million people who proudly say: "I'm better because Chiropractic exists." And there are 2 million more who annually come under its care.

This is what B.J. built up. This is the result of farsighted thinking when a boy told his father that Chiropractic was too important to keep a family secret.

He told his father that many people needed Chiropractic, that men would have to be taught the methods so they might help spread the healing art. There are now many thousands of men and women who practice Chiropractic.

And yet, there was a time when just one man, one irresponsible Chiropractor, almost destroyed the art B.J. dedicated his life to. This happened when . . .

An important star in vaudeville called on a New York Chiropractor for help. The star was having trouble; medicines didn't help.

The star had heard about this new healing art and decided to see if what was said was true. She placed herself in the hands of a Chiropractor who was drunk.

The Chiropractor placed the star across a divided adjusting table, spread too far apart. His drunken stupor eradicated all his ability at his art. He pounded at her lumbar vertebrae . . . and the pressure forced her stomach down between the divided table. The drunken practitioner broke the back of the vaudeville star who was then at the peak of her career.

The star was a close friend of Mr. Albee, the owner of the famed Orpheum, Keith and Albee vaudeville circuits. The chain included thousands of theatres in the U.S. and Canada, and played to more than 8 million people daily.

When Mr. Albee heard the story of what a drunken Chiropractor did, he issued an order to all the performers who played his chains:

"Every chance you get, ridicule Chiropractic until we have the world laughing at it instead of looking for it."

Many of the acts that played in Albee's theatres followed the directive, and the more than 8 million people who attended vaudeville shows daily heard such remarks as:

"Judge, I did not beat up my wife. We were just play acting. She was playing patient and I was playing Chiropractor."

Around the nation the jokes were being told:

The comedian would walk out on the stage, limping and holding both hands to his lower spinal region:

"Boy," he would say, addressing the audience, "My Chiropractor told me a joke yesterday while he was working on me and it really fractured me."

There was the routine where a comedian dressed in ragged comic clothes would come on stage throwing punches around in an imitation of a prize fighter.

He would throw a couple of punches and then double over laughing.

"Hey, what are you laughing about . . . and why are you making like a fighter? You couldn't fight your way out of a paper bag."

"Oh yeah," said the first comedian, "Oh yeah. You know that guy who was always pushing me around. Well just a little while ago I beat him up. I punched him in the mouth, then in the eyes, back to the mouth, in the nose . . . boy, I made a mess of his face."

The comedian would throw a couple more punches in the air and continue:

"I didn't stop hitting him until that cop hauled me off to the judge."

"What happened? How did you get out?" asked the straight man.

"That was easy. I just used my old noodle," said the comedian. "When the judge charged me with fighting, I said: 'Now wait a minute judge, you got this all wrong. I wasn't fighting, I was helping the man.'

"Well the judge just looks at me and says 'You beat a man up so bad he has to go to the hospital and you say you were helping him?'

"And here's where the old brain is put to work . . . I says: 'Judge, I'm the guy's Chiropractor.' He let me go, was the punch line."

Audiences howled at this joke and many more like it. Even old jokes were changed around and brought into the campaign against the baby science:

"Who was that drunken bum I saw you with last night," said the male comedian to the female comic.

"That was no bum, that was my Chiropractor," was the new switch.

Or: "Why did the Chiropractor cross the road? To get to the other bar."

The jokes became rougher as the comedians warmed up to the newest whipping boy:

"You know who is the smartest guy in the world?" said the comic to the straight man. "No, who?" was the feed line.

"A Chiropractor," said the comic. "You pay him to give you a back set."

A famed vaudeville puppet act used this routine: One puppet would come on stage, stagger over to a second puppet and begin pulling its arms.

"Hey, what do you think you're doing?" said the second puppet.

"I'm studying for my Chiropractic test," answered the first puppet.

Then there was the routine where the drunk staggered in late and his wife was waiting up for him:

"Drinking again; don't lie to me, I saw you in the bar before," said the wife.

And the drunk answered: "Honest baby, I wasn't drinking in that bar . . . I was getting a Chirop . . . pr . . . pic . . . bone treatment."

It didn't take long for audiences to get the idea that Chiropractic must be a joke.

Chiropractors were all supposed to be drunkards. People to be laughed at. The profession began to feel the effects.

Patients dropped out by the thousands. Chiropractors were being pointed out and ridiculed. Enrollment at colleges dropped. The profession turned to B.J. and urged him to do something.

Here was another fight B.J. had to win. He had fought many battles before to protect the new science and he didn't hesitate to undertake this one. The future of Chiropractic once again depended on B.J. for its salvation.

But what could he do? He could not undo the drinking of *one* Chiropractor. He could not undo the damage caused by the drunk pounding on the vaudeville star's back. He could not undo the paralysis that occurred, and he was helpless to recover the losses of patients taking place in Chiropractors' offices all over the country.

Theatrical people are clannish; injure one and you injure all. Help one and you help all. This was the straw B.J. had to grasp if he was to save the science.

B.J.'s chance came one evening while watching a vaudeville show in the Columbia Theatre in Davenport. He noticed the show was not running smoothly. He sensed something was wrong but could not pin it down.

He thought about the situation and then his inborn intelligence, his Innate hit upon the problem and the solution. B.J. sat in the theatre feeling helpless and listening to each act knocking Chiropractic, in the town where it was born, but now he had an idea how to help his and their professions.

B.J. realized in every act, actors and actresses were sick. Singers had colds, acrobats had kinks in their backs, the pianist had rheumatism in his fingers and so it went.

B.J. walked back stage and looked for the theatre manager, who was a student in his school and a friend of his. He asked the manager to gather all acts backstage after the show.

When the vaudevillians were assembled, B.J. told them what he detected and asked them to come to his office at 9 A.M. the next morning to get free Chiropractic service.

Because it cost nothing, vaudevillians were willing to try out Chiropractic. They went the next morning and got free adjustments. At the end of the week, when the acts packed for their next town, B.J. gave each person a letter introducing them to a Chiropractor in their stopping off place.

The letter requested each Chiropractor to give the bearer Chiropractic adjustments free of charge. It stipulated that the practitioner stick to straight Chiropractic and not use all innovations and tricks some practitioners were resorting to.

The letter, addressed to the doctor, read: "This will introduce you to, (here was put the name of the performer), introduced to us by (here was put the name and address of the Chiropractor). He is of good people of the road, the Knights of the Grip.

"His path through life is strenuous with many downs and many ups. He is a booster for us and will do much for you. He has troubles that need adjusting. Get busy.

"Give him straight, specific, pure and unadulterated type. He knows that adjusting subluxations in the spine is Chiropractic and that anything else given him under the guise of Chiropractic is proof that you are not a thoroughbred, so cut out the electricity, baths, stretching machines and the rest of the bunk.

"Give him of your best and charge it to profit and loss. If, in the conduct of your business you do not agree with me in this policy, make no charge to him, make out a statement and send it to me.

"I send you, with this kind friend, my best wishes and best regards for all they will bring. I am,

Chiropractically yours,"

The letter was signed by B.J.

The word spread throughout the vaudeville world. Performer told performer about this free Chiropractic service and, even more important, about how this new art was actually effective.

Other vaudeville acts wrote and asked B.J. for letters; B.J. sent them. (At one time he was sending out as many as 8,000 letters annually.)

B.J. extended this service to Evangelists and their helpers; to travelling salesmen; to anybody whose business put them on the road. It was these traveling men who would spread the word. They were living proof of the help given by Chiropractic.

The plan worked. Acts began boosting Chiropractic. Audiences heard the word Chiropractic used in complimentary terms. Jokes about the profession became scant. Business took an upturn. Patients flocked back to practitioners; students flocked back to schools.

B.J. was satisfied in a short time, vaudeville would atone for the damage it caused. And in passing weeks, his faith was justified.

A letter came from Mr. Albee asking B.J. to drop in next time he visited New York. B.J. did.

Mr. Albee challenged B.J.'s right to tell the acts to plug Chiropractic "while playing in my theatres."

"I didn't tell the good people of the theatre anything; it wasn't necessary," B.J. said.

"They are doing it of their own free will, without suggestions from me," he said. "They are doing it because they found for themselves how Chiropractic gets them well."

Now B.J. was ready for the finale in his campaign to restore Chiropractic to its former dignity:

"Mr. Albee, when you have one bad act or one bad actor or actress, and it doesn't go over, what do you do?"

"I call them in and cancel their act," was the reply.

"It is that simple in your business," said B.J. "But once we have graduated a Chiropractor, we have no strings on him. We cannot control his actions. He is on his own. What he does or doesn't do is his business. He has a state license which we can't cancel."

"He can turn out to be the best practitioner in the field or he can get drunk and injure someone. We have no way of calling him in and cancelling his practice. Do you see what I am driving at?"

Mr. Albee admitted B.J.'s defense made sense.

"So Mr. Albee, how fair were you when you hurt a world-wide profession because of *one man's* actions. Would you be as quick to condemn all vaudeville because one act is bad?"

B.J. had made his point; Mr. Albee saw the justice of his argument and the injustice of his own hasty actions.

As a token of apology, Mr. Albee presented B.J. with a gold engraved membership card to NVA House, a hotel for theatrical people in New York.

Vaudeville is dead now. But Palmergrams, the letters given acts introducing them to Chiropractors, still go on. Chiropractors still honor the letters. They are renewable once a year upon the request of any Chiropractor, who in turn sends the expired letters back to B.J.

This episode had its moral: There is no such thing as an unimportant man. One Chiropractor, a drunkard practitioner in New York, almost ruined the entire profession. It could have been a man in a backwoods town in the northern New England states; it could have been a man in a middle-sized community in Texas; it could have been any Chiropractor, everyone fits in the great scheme of things.

B.J. gained two things out of this episode: he drove home the lesson— if you drink, don't adjust; if you adjust don't drink. All B.J. got for this service was autographed pictures of each person to whom he issued a Palmergram. He has now more than 8,000 photographs of people in the theatre, vaudeville, movies, radio and TV.

The pictures completely cover the walls and ceiling of the B.J. Palmer Chiropractic Clinic assembly hall.

To go back for a moment to the period when vaudeville was attacking Chiropractic, some help in the battle to restore the profession came from a famous song writer, Dave Stamper.

Dave had been taking Chiropractic service for many years prior to the episode. He wanted to repay the men who had done so much for him.

He went to Flo Ziegfeld, for whom he was writing music for a review, and suggested that Flo set up a Chiropractic adjusting table in one of the dressing rooms for the cast.

Flo did. He retained a New York Chiropractor and paid for his whole cast.

Dave, who wrote 23 of Ziegfeld's shows and is a charter member of ASCAP, is to this day taking Chiropractic adjustments and boosting its healing help.

19

$$\diamond\!\!\!\!-\!\!\!\!\diamond\!\!\!\!-\!\!\!\!\diamond$$

THREE STEPS FORWARD

Bartlett Joshua Palmer was always seeking better ways to deliver better service. He could never enjoy watching how far Chiropractic had developed. His active mind searched for the new, for the not yet uncovered. He was a scientist.

He was also a lover of the arts. Beauty and Nature were to him as food and sleep are to most.

He relaxed with music; he worked for science. He knew no bounds in his relentless search for more information about the body.

In the years 1920 to '22, Doss Evens, a graduate electrical engineer, attended school at PSC. Upon graduation, he was asked to join the faculty. His contributions to the science proved invaluable.

Doss spent five years trying to build an electronic instrument which would prove the theory of Chiropractic. He spent endless hours in the laboratory working and reworking his ideas. In 1925, the Neurocalometer was granted a process patent to the Palmer School.

It proved to be a big stepping stone in scientifically proving the principle and practice of Chiropractic.

Its function was to locate nerve interference in the spine. After an adjustment, it was again employed to recheck the spine and see if the interference had been corrected.

Before the invention of this scientifically proven instrument, Chiropractors used highly trained fingers to explore the length of the spine. They would glide their skilled fingertips over the spine until they came in contact with little hot boxes—heat radiated through the skin from the places where the nerve was pinched.

This instrument discovered these areas with scientific accuracy. It had a two-pronged instrument, extending out from a dial. The prongs would be glided over both sides of the spine and when it contacted a hot-box, the result would register on the dial giving the Chiropractor exact locations of interferences, pre- and post-checks.

The instrument was employed again after the adjustment as a check to see that all interferences were released.

There were no electrical attachments to the Neurocalometer. Its operation was governed solely by heat emanating from the pinched nerve. The operation is comparable to an electrical short circuit.

The instrument was further developed at PSC to connect it to a graph allowing the Chiropractor to permanently graph patterns of the patients' problems. The graph also provided a file record of the Chiropractors pre- and post-checkings of the patient.

Once the instrument was proven beyond doubt, B.J. decided to take it out of the experimental category and introduce it to the profession. He called together the school's faculty to tell them of the latest step to be made.

The faculty, which B.J. assembled, consisted of some of the finest Chiropractic brains within the profession. When they were told by B.J. of the plan to introduce the Neurocalometer into the curriculum, some responded by threatening to leave the school if such action was taken.

The situation was painfully familiar to B.J. Had not this happened 16 years ago when B.J. introduced the spinograph into the curriculum?

Again B.J. was faced with a decision: Do what he thought best for the science he dedicated his life to, and risk making dangerous enemies out of friends, or bowing to the demands of the faculty and cheat Chiropractors out of a valuable asset.

He decided for the profession. He suffered great personal grief by the insipid action of the angered faculty and almost saw the profession and the reputation of its discoverer ruined.

He made his decision . . . let the axe fall and the chips fly where they may; the instrument was added to the Palmer School curriculum.

And, as in the past, some of the members of the faculty left PSC to start their own college.

Fortunately, for the profession, these men didn't leave PSC with hate in their hearts. They simply felt the instrument was not suitable for Chiropractic.

The instrument proved itself in years to come. Its importance in the study of patient problems equaled the importance of the x-ray.

Medical scientists had known for years, from their study of anatomy and neurology, that bundles of nerves emanated from the spinal cord through openings between vertebrae. But they did not know where the nerves went or what their general function was.

It was B.J. who through the development of the Spinograph and the Neurocalometer proved that every tissue and every organ has a corresponding cell in the brain and the brain, like an electrical dynamo, generates the nerve energy. This energy is sent down through the spinal cord, which is actually a continuation of the brain. It then goes from the spinal cord out via the bundles of nerves to every tissue and organ in the body.

If there is any interference in this flow of energy from brain through spinal cord over nerves to tissue cells, organs will not receive their proper nourishment and in time will degenerate.

Clearly it is evident no Chiropractor can technically say he makes sick people healthy. B.J.'s research proved that the real power to heal comes from within the body.

This ability of the body to heal itself was named by B.J., Innate Intelligence. This means the body will take care of itself; the Chiropractor's job is to correct interferences in the body when the machinery gets entangled.

Doctors aid, but the Innate Intelligence directs and its power cures. If a surgeon makes an incision, it is Innate which forms the scar tissue which closes the breach. If a doctor sets a fractured bone, it is the body's Innate Intelligence which knits the fracture back together.

The impact of this Neurocalometer was so tremendous that it almost proved a boomerang against B.J., the PSC and Chiropractic. It was publicly introduced first at an Eastern seaboard symposium in New Jersey. The fact that it provided a more efficient service was so obvious that almost all those at the symposium wanted them as soon as possible. B.J. taught them its use and promised a traveling school to cover all groups in the field. What would it cost? Nobody had given that matter consideration. B.J. was anxious to help all Chiropractors so he arbitrarily placed the sale cost at $100. On his return home, his bookkeepers showed him that for every sale he made at $100, he would lose $400 with his traveling school demonstrations. The price was immediately raised to $500. Later, it was thought advisable that it was better not to sell the instrument outright for it might be used carelessly and thus do harm. Therefore, it was decided to have the sale based on a lease-rental plan, with monthly payments and with repairs made available at no cost. Today, many thousands are in use. It has been invaluable when competently used. This method of sale kept the control of this instrument in the hands of B.J. and The PSC. Other schools were granted the right to use it also, but, because it added prestige to The PSC, many schools denied the instrument had any value. Since then, various types of instruments purporting to perform a like service have been offered to the profession.

B.J.'s work and discoveries and farsighted thinking kept hypoing Chiropractic advances in the healing arts. The new idea, the new invention, the radical step were the things B.J. thrived upon. The same pioneering spirit that led D. D. Palmer to the discovery led B.J. to constant rediscovery. He wasn't afraid to be different. If there was something new to be done, B.J. did it.

Throughout the years the men in the field put a constant demand on B.J. to build a personal clinic that would explore the problem cases and correlate the information gained. Then this information would be used in a scientific research program.

B.J. certainly was the man to turn to. He was a leader and his school had on hand latest scientific knowledge necessary to deal with stubborn cases.

B.J. invested $1,000,000 to build the B. J. Palmer Chiropractic Research Clinic.

The purpose of the duality of both medical and Chiropractic sections was to dispute those medical critics who said, "Patients who go to Chiropractors are hypochondriacs. They're not actually sick, they just think they are. It's all in their minds." To disprove this theory, the same medical tests were made on the patients before and after treatment at the clinic. So long as these sick people went to the M.D.'s their sicknesses were supposed to be genuine. But the minute they went to a Chiropractor, they ceased to be ill, they merely imagined their sicknesses!

The Chiropractors in the field sent problem cases to the clinic. Upon entering, the patient was examined by the medical staff who used all the latest medical scientific instruments. Then B.J. examined the patient with all the scientific instruments that the Chiropractic profession had discovered.

When the patient completed his Chiropractic adjustments and health service, the same medical staff re-examined the patient. Their new findings were correlated with the Chiropractic findings to prove the correctness of Chiropractic the patient received.

When the patient was discharged from the clinic, he was sent back to his Chiropractor, along with a complete transcript of the patient's case history and the clinic's findings. With this information the Chiropractor in the field can render better health service to his patient.

The clinic was the best money could buy. Within its walls there is a complete rehabilitation laboratory, a private auditorium where B.J. lectures to patients, B.J.'s osteology studio which he built over the years at a cost of over $500,000. The studio contains 25 thousand specimens and is the largest collection of spines in the world. Only Harvard University, which contains the second largest collection, comes anywhere near the clinic.

In the rehab of the clinic is one 40 foot long, 20,000 gallon aquarium with tropical fish. (When he designed this B.J. was recalling his youthful days when he sold various types of goldfish to the public from his father's infirmary.) The fish tanks serve as a relaxation to patients.

The clinic became so famous that one of the foremost doctors in the U.S. came to it for assistance. The doctor's wife had been given up as incurable. The doctor consulted with B.J. and then decided to send his wife as a last resort.

The doctor gave B.J. all his medical findings on his wife's case, which B.J. refused.

"What do I want with your findings?" B.J. told him. "No one knows the findings better than you and you were not able to get her well.

"If you are going to place your wife in my care then I must be allowed to care for her my way. I will give her my Chiropractic analysis and adjust her based on what I uncover.

"If you don't have confidence in me or my profession or in my clinic then we are finished before we start."

The doctor agreed with B.J. and turned his wife's case over to B.J. without strings attached.

B.J. made his analysis and adjustments.

The Chiropractic adjustments were able to do what medical science had failed on. The doctor's wife left the clinic and lived in comparatively good health for years after.

A complete case file is kept on every case. All files are numbered and are stored away for ready reference. Everything in The B. J. Palmer Chiropractic Research Clinic is done methodically and is based on scientific research. One of B.J.'s slogans is "The first consideration of every person in this clinic is to do everything just exactly right." This principle is strictly adhered to by all.

Because of B.J.'s work, the prominent physician has referred many problem cases to B.J.'s private clinic.

Again, in this one case, as in so many similar cases, Chiropractic proved its abilities and justified its fight for recognition.

B.J.'s clinic converted another medical man into realizing that Chiropractic was not based on guess work or mysticism. He again proved Chiropractic is science based on study and research; that it doesn't depend on pills, powders or potions but on skill, training and knowledge.

20

LITTLE BIT O' HEAVEN

B.J. INTRODUCED A NEW INSTRUMENT into the profession and science of Chiropractic. Some of his faculty left him and people thought he was way off the beam. For years there was not a day that B.J. did not receive almost 200 letters of the most vicious and condemning types attacking his personal and professional integrity. This B.J. could take, but the letters telling him that he was ruining a science for which he had struggled and sacrificed added pounds of punishment to an already tired body.

No matter how strong a man, no matter how positive and sound his thinking, the constant bombardment of a derogatory nature acts like dripping of water on a piece of granite. In time, something must go, and so it was with B.J. He could feel his grip slipping as something was slipping within him.

B.J.'s mind was cracking under the injustice and persecution. If this had been B.J.'s first meeting with persecution the effects might have been less damaging. As it was, he became unreasonable even with his closest friends who worried about his health and the future of Chiropractic.

"B.J. sure is hard to get along with these days," one friend said to another.

"You said it. I said good morning to him a bit too slowly this morning. He almost snapped my head off."

"It is understandable. He has had a hard time of it."

"I think B.J. needs a rest. He works so damn hard. First he had to build up the new field of Chiropractic. He did a great job, but he wasn't satisfied . . . He had to do a better job. It seemed perfectly natural to him to go into radio, another unknown field, build that up and then build Chiropractic still further."

"I wish there was more we could do to help him. I'm a bit worried about Chiropractic without B.J. in control of all his faculties. He should take a rest."

"We really cannot do too much to relieve him of his burden, but if we can talk him into taking a rest, that might do it."

"You're right."

Everyone knew that at this period of his life, B.J. had worked for 18 hours a day, 365 days a year. They also knew that B.J. only allotted himself 6 hours of sleep per day during the time when he took over his father's practice and school. They suggested he go to Pass Christian, Mississippi. There, they told him, he could rest and occupy his mind with thoughts other than those of degradation. There, they told him, he could regain his confidence and courage feeling strong enough to prove he was right and the world was wrong.

B.J., of course, could not agree to the plan. Why should he?

He consented to go . . . for a while.

B.J. was given the best care at Pass Christian, but it didn't seem to be enough. For one thing, there were always people around him. He realized he was not getting proper rest.

He was dictating on the average of 100,000 words a day to a reporter. Although in a wheelchair, he was forced to think about those who were trying to further a science which would better humanity. He realized no one can really dictate a form of diversion to another; he would make his own.

While B.J. had been in Pass Christian a few thoughts had run through his head. He did not tell anyone about them because he felt they would not understand, but he must try them. With an employee, Wilhelm Stahmer, he went up and down the banks of the Mississippi River gathering glacial deposit granite boulders.

When they gathered as many as they wanted from the banks of the river they went into the fields and collected rocks by the ton. These they stored away and separated into various piles.

(B.J. had confided in Stahmer, and in no one else, because Stahmer had been a rock man for the former Kaiser's Pottsdam Gardens in Germany.)

Working side by side these two began putting rocks together into patterns and designs. They continued to do this for about two years. Wilhelm devoted all his time to the project, while B.J., feeling better, stole as much time as he could from his enterprises. The two sweated and toiled and were pleased with what they found. Out of near tragedy, B.J. realized he was forming beauty just as Carrie Jacobs Bond had written beautiful tunes to overcome tragic deaths.

Besides patterns and designs, the two men built fish ponds, waterfalls and other things of beauty. B.J. brought in rose quartz crystals by the car load from South Dakota and these were fitted in with the fish ponds and falls and all the other objects of beauty collected during tours of the Orient, all of which was under glass in a green house 80 feet long, 40 feet wide and 40 feet high.

B.J. thought it was a beautiful thing, but they could not find a name for it. B.J. was proud of their accomplishment. Looking at the beauty of the rock garden made him forget all the persecution which had piled on as the years passed.

When B.J. looked at the designs and patterns he and Wilhelm had made, he forgot that people scorned and scoffed; he forgot that people were trying to destroy his dream of a place for Chiropractic in the world of science. Forgotten also were the days spent in a courtroom while he was being accused of murdering his father, a father who, towards the end, was unaware of the fact the son was trying only to do his best to perpetuate it all.

He toyed with names and tried to find a suitable one. It relaxed him and made him feel good, but he could not think of a name that fit. Others in the community had given it a name, they laughingly called it "B.J.'s Folly" or "Foolish Pastime."

B.J. returned to normal. Friends noticed he was better in control of himself than ever. They called and asked if they might see the garden. This was an escape valve for B.J.'s irritation and people are always curious about other people's escapes.

"It is truly beautiful," a woman friend said. "How did you manage to do this?" she asked pointing to something. "And," she asked after that had been explained, "What is that shiny stuff?"

Everyone who came to see the gardens marvelled at their beauty and asked B.J. questions. These people went upon their merry way and exclaimed about the garden to their friends who decided they must see it, too. The general public came to ridicule and went away feeling beauty had touched them.

B.J. realized he and Wilhelm were spending a lot of time in the garden. Both were answering questions and showing so many people around they had to neglect their other duties. B.J. thought that fewer people might come if they had to pay to see it. Instead, more people came; people who had gotten private tours free-of-charge came again and again.

Fees were delivered from curious hands to B.J.'s and still the garden remained unnamed, all of which was plowed back in further beauties. One day a little old woman came to visit the gardens. She fell upon her knees and prayed out loud. She had been overcome with its beauty and could not believe that earthly beings had put this together.

"Thank you, dear God in Heaven, for allowing us this little bit o' Heaven," she prayed.

Having seen the woman fall, B.J. had run to her side to render aid possible. He stopped short when he realized she was praying and listened. He heard her say "for allowing us this little bit o' Heaven." That was it! That was what he would call his garden . . . Little Bit O' Heaven!

Over two million people came to see B.J.'s bit of folly, bit of beauty, Bit O' Heaven. They came back again and again. No one realized this had been an insane asylum to B.J.; no one realized B.J. had been a patient under Stahmer and that the garden was therapy for B.J. The over 2,000,000 people who came to gaze at the work of art went through the garden for 50¢ apiece and came out talking about the "work of a genius" when they had expected to see "the follies of a madman."

Hardly anyone who visits the Tri-cities misses the sight of Little Bit O' Heaven, which B.J. keeps up. The rock garden in all its glory represents Mind Over Matter. He is rightfully proud of it.

The rock garden also represented something of his mother's love of beauty which he inherited and his father's spirit to do the hard job different.

Laughter didn't stop B.J. from going ahead and creating his garden. Scoffing didn't stop him; insults didn't; ridicule didn't.

By completing the garden, B.J. proved he was back to normal; that he again was strong enough to withstand all that was thrown at him and still keep moving ahead.

21

———•◆•———

SOME DENIED

ONE CHIROPRACTIC COLLEGE saw fit to dispute the possibility of a vertebral subluxation, producing pressure, interfering with nerve force flow, as The cause of disease, contending the intervertebral foramina WERE SO LARGE and the NERVE SO SMALL that no pressure WAS possible.

Why a Chiropractic college should deny the fundamental on which CHIROPRACTIC was based is beyond understanding. If this issue remained unchallenged, CHIROPRACTIC at tap-root would be denied. In THEORY B.J. proved his point because he GOT WELL. But it had to be proved scientifically, so there would be no question. Who else but B.J. could or would prove this theory?

After unsuccessfully seeking places in America, B.J. was compelled to go to the Spalteholz Labs in Dresden, Germany, to prove or disprove Chiropractic foundation principle and practice.

In Germany, B.J. raised this question: "With a vertebral subluxation, can there be SUFFICIENT occlusion, with SUFFICIENT pressure upon nerves, which could and would interfere with quantity flow of nerve force through the intervertebral foramina?"

This was a new question IN SCIENCE, neither proved or disproved, although it had been denied by medical men. Drs. Spalteholtz, Guenther, and Mueller accepted the challenge. This was THE FIRST time THIS question ever had been anatomically and physiologically raised in any laboratory. B.J. proposed proving it on cadavers. He was promptly told this approach would prove nothing, because:

—Bones, being the hardest substance, DO NOT shrink
—Brain and nerves, being the softest body substance, DO shrink
—Forty to fifty per cent within 24 hours after death
—Upon death, bodies are embalmed in formaldehyde, which further shrinks them
—Cadavers are dissected in rotation, some as long as 18 months after death
—By that time, bones have shrunk less than 1 per cent
—Brain, spinal cord, spinal nerves as high as 85 per cent
—Thus, dissection COULD NOT prove the answer we needed. There was only ONE way this question COULD BE answered: that was through a quick deep-freeze process to be applied IMMEDIATELY AT DEATH.
—Special permission from the German government was necessary to do this work on such bodies. This permission was granted and frozen sections were sawed before ANY shrinkage COULD take place.

The quick deep-freeze process on many bodies proved that the brain filled the cranial cavity; that the spinal cord filled the neural canal, and that desiccated nerves filled intervertebral foramina.

This proved that any sufficient occlusion could produce pressure and interfere with the normal quantity flow of nerve force. This was the first time this had been proved scientifically.

The Spalteholtz Laboratories issued a report on their findings and stated that this proved Chiropractic was based on a proper scientific premise. This report has never been denied by the medical profession nor have they denied the anatomical or the physiological premise of Chiropractic!

The final results of these experiments—which cost $5,000, by the way—were many photographs of the work done as well as a wet specimen which now is in B.J.'s Osteological Laboratory. All students have the opportunity to study it there. Scientists from other fields are privileged to study it too, at any time upon request.

22

THE STORY OF THE PATHFINDER

THE PROBLEM OF the ex-convict is one of the most troublesome in our society and one that is always difficult to solve. On the one hand, we call our prisons "correctional institutions" and base our prison programs on the belief that a man behind bars will learn the error of his ways, that he will "correct" his habits, and that he will emerge from the penal institution determined to be a decent citizen. But on the other hand, no sooner does a released prisoner or a parolee apply for an honest job, then we tell him, "Sorry, we don't take ex-cons here!"

Even if the parolee or ex-con neglects to mention that he's been in prison, it isn't very hard for the prospective employer to find out about the man's record. He usually asks the applicant where he's worked the last few years, what recommendations he can give, what the name of his last boss was. If the applicant supplies phony names, he's sure to be found out and given his walking papers. If he confesses that his last job was in the machine shop of Sing Sing or Leavenworth, then the employer becomes horrified and sends him packing forthwith.

The result of this system is that the ex-con is practically forced to go back to crime to feed himself. If he has a family to support, the temptation to rob and loot becomes virtually irresistible. When he is caught for the second time, we usually write self-righteous editorials which begin, "Once a criminal, always a criminal."

After B.J. had been established in Davenport, he met an insurance agent named Frank J. Wright. Wright had come into contact with a number of parolees and ex-convicts and had discovered that many—if not the great majority—of them were only too anxious to do the right thing, to live honestly, and to black out their past by becoming good citizens of the future. But to do this, they told Wright, they desperately needed help from society.

Wright decided to help them. He organized a club called the Pathfinders Club of America. The object of this club was to help ex-convicts find jobs and thus keep them from reverting to crime. He solicited big corporations like General Motors, Ford, Standard Oil, and Swift, for their help. At first, their personnel directors were extremely skeptical, but Wright managed to convince them that these former prisoners would be so grateful for the opportunity of working for them, that they would make the most conscientious employees in their shops.

Wright induced may leading businessmen and civic leaders to join his Pathfinders Club. These people helped "sell" the big corporations on Wright's idea of providing gainful employment for men who had learned their mistakes behind bars.

Wright held meetings for his Pathfinders Club in the basement of a Methodist church in Davenport. He had ex-convicts come to these meetings to talk about their difficulties in gaining employment and to explain how they would repay society if they were given a chance to earn an honest living. At one of these meetings, however, Wright unwittingly invited a former prisoner who had had a chance at honest employment, but had been so inefficient and surly on the job that his boss had been forced to fire him. This ex-con was a single bad apple in a very large barrel—he was the only one of the ex-cons who had been helped by Wright's group who had violated his trust and faith in him. When the elders of the church found that he had been invited to this meeting, they threw Wright and the Pathfinders Club out of their institution. Wright pleaded in vain that he had not known of the man's poor record, that in any case when you were trying to help thousands, you had to expect that one or two would go wrong. "Why hurt the chances of the 998 good ones, if just one or two fail to live up to the opportunities you give them?" he asked.

Wright's plea did him no good. The church officials refused to allow any more meetings in the church. Embittered, Wright left town and moved to Detroit. There, he patented a quick adjustable monkey wrench which he sold to Ford for $50,000. He used the money to set up a new branch of his Pathfinders Club in the Motor City.

Meanwhile, B.J., who was a charter member, remained active in the Pathfinders movement. About a year after he first joined Wright's club, he conceived an unusual idea.

B.J. had long held the opinion that many prisoners were sick people, not deliberately malicious. His study with so-called criminals convinced

him he was right. He became convinced, which he later proved, that
Chiropractic could and did render a health service to many of this type
of warped sick minds which directed their hands to commit crimes they
otherwise would not have committed.

B.J. met convicts of all varieties. He met confirmed criminals whom he
felt could never be salvaged. They had become so hardened and their
minds so warped, that he felt no amount of rehabilitation could possibly
bring them back to where they would be decent citizens of society. But
he found others who were not criminal by nature. These people had
committed their crimes in moments of great passion or anger. They had
been driven by such a violent fit of emotion that they could not contain
themselves and they had acted criminally before they could stop themselves. These men, he felt, could be returned to society and could be
easily rehabilitated.

B.J. met convicts who had been sent to prison on circumstantial
evidence. Some of these men, B.J. felt, were undoubtedly innocent. But
unfortunately, they didn't have enough evidence to petition for new trials
and had to undergo undeserved punishment. B.J. was also horrified to
find many young boys thrown into cells with hardened, vicious adult
criminals.

Every man jack in prison longed for the day he would gain his freedom. B.J. became convinced that the majority of convicts in prison
thought a great deal about the old maxim, "Crime Does Not Pay," and
came around to believing it. Being proud men, most of them were brag-
garts and said things they didn't really mean. Deep down, however, they
were men who wanted to go straight and were willing to abide by
society's rules—providing society gave them a chance.

Prisoners were men of every vocation. He found ministers and
evangelists. He found bankers, writers, painters, artists, engineers, and
government officials. The mechanical trades were all represented. Many
prisoners were talented men. In addition to work they did in the prison
factory, they had hobbies which brought them in extra money for smokes
and candy.

After that time, he visited many prisons around the country, and
gave lectures there. He made it his avocation to help reform our
convicts. He also tried to help improve their conditions while they
are under sentence.

In some penitentiaries where B.J. lectured, he found wardens who
permitted men to keep canaries and other pets in their cells. These
wardens also permitted baseball games on Sunday afternoons, and even
allowed outside teams to come in and play against convict teams. Their
theory is that even prisoners are human beings and they have to be
treated as such. B.J. has always been in favor of humanitarianism in
jails, and in his lectures has encouraged and applauded the efforts of
understanding wardens. It should be noted these wardens are not

"suckers" or "patsies"—they enforce discipline and they crack down on prisoners who break rules or start trouble.

In various prisons which B.J. has lectured, he found many convicts who had substantial quantities of good in them. This is the principal reason B.J. has participated so actively and so wholeheartedly in a program for rehabilitation of prisoners. Men and women go to prison for committing crimes against society. Admittedly, society has the right to incarcerate and to punish evil-doers. But once convicted men and women serve their term as required by law, they deserve every opportunity we can give them to obtain honest employment and live a decent life. When society discriminates against ex-convicts and thus prevents them from going straight, then society itself is guilty of criminal action.

B.J. found the greatest single problem in prison is sex. Sex is a natural human instinct and yet we treat it as a shocking and disgraceful taboo. As a result, it creates more tensions and frustrations in relation to the problem of sex than we do with any other human problem. Our whole hypocritical attitude toward the sex question begets and fosters crime and anti-social human behavior.

When men and women are imprisoned, to associate only with individuals of their own sex, they are automatically deprived of a natural and normal function. As a result, they resort to perversions which disturb their mental and emotional framework and may cause them physical damage as well. Actually, the deprivation of a normal function to a human being is itself a "crime"—it is a crime committed by society against people who have been convicted for crimes of their own.

Many men and women in prison are not homosexuals to begin with, but they pick up the habit behind bars. They take on "wives" or "husbands" in the lower bunk. By the time they are paroled or have served their full time, they have become chronic perverts. They pursue this secret vice after they get out and thus spread homosexuality throughout the communities in which they settle.

Some foreign countries are much more enlightened and much more practical when it comes to handling the sex problem in prison. They permit wives of male prisoners to visit them for conjugal purposes. They also permit husbands of female prisoners to make similar visits to jails. This prevents their prisons from being turned into cesspools of mass perversion.

Some foreign countries also accommodate single prisoners who have no wives or husbands who may be certified for conjugal visits. In the case of these unattached prisoners, women are procured for them. If they are female, they are allowed to have male visitors of their choosing on occasion. Some people feel this is creating a system of immorality in prisons. It is true there is a moral question as to whether such sex activity should be allowed. On the other hand, the only other alternative is to invite perversion, for the record shows conclusively that when convicts are denied natural sex activity, they turn automatically to unnatural sex relationships.

In addition to preventing perversion, this arrangement to provide natural sex functions for prisoners tends to prevent rebellions in our penitentiaries. Prison experts say that sex-hunger is one of the main reasons why prisoners kick over the traces, create armed riots, and attempt to "bust out." B.J. has always felt that when all advantages and disadvantages of providing sex companionship for prisoners are measured, advantages clearly outweigh disadvantages.

B.J. has always had definite ideas on another important question relating to crime and punishment—the question of capital punishment. B.J. opposes capital punishment as a form of legalized murder. He feels that no state government and no federal government has the right to take a person's life, no matter what crime this person has committed against society. They have the right to imprison him, of course, for as long as they see fit, but B.J. feels that only a Higher Force has the right to take a life. He has found that capital punishment is not a deterrent to crime and that therefore the theory that we have to electrocute men convicted of murder to prevent others from murdering does not hold up. A man bent on committing murder does not weigh his possible punishment—he acts in an inhuman frenzy and he is not influenced by practical considerations.

Another reason B.J. opposes capital punishment is that there is always the possibility the state will kill an innocent man. There have been any number of cases of men who have been convicted on false or misleading testimony and who are later found innocent. When we employ capital punishment, we close the books on a man's case forever. If we later find he was innocent, we can no longer do anything to help him.

In the years that B.J. has been a member of the Pathfinders Club of America, he has had enrolled many parolees and ex-convicts as students of the Palmer School of Chiropractic. B.J. has even advanced these prison graduates money to pay their tuition fees. He never disclosed their backgrounds to any of his students, but instead preserves their secret. The only request B. J. makes of these ex-convicts is that they repay the loan of tuition money when they are well established in their practice. B.J. charges them six percent interest, but puts this interest money in a fund which is used to help other ex-convicts rehabilitate themselves.

To date, nearly 300 ex-convicts have been made able to study at the Palmer School through B.J.'s generosity. Nobody in B.J.'s organization, except for B.J. himself, knows the true identity of these ex-convict students. B.J. has found that too often people who profess to be holier-than-thous will employ the sin of gossip to destroy hopes and opportunities of men and women with criminal records.

The most tragic example of the damage gossip can cause involved Mary S., a woman whom B.J. helped after her discharge from prison. She came from South Dakota and had been imprisoned for running a house of prostitution. She had used her period behind bars to reflect bitterly on her sordid past, and had finally decided to make restitution for her anti-social actions. She felt the best way to make restitution was to help others in sickness, and possibly save their lives. She therefore decided to study Chiropractic. B.J. personally enrolled her in the Palmer School.

Everything went smoothly until one unfortunate day a new student came into class. He had once been a patron of Mary in her prostitution days and he recognized her immediately. To make matters worse, he gossiped about Mary to his wife and the wife quickly broadcast the information to wives of other students. Gossip about Mary's background immediately spread throughout the student body.

The effect was disastrous. Men began chasing Mary, pawing her, and hanging around her, waiting for an invitation to "come up and see her sometime." They gave Mary no rest or peace. B.J. told her to ignore the leeches, and to carry on as if nothing had happened. "They'll get tired of talking about you in time, and then you will forget they ever bothered you." he said. But Mary was unable to shake off her feeling of despair.

One day, B.J. was called to examine a typhoid fever case who lived in the same boarding house as Mary. As he passed Mary's door, he noticed it was half open. Glancing inside, he was horrified to see the former prostitute standing in front of a mirror with a gun in her hand. Impulsively, he burst into the room and shouted "Put it down! Throw that gun away!"

Mary looked up, startled, saw who it was and dropped her gun. B.J. demanded to know what she'd been trying to do with the gun, and she confessed that she was attempting to commit suicide. Then suddenly, she broke into a wild fit of sobbing. "I want to die," she screamed. "I want to die!"

"You're being selfish, you know," B.J. shot at her. "People who need you and love you don't want to be deprived of your help and guidance and devotion."

"Nobody is interested in me," she cried. "Nobody cares what happens to me."

"What about your daughter who needs you and loves you?" B.J. demanded. "Also, if you take your life now, you'll be cheating the many Chiropractic patients of the future who would want to come to you for health. As a practicing Chiropractor, you can add many long years to people's lives, and save the lives of some now deemed hopeless."

B.J. insisted the woman put the gun away in the drawer, and never take it out again. Still sobbing, she followed his suggestion and put the gun away. She went back to school, did well in her studies, and is now a practicing Chiropractor with an excellent practice. Her patients swear by her and call her a most dedicated woman.

B.J. points out that this story emphasizes, once again, the fact that convicts CAN be redeemed if we are willing to help them. The tragedy of so many of our ex-convicts is that they don't get this help very often. People who are the first to make big speeches about the "value of re-habilitating Criminals" are the first to deny them the right of re-habilitation, when it comes to doing something of a practical nature. These people are the kind who will never forgive a person a past sin. By means of Gossip and slander, they make a mockery of the Christian ideals of forgiveness, repentance and rehabilitation, and thus create lifelong criminals out of people who otherwise could rise above their past and become honorable and decent neighbors in the community.

Incidentally, the gun Mary was going to use to destroy herself is now mounted in B.J.'s museum. After Mary established herself in Chiro-practic and rebuilt her life, she gave the gun to B.J. to assure him she would never have need to look at it or use it again.

23

———◆———

'TIMPOGRAPH

In 1935 THE TIME HAD ARRIVED for B.J. to prove certain answers to certain problems. B.J. knew the crux around which everything Chiropractic revolved was that:

(1) a REDUCTION in the QUANTITY flow of mental impulse nerve force between Innate above and function below, between brain and body, was the cause of all disease. If this were NOT so, there was nothing to Chiropractic.

(2) a RESTORATION of this reduction in QUANTITY flow, between Innate above and function below, between brain and body, would change sickness into health.

In 1935 B.J. began to wonder if there were some way he could MEASURE, EVALUATE, AND CALIBRATE this QUANTITY flow.

He began to experiment with developing an instrument which would do these things. Eventually he built two different instruments and finally perfected the ELECTROENCEPHALONEUROMENTIMPOGRAPH.

B.J. knew that if he could MEASURE THIS QUANTITY FLOW he could prove the effectiveness of what he was doing in adjusting subluxations. He had to be sure that what he was doing would restore the QUANTITY flow. If he was restoring the flow, the patient would get well—other things being equal. If the patient did not get well, something was wrong.

Ever since the beginning, B.J. had tried to perfect adjusting subluxation to accomplish this one objective.

There was ONE way to prove if his work had been effective. He would test Chiropractic adjusting, measure the flow BEFORE AND AFTER, and find out.

This instrument brought forth far more information than B.J. expected.

Because of its 8 multiple pick-up detector electrodes
—placed at 8 objective comparative spots
—simultaneously graphing 8 at same time, same person
—permitting any length of time to make a complete test
—placed at pre-determined strategic points between brain and body,
Innate source of function at epiphery and its expression of periphery
—by measuring, evaluating, and calibrating interpretation of QUANTITY
flow of mental impulse nerve force supply, differentiating between normal quantity in brain and abnormal quantity in body
—it was possible to prove or disprove the ultimate Chiropractic objective whether ANY adjustment, given ANY place, ANY time, ANY manner, did or did not restore NORMAL QUANTITY FLOW of mental impulse supply below subluxation adjusted, or misalignment corrected.

—or, in reverse, reduced the already impeded flow to make case worse. With this instrument, B.J. could AND DID prove, with scientific accuracy, the value of Chiropractic adjustments.

Problem cases enter The B. J. Palmer Chiropractic Research Clinic, the BJP CC with certain symptoms or pathologies which they sense and feel.

The usual Chiropractor has similar cases, asks questions, possibly writes answers on a printed form for his records. The patients describe locations, intensities of feelings, discomforts, pains, miseries, etc.

The Chiropractor has TWO usual Chiropractic analytical instruments —the Neurocalometer to locate heat-break readings and the x-ray to give him inside information as to the position of vertebral subluxation.

He adjusts and from day to day, he will check these mentioned. Beyond that HE ASKS THE PATIENT HOW HE (or she) IS FEELING. From these checks, AND THE REPORTS FROM THE CASE, he determines whether he HAD adjusted in the RIGHT PLACE, the RIGHT way, at the RIGHT time, and DID NOT adjust when he shouldn't have adjusted. From this information too, he determines whether the case is being restored with the normal quantity flow of mental impulse nerve flow, or not. He is prone, without other evidence, to rely HEAVILY on verbal opinions expressed by the case.

Similar problem cases coming to The B. J. Palmer Chiropractic Research Clinic have another fundamental method of checking which is superior to those mentioned, except for Neurocalometer and x-ray, via the 'timpograph. At Palmers, they take a pre-check 'timpograph before any adjustment is given. It is MATHEMATICALLY calibrated and deciphered by a specially built measuring device as to quantity of mental impulse manufactured IN THE BRAIN and a simultaneous pre-check is made of some SICK PORTION OF THE BODY TO EVALUATE the difference between normal-brain production and the amount of production in SOME SICK PORTION OF THE BODY. At some predetermined subsequent time a similar 'timpograph post-check is taken. The two graphs are mathematically evaluated and compared. In so doing they can TELL THE PATIENT whether he (or she) is getting better or worse by measuring RESTORED QUANTITY FLOW between brain and body. It is NOT necessary FOR PATIENT TO TELL the Chiropractor, but the Chiropractor tells them! At the same time, they HAVE A RECORDED COMPARATIVE 'TIMPOGRAPH GRAPH RECORD.

The B. J. Palmer Research Chiropractic Clinic has TWO Chiropractic comparisons, within the scope of the Chiropractic primary factor:

—brain normal production with abnormal organ below-paralysis

—below-par organic abnormal condition in its rapidity coming UP TO par level or normality.

24

---◆---

MUSEUM PIECE

HEINRICH DUERRINGER WAS ONE of the great practitioners of Chiropractic. It was a freak accident that brought him to Chiropractic and to the Palmer School.

Heinrich was a German immigrant who, when he first came to this country, worked as a gardener on an estate near Stamford, Conn.

One day a truck that was unloading manure on the ground turned over burying Heinrich under tons of fertilizer. The accident fractured his spine. He went to a PSC graduate in Stamford for relief from the pain and became well.

The Chiropractor's restoration of health so thoroughly made Heinrich a convert to the profession that he decided to study at the Palmer School.

Heinrich had an extensive educational background in Germany which helped in his studies, although he had a great deal of difficulty reading English. He had the keen, curious mind of a scientist.

In class he would always ask, "vy?" when the instructor made a flat statement. He was regarded as the class nuisance. More than a few members of the faculty complained to B.J. about this bothersome fellow with the troublesome questions. B.J. liked Heinrich. He liked a man who wanted to know everything and wasn't satisfied with just knowing what he was told.

In spite of his language handicap, Heinrich Duerringer learned Chiropractic . . . not just book learning, but he thoroughly understood the basic principles. His hands acquired the skill of an experienced man; his head acquired the basics, from which all else follows, B.J. once told him.

Now Heinrich had to get experience. He and his wife, Toots (a nickname given her by students), moved to New York City and opened a large room in Columbus Circle. He had left PSC with $10 in his pocket.

Heinrich's first patient got the kind of treatment that didn't come out of any Chiropractic book. The man attempted to tell Heinrich how he wanted to be cared for.

Heinrich threw the man out of his office. He knew his profession and he wasn't going to let anyone tell him what to do. He lost a fee he needed, but he gained self-respect and convinced one person he was honest.

This patient sent dozens of people to Heinrich in following months. Then, one day, he returned to the office.

"You did dose patients a great favor by sending dem to me. I helped dem," said Heinrich.

"And now you are back t'inking you have some special privileges . . . t'inking you now may be able to tell me how to be a Chiropractor.

"You can't. I told you vonce, now I'm telling you again: Get out of my office and stay out," and Heinrich again threw the man out.

Heinrich's business grew. He eventually outgrew his office on Columbus Circle and moved to a larger suite of offices in the Marbridge Building on Broadway opposite the McAlpin Hotel.

Whenever B.J. visited New York, he would make it a must to stop in and see his friend Heinrich. Heinrich's home and the home of Rufus St. Onge in Seattle were the only two that B.J. did visit. He made it a rule never to visit a Chiropractor's office when he travelled. If he visited one, he would have to visit everyone.

When B.J. called on Heinrich, the two went across the street to the hotel for lunch. Heinrich had a table reserved there which was always ready for him at 12 noon.

Once, when B.J. was with him, someone was sitting at Heinrich's table. He let out a howl which caused everyone in the dining room to stop eating. The headwaiter immediately cleared his table, apologized and the table was never taken again at noon.

Heinrich had one hobby . . . buying things from a "fence." This is the way he worked it:

After finishing his meal at the hotel, Heinrich walked out the back door and up to Madam Trigger's, who was a fence for stolen goods.

Heinrich would buy anything from her, as long as the price was right. His main pleasure was bargaining with her over price. He knew she paid less than face value for the stuff, and he wasn't going to let her rob him.

Heinrich's house was a museum with no theme . . . it consisted of a little bit of anything.

Heinrich's practice had become very successful. He would run up to 100 patients a day and employed two Chiropractors as assistants to take care of house calls.

He was successful because his patients had confidence in him and respected his professional honesty and fairness. He did not discriminate between rich and poor. Money did not have privilege. B.J., when pointing out Heinrich's professional ethics, uses this story as an example.

B.J. had dropped in on Heinrich's office one day without informing the German Chiropractor he was coming. He sat in the waiting room, waiting for Heinrich to come out. Beside him were sitting two women. One was a typical Italian scrub woman. Her knees were calloused from scrubbing the floors; her face was wrinkled; her hands were red and rough; her clothes were shabby and old.

Along side her was a woman who was all that the scrub woman was not. This woman's clothes were the last word in style and material. Her furs were the best money could buy. She had a little dog on her lap and her colored maid stood beside her chair.

When Heinrich came, he looked around the waiting room. B.J. sat in the corner, his face hidden by a magazine so Heinrich could not recognize him.

"Who came first?" Heinrich asked.

The Italian woman, a meek person, didn't speak. The rich woman insisted she be taken first.

Heinrich finally got both women to admit that the scrub woman had come first.

"If you are here first, den you go in first," Heinrich said to the Italian woman.

The rich woman was furious. "How dare he take her before me? Who does he think I am?" she mumbled so it was barely heard.

B.J. then asked the woman what she thought of her doctor.

"My first reaction was to leave and never come back," she answered. "But after I gave it a second thought, I realized that this doctor was the man I wanted. He thought nothing of my money. He was just being fair and honest.

"We rich are used to having every one bow down for us. It is a pleasant surprise to find an honest, independent man.

"I also realized if this doctor thought little of my money, he would give me honest service and not try to make up things just so he could charge me higher fees. I now have complete faith in him. And faith is a wonderful thing to have in a doctor."

B.J. told Heinrich what the woman had said. Heinrich brushed it off.

But B.J. did find out the woman he had talked to in the waiting room was none other than the wealthy and famous Mrs. Duke.

When B.J. told his students this story to point out the power of professional honesty and fairness it got the hoped for reaction from students.

B.J. visited Heinrich's home in Stamford, Conn. On these occasions, Toots would see that B.J. got his favorite food . . . lobster. Dinner would consist of lobster soup, boiled lobster and broiled lobster tails. One time, after dinner, B.J. spotted an Indian necklace made up of 28 pieces of genuine elk tusks. Heinrich had paid 25 cents to Madam Trigger for it. (Today it is worth $26 a piece.)

B.J. asked Heinrich if he could purchase the necklace from him.

"I'd like the necklace, not because of its value, but because I am an Elk and the necklace means a lot to me," B.J. said.

"My goot friend, I am sorry, but the necklace means a lot to me also. It is like the many tings you have in your Palmer School Museum. They represent memories and moments.

"This necklace also to me represents something. Maybe not so fine as the tings in your museum, but to me it is a big bargain I got from Madam Trigger—and my hobby is buying this thing.

"Maybe someday, you will get the necklace and it will be with my blessings," Heinrich said.

B.J. understood and never said anything to Heinrich. But he knew that if he was ever to get the necklace it would have double value to him: value because he was an Elk and value because it meant so much to Heinrich.

No one could talk about Heinrich in a derogatory manner to B.J.; no one could make fun of him, or comment on his office manners. He was B.J.'s friend and B.J. didn't hesitate to let a culprit know this.

Heinrich had the opportunity to pay B.J. back for the interest B.J. had taken in him and the friendship he had given Heinrich. The payment was in the form of saving B.J.'s life.

It happened one night when B.J. was given a banquet in his honor at the McAlpin Hotel. The word got around that a disgruntled Chiropractor was going to shoot B.J. when he made his appearance on the rostrum. Although everyone heard about the threat, no one knew who the Chiropractor was.

B.J. was asked not to speak in fear of what might happen. He refused to be intimidated. He told the committee that the people expected to hear him and he was not going to let them down because of a rumor spread by a crack pot.

The committee figured the best thing to do was to place men strategically around the man in question so they could grab anyone who acted suspiciously.

Halfway through B.J.'s talk, a man in a third center row of the lecture hall started to stand up and at the same time reach into his hip pocket.

He was unaware, as he took the gun out, that the guards had spotted him and were closing in on him.

He raised the gun. His action was stopped midway as a group of men pounced on him. A short struggle ensued. B.J. spoke from the platform:

"What's happening there?"

"We got him. Don't worry. Everything is okay now. We'll call the police," one of the men answered back.

Heinrich, who was short in stature but loud in voice, started to yell:

"I'll fix him good. Police we don't need. I will teach him a lesson he would never forget. Just let me get my hands on him."

Heinrich turned towards the man. With his fists shaking he yelled "Du bist ein . . ."

B.J. cut him short. Like two men in one body, B.J. told the men to take the attempted assassin into a side room, urged the men not to call the police and directed his attention toward Heinrich in an effort to quiet him.

After quieting Heinrich, and telling everyone to proceed with the program, he went to the room to have a talk with the disgruntled Chiropractor.

The two had a long talk. B.J. scotched rumors the man believed about him. The man thanked B.J. for his help, kindness and consideration. He came to the hall hating B.J., determined to kill him and left mentally readjusted and with a new friend . . . B.J.

About 3 A.M. one morning, B.J. received a long distance call in Davenport. It was from Stamford, Conn. A broken German girl's voice said, "Heinrich is sick, come at vonce."

B.J. caught the Golden State Limited at 4 A.M. In Chicago he boarded the Twentieth Century Limited for New York. In the city, he took the next express for Stamford. Heinrich's chauffeur met him at the station and drove him to the house.

B.J. met the M.D. that Toots had called. The M.D. told B.J. he advised Heinrich to take insulin shots for his diabetes, but Heinrich had refused. He would not take them unless B.J. advised him to.

B.J. went up to the bedroom and found Heinrich in a deep coma. He woke him and they talked. B.J. then went down stairs and told Toots he could give Heinrich an adjustment but it would do no good.

"Heinrich is just a few hours away from death," he announced. (He did die at 3 that afternoon.)

The conversation was broken by Heinrich's shouts:

"I won't do it. I won't do it."

B.J. rushed back up stairs . . . Heinrich's niece stood just outside his room.

"I told him you had advised the M.D. to give him the shots," she told B.J.

B.J. rushed into the room, but it was too late. Heinrich had lapsed back into the coma. He never came out. He died that afternoon without knowing that B.J. had not betrayed him.

In 1948, at the annual home-coming, Heinrich's chauffeur, who was then a PSC graduate, presented B.J. with a bronze bust of Heinrich given the chauffeur by Toots after Heinrich's death.

The bust now stands in B.J.'s osteological laboratory. In a room at the Palmer home there hangs this Indian necklace made of genuine elk tusks.

This was given to B.J. by Toots . . . it was from Heinrich who knew what it meant to B.J.

Heinrich's death lost to the profession one of its greats. If there were many more such as Heinrich Duerringer in the Chiropractic profession it could lick scoffers firmly and finally.

He was honest, fair and a credit to Chiropractic, its practitioners and its leaders. Heinrich was a doctor of Chiropractic in every sense of the meaning the title holds.

25

A FAVOR FOR GRAHAM

THE LATE GRAHAM MCNAMEE WAS undoubtedly the greatest sports announcer who ever lived. His was a voice that carried into many millions of homes and described so colorfully and effectively the sports highlights of the day, that it helped popularize sports among men and women who normally had no interest in athletic pursuits.

McNamee was a man who never forgot a favor. There was the time when the distinguished announcer and M.C. was engaged to sing before the Iowa Federation of Women's Clubs at Davenport. He was due to arrive on the 2:30 train. A group of women were to meet him, escort him around the city and then bring him back for dinner at six o'clock. Thereupon, they would escort him to the Masonic Temple where he was to sing.

B.J. knew McNamee had no desire to spend the day with a group of women. As a friend of McNamee, therefore, he decided on a plan to get the famed broadcaster out of his afternoon commitment. He wired McNamee, asking him to meet him at Moline, across the river from Davenport. B.J. promised to hide McNamee out until the time that he had to go to the Temple.

B.J. took McNamee off the train at Moline, and hid him at his home until it was time for the women's meeting. McNamee was so grateful for this, he literally fell over himself thanking B.J.

The female clubwomen were frantic, however. When the sportscaster failed to get off the train at Davenport, they thought something serious had happened to him. They phoned all hotels and hospitals without results. Finally, they phoned B.J. to ask if he had seen McNamee. B.J. told them truthfully that he knew where the sportscaster was, that he had taken him there because McNamee badly needed rest before the meeting.

The women were enraged and began to spread rumors about McNamee. They said he was dead drunk, and that B.J. had hidden him so the public wouldn't know what a lush he was. B.J. denied these charges, but few people would believe him. The charges were disproved however, when McNamee appeared at the women's meeting that night, looking as fit and as sober as the proverbial judge.

While announcing the famous Dempsey-Tunney fight a few months later, McNamee paid tribute to B.J. He announced that "my dear good friend Dr. Palmer of Davenport is now coming down the aisle." This remark was heard by 30,000,000 fans.

Later, at a Fourth of July party given for McNamee, B.J. was one of the few outside guests invited. The party was held at the estate home of Maj. Lennox Lohr. *Life Magazine* was there, to take pictures for its "Life Goes to a Party" series.

B.J. and the *Life* photographer were the only outsiders invited. B.J. became friendly with Major Lohr, and this friendship later proved beneficial to both men.

Innate had prompted B.J. to send his wire to McNamee and Innate was proved right. McNamee showed his gratitude by helping B.J. in many ways throughout his lifetime.

26

<hr />

THE STRANGE STORY OF MARGARET

FROM TIME TO TIME we read stories about people who have religious visions. Sometimes the person who sees a vision or thinks he sees it, insists the vision is that of Jesus Christ or the Virgin Mary. Most of these so-called visions are undoubtedly hallucinations, brought on by an over-active imagination or by a form of self-hypnosis. Some visions are pure frauds. They are conceived by shrewd promoters who believe that if they convert some piece of property into a Mecca for tourists, they will pick up money from tourists. One way to make a place a tourist site is to get publicity about a "vision" taking place there.

In addition to "visions," there are people who claim to receive secret signs from the Almighty or insist the Almighty has touched them in some miraculous way. Most of these so-called signs, marks or blemishes are also the products of wild imaginations. Often, they do not even exist— the person affected simply THINKS they exist. Or if they do exist, they are likely to be self-induced either through hysteria or a simple desire to pull a prank and fool the public.

During the course of his career, B.J. has seen several of these so-called "blessed" people, people who claimed to have seen visions or been marked by God or the Mother of God. He has exposed them as out-and-out charlatans. He has met hundreds of spiritualists who claimed to have had divine guidance or a divine message and by cleverly cross-examining them, was able to unmask them as congenital tricksters.

In all of B.J.'s long experience, however, there was no case to match that of Margaret, the girl with the "stigmata." Until this day, B.J. is baffled by the Margaret case. It remains his personal "Believe It or Not" episode.

Margaret was a schoolgirl studying botany in an exclusive girls' school in Illinois. She loved flowers, plants and trees, and from time to time, would wander off to nearby fields, to collect baskets of flowers, and study the vegetation. Near Margaret's school, there was a seminary for priests. One day, while Margaret was picking flowers, she saw a young priest coming toward her.

"Hello there," the young man said. "I see you like the flowers here."

Margaret had always led a sheltered life, and was very shy with boys. She turned away, her face beet-red with embarrassment.

"I'm not trying to be fresh or to pick you up," the young man said quickly. "I'm not interested in girls that way. You see, I'm a seminarian . . . I'm studying to be a Catholic priest."

It turned out that the young man was interested in botany. He and Margaret began to meet almost every afternoon and became close friends. But it was an unusual kind of relationship. Instead of talking about the usual boy-girl things, they talked about plants, trees, and forests—and about religion. The young man was fanatically religious. "I'm going to spend my life in the service of God," he told Margaret. "Being a priest means I'll miss many of the pleasures of the flesh, but it doesn't matter to me, because I regard these things as unimportant."

Although Margaret was a Protestant and had never been particularly interested in religion, the young man's passionate zeal was contagious. Margaret too began to visualize herself as a devoted servant of God, and began to tell herself that earthly pleasures were unimportant and that spiritual values were the only things that counted in life.

She began to study Catholic dogma, decided she wanted to be a Catholic and after a period of instruction, was accepted in the Catholic church.

It has often been said that a convert is more devoted to his religion than those who are born into it. Certainly, this was true in Margaret's case. She lived for nothing but her religion. Her roommates would find her praying so fervently at odd hours of the day and night that she seemed totally unaware that they were in the same room with her.

One night, after Margaret had literally prayed herself to sleep, she stirred in a fervor of religious ecstasy. She began to cry out in her sleep. Her roommates hurried to her bed and woke her up. "What's the matter, Margaret?" they asked her. Margaret put her hand to her left breast. "Somebody branded me here," she said. "It hurts me terribly."

The girls took Margaret's hand away from her breast and stared. On the upper part of the large breast, above the nipple, was a strangely-colored blemish. It was shaped in the form of a crucifix.

Margaret looked down at the blemish and said excitedly, "It's a sign from the Lord. You see the crucifix! The Lord has touched me!"

A few Catholic girls who were students at the college heard Margaret shouting and hurried into her room. They stared at the odd-shaped blemish and said, "It's a religious stigmata. Margaret has been blessed."

They knelt in front of Margaret and begged her to bless them. Margaret slowly recited a blessing over them.

A "stigmata" is defined in the dictionary as a speck or a series of specks, caused by extravasion of blood. The extravasion may result from a nervous influence, as in hysteria, or by capillary congestion. In Margaret's case, her "stigmata" was quite large and was elevated, like a huge welt. At first, the Father Confessor would not accept this as a truly religious sign. But then on Holy Week, a remarkable thing happened to Margaret. The stigmata began to change color. On Good Friday, she suffered violent pains in her breasts and blood began to drip from where the nails were in the body of the stigmata. The pain continued on Saturday, then ceased on Easter Sunday.

When this remarkable occurrence was reported to the Father Confessor, he exclaimed, "My God in Heaven, the girl must be blessed!"

For the next few days, every Catholic girl in the school came to Margaret, and asked to be blessed. They regarded her as a saint. It was decided to move Margaret to Mercy Hospital in Chicago, so she could undergo extensive physical tests. The doctors there told Margaret she was suffering from a general arthritic condition. This would account for some of the pains she suffered the year round. But they had no explanation to offer as to why Margaret should suffer so intensively on Good Friday, and why her pains should abate on Easter Sunday.

A married Catholic couple of students in B.J.'s school at Davenport knew B.J. and knew of his experience in exposing fraudulent spiritualists. They asked if he would examine Margaret and determine whether she had experienced an authentic religious phenomenon or whether her stigmata could be explained scientifically.

It took several weeks before B.J. was able to get permission to see Margaret at the hospital. His first interview with the girl was held in January. Arriving at the hospital, he was escorted down the hall by the Sister Superior. As he approached Margaret's room, he suddenly asked to be permitted to go on from there alone. He didn't want any distractions when he was alone with Margaret.

He approached the door, and knocked. A voice inside said, "Come in." He turned the knob and tried to open the door. At first it wouldn't budge. Then B.J. leaned on it heavily, and it moved slowly, as if a sandbag were placed against it on the inside and had to be forced back. Once B.J. stepped inside, he looked on the floor to see what kind of obstruction was blocking the door. There was nothing there!

B.J. went out again and tried the door a second time. Again, he met this strange resistance and he had to use every ounce of his energy to get the door open. "How come?" he asked Margaret. The girl simply shook her head. She had no explanation.

B.J. asked permission to sit on her bed and examine her. "It's all right with me as long as the Father Confessor has given his permission," she said. She opened her nightgown and exposed her breast. Sure enough, the stigmata was there, shaped in the form of a cross.

B.J. knew all the tricks of tattooing and branding. A stigmata of this type could have been branded with a hot iron, resulted from an acid burn, grafted on, or tattooed. "Do you mind if I examine this blemish with a microscope?" he asked the girl. The girl looked startled, but said she had no objections.

B.J. had brought along a high-powered pocket microscope. It was powerful enough to expose the marks of a burn or to show any grafting operation. But it did no such thing. After five minutes of the most minute scrutiny, B.J. looked up from the stigmata in amazement. It was not a burn, it had not been grafted on, there was no artificiality connected with it. It was genuine!

"It's real all right," he told Margaret. "I don't know how to explain it." Suddenly, Margaret turned her head and began conversing with an imaginary person. "Margaret, who are you talking to? There's nobody here but me." B.J. asked her. "Mother Mary just came to me," Margaret exclaimed. "She told me to warn you of danger."

"Danger?" B.J. asked. "That's ridiculous."

"Please, please, believe me, there is danger. Mother Mary asked me to tell you not to take the Twentieth Century Limited when you go to New York next week."

"I have no intention of going to New York," B.J. said. "Are you sure you know what you're talking about?"

A few days after B.J. left Margaret, he got a call from a radio executive in the east, asking him to come to New York for a conference. B.J. had dismissed Margaret's warning from his mind, so he blithely made a reservation on the Twentieth Century. Because of the press of late business, however, he missed the Century and had to take a later train. The Century had a wreck en route!

The wreck brought home to B.J. the astounding reminder that Margaret had been right in her prophecy. Furthermore, the prophecy could not be explained in any scientific manner. Margaret couldn't have read B.J.'s conscious mind—when she had her conversation, there was no thought of going to New York in his mind. He had given her no cues or hints about any possible trip. Could it be that B.J. had an innate personality who knew of this forthcoming trip even though B.J. himself had no conscious knowledge of it? If that supposition was true, then Margaret too, must have had an innate personality who was in some mysterious fashion able to contact B.J.'s innate personality. Or could it be that Margaret had actually acquired a saintly character, that she had established authentic contact with Mother Mary and then had been used as a messenger to convey a warning to her bedside visitor? B.J. admits he is still mystified.

B.J. returned again to see Margaret in the spring. He asked permission to visit her during Holy Week so he could see for himself what happened to her stigmata. "Of course, you can come," Margaret told him. "I have no secrets."

B.J. came on Monday, Wednesday, Friday and Easter Sunday of Holy Week. Everything happened as Margaret predicted. The mark on her breast changed to a light purple color, then to a dark purple. Then drops of blood began dripping from the nail wounds on the stigmata. On Good Friday, the pain increased sharply. On Easter Day, the pain ceased.

Could the wound and bleeding have been produced artificially? B.J. knew that in India and other Asiatic places, Holy men torture their bodies in all sorts of ways. But Margaret's body was not in constant torture. B.J. could not find any natural explanation of why the pain would be aggravated on Good Friday and end on Easter Sunday.

During B.J.'s Easter Week visit, Margaret suddenly began another conversation with an invisible person whom she insisted was Mother Mary. At the end of her conversation, she said to B.J., "Don't worry about the property you're trying to buy. The owner will come to you one week from today at 10 in the morning and he will accept your price."

B.J. had indeed been negotiating for a piece of property and at the time of his visit, was having trouble closing the deal. Had Margaret read his Innate mind again? Whatever it was, her prediction proved accurate. A week later, precisely at 10, the man with whom B.J. had been negotiating came and told B.J. he would accept the terms he offered previously for the property.

After Margaret got out of the hospital, she moved to Glendale, California. She became a patient of one of B.J.'s former students. This Chiropractor wrote B.J. the stigmata was still on the girl's body. Two years later, after Margaret had married, B.J. visited her on the west coast. The stigmata still had not faded away, and on Holy Week, Margaret was still experiencing the same symptoms.

The story of Margaret remains one of the most bizarre in B.J.'s long and rich experience. Margaret may or may not have been specially blessed, but B.J. is certain of one thing—if there is a scientific explanation for her condition, neither he nor any one else has even been able to find it!

27

THE MAN WHO MADE US

THE MAN WHO HAD ADVANCED the art of Chiropractic by innumerable years, Daniel David Palmer, died long before his science took its rightful place among Mankind.

He died, but he left a heritage for his son, and his son did not fail.

Although D.D. felt his son had cheated, robbed and fooled him, and although D.D. died hating his son, the son, Bartlett Joshua Palmer loved and respected his father.

He knew his father's hate was the result of his life-time battle for his science . . . a battle which took so much it weakened his body and mind.

Shortly after D.D.'s death, the Chiropractic profession built a monument to the founder. B.J. placed a bronze bust in the middle of the Palmer School campus and with it he placed an urn with his father's ashes in a glass enclosure.

On the 50th Anniversary of the founding of Chiropractic, in 1945, B.J., in a nation-wide speech to the profession, told about: "The Man Who Made Us, Whom Some Now Deny":

"If D. D. Palmer, fifty years ago, had listened to the smug, satisfied, complacent, conformist, opportunities, so-called educated people, there would never have been a Chiropractic, Chiropractors, and you would not be here today celebrating his memory.

"So-called educated people believe in disease being a thing, symptoms and pathologies to diagnose, something to treat and cure, something material to be cut out.

"D. D. Palmer believed 'dis-ease' was a condition in which matter found itself. Whether diagnosed or not, its cause was mechanical and needed adjustment.

"Smug people believed in disease having its cause and cure outside of the body.

"D. D. Palmer believed all cause and cure for each 'dis-ease' was inside the body.

"Satisfied people believed in germs, effuvia, in immunizing and vaccinating the community, etc.

"D. D. Palmer believed these were the result—effects of 'dis-ease.' Conformist people believe in privy practice, violet rays, pills, potions, powders, dope via mouth and injection.

"D. D. Palmer believed there was nothing that could come from outside inside, that could or would cure anything.

"Five thousand years of medicine established it as a proper, legitimate, accepted, fixed and stable as well as correct method to be believed, taught, and practiced. It was and is still a failure in getting sick people well. If they got their sick well, there would be nothing for Chiropractors to do, nobody for Chiropractors to adjust.

"It has taken Chiropractic less than fifty years to work from the idea in the mind of one man, from a correct basic principle and practice an established and proven science, to locate the specific for the cause and specific for the correction of that cause, to get sick people well.

"D. D. Palmer was an uninhibited individualist. He lived a life that was an extremist's in that respect. It takes an extremist to produce radical thoughts. 'Radical' thinkers differ from conservatives. 'Conservatives' are those who think today what was thought yesterday. Every man who ever brought forth anything new was an extreme radicalist in his day.

"D. D. Palmer drove a pair of spotted Indian ponies. He and his wife rode a tandem bicycle over the streets of Davenport. He was a magnetic healer. He wore long hair down to his waist, black as coal. He wore a broad-brimmed Stetson hat, made to order, which you can see in our museum case. He gathered and collected the finest and largest collection of animal game heads and antlers in the world, all of which were presented to and are now in the Davenport Academy of Sciences, some of which were returned to us and now hang on our hallways. He invited people to see them.

"He bought and sold goldfish as a hobby—thousands every day. We were their nurse-maids. He thought differently, he lived differently, opposite to what inhibited individuals did. He was indifferent to what inhibited people might say about his 'peculiarities.'

"Whether he did any or all of these for relaxation, to change pace, to break the monotony of the daily grind of sitting at the bedside of sick people; or for the purpose of rejuvenating himself from that constant, every-fifteen-minute drain on his vitality, is beside the point. They were all foreign to anything allied to magnetic healing or Chiropractic work which came later. The fact remains he gave vent to a pent-up desire to want to do them; and in giving vent, he was developing a breaking down of a line of uninhibited thought which permitted him later to be free in giving full and untrammelled values to his Chiropractic reasoning.

"Men who have these inner urges are much like volcanoes—suppress and choke them back, and some day there'll be an explosion with consequent damage. All of these came from fires raging within himself, including his Chiropractic.

"Eventually, out of all this characteristic uninhibited thinking and living, came a new line of uninhibited thinking, viz., discovery of the vertebral subluxation as the cause of 'dis-ease'; and a method of correcting by hand only. He did not re-discover this from the Greeks, but he did tap his Innate and let it flow from inside out. His new reasoning came from the only source where such had always existed, was known, and how to correct it was also known, viz., Innate Intelligence of all people of all time; for the production of vertebral subluxations and their reduction have been going on within the cognizance of Innate for millions of years in millions of people—all well known to Innate but never known to education till 1895 when D. D. Palmer drew it out of the void of the mental vacuum and forced its understanding into the consciousness of men.

"Had D. D. Palmer been an inhibited person, thinking same thoughts as those who surround him; had he done same things same ways as others of his day, he would have been one of the mass, coming and going as they, knowing no more, no less, and no different than they, and he would have left no imprint upon history, and you and we would have been products of our new day the same as those who surround us now.

"Only from an uninhibited individual who lives an uninhibited life can come uninhibited products.

"It's the so-called highly touted, super-educated who are inhibited. Education breeds inhibitions with all its stifles.

"It's the inhibited who choke progress. Let an uninhibited one come forth with a new idea, ideal, plan, method, system, device, or invention —it's the inhibited who say it can't be done, and build barricades, barriers and hurdles to prevent its coming into its own.

"Chiropractic is an uninhibited product. Chiropractors should be uninhibited individualists. Chiropractic as an uninhibited product cannot long live or survive in a body that is inhibited. Chiropractic today is surrounded with inhibited people who think we must be conformists, and agree with all others to attain its opposite end.

"Even as a magnetic healer, his theories were different from others of same thought. Others rubbed and stroked the body for a period of time each day, thinking to impart their body magnetism from their bodies to that of the patient, imparting strength from them to him.

"D. D. Palmer would find the organ that was sick, debilitated, run-down or weak, and placing one hand on the abdomen or chest over that organ and the other on the back under that organ, would hold his hands still for a period of fifteen minutes daily, thus flowing his magnetic strength through that organ, thus rebuilding or strengthening the sick organ rather than trying to build the entire body.

"It was easy to go from that theory to the next step of why this organ was weak and sick. Why did it not receive its organic strength? Where did its strength come from when it was healthy? Why was it not getting there when it was sick? Thinking along those lines led him back to the nervous system conveyance or energy flow from that back to the blocking obstacle, the barricade, which stopped the flow from getting where it was to where it should be.

"Everybody in his day believed in impure, obstructed, stagnated, all-disease caused by blood flow. He denied this as having no sense or foundation. Having once 'discovered' the vertebral subluxation, it was but another step to its 'adjustment by hand only.'

"Gradually ideas accumulated into a major premise which he announced in 1895, although in the borning five years previous. When that stage of understanding was reached, a new name for a new system was inevitable.

"We could recite 'peculiarities' of this man by the hour. He was a 'marked' person. Many older people of Davenport still recite the un-inhibited things he did. Time will record these as unimportant.

"Time will record, as it does all individuals, that it took this kind of an uninhibited individual to bring forth that for which his name will go down in history, viz., the sum total of that type of thinking and acting known as Chiropractic.

"Many people lived then who ridiculed him because of his foreign and peculiar freedom of thought and action which expressed themselves radically to the disadvantage of the listener. They could not see then what we see now, that all this was necessary as a formulative process to develop the man to develop Chiropractic.

"You and we today forget the eccentricities of this man; they fade out of memory. We pay homage, fifty years later, to the one great thing that these minor issues led up to his producing.

"While he lived, people remembered and resented the odd and peculiar things he did. They enlarged upon and nursed them. They told and retold them, often exaggerating them beyond belief. He could not see why they did not see what he saw. He could never understand why they could not understand what he understood. He would spend patient hours with anyone who tried to understand. He ended all conversations abruptly with ones who interfered with his work. Today, were he here, he would be the first to damn every person who would erect a monument to his memory, and then deny everything Chiropractic he discovered and gave to the world.

"Time has a way of eradicating issues of no importance to time. Time has a way of making permanent issues of importance to mankind. D. D. Palmer will go down in history as having 'discovered' the secret wherein lies the cause of all 'dis-ease' and a method of correcting same by hand only. All else that made him unreasonable and distinctively different will be forgotten.

"All his thinking was off the beaten path; he took the side roads; he wandered alone into the jungle, cut down virgin forests and beat out a new road.

"The price he paid was to be alone, followed by few, shunned by many, misunderstood by most, fought on all sides by those who profited most from his labors. But the sum total of that life led eventually to the great accomplishment for which history will know him best.

"D. D. Palmer went through life a stranger to all but a sincere, honest friend within himself to himself. He knew, as none others did, what he was doing for them. They sponged on him; they picked isolated sentences from his writings and twisted them to mean the opposite of what he believed and taught; they thrice denied him, even as many are doing today.

"They glorify his name, they erect monuments to his birthday at his birthplace; they praise Chiropractic and then say he stole it from the Greeks; and spit on what he stood for and fought so strenuously to preserve for the sick people he loved.

"If he were alive today, he would damn with no faint praise those who do these things to his Chiropractic and those who would fence it in so the sick people could not get it."

B.J.'s tribute to his father left the listeners stunned. Many of them had known little about D. D. Palmer. They knew he was the founder; they knew he was B.J.'s father and that was about all.

But here, on the 50th Anniversary of the founding of Chiropractic, they found out about the "Man Who Made Us."

They rediscovered the pioneer. They learned of the fight to further a healing art.

The students and newer members of the faculty heard B.J. speak with love and affection about the man who died hating and attempting to punish his son.

D.D. clamed on his death bed that his son had robbed his science from him. D.D. died fearing that his name would be white-washed from Chiropractic journals. D.D. never really knew or understood his son.

B. J. Palmer spent his life building up the science his father discovered but never once did he deny his father the credit for the discovery.

The son made his father legend. D. D. Palmer may never had achieved such greatness if it wasn't for the work of the son and, in turn, B.J. may never have achieved such greatness if it wasn't for the discovery of the father.

28

---❦---

TV AND B.J.

IN RADIO, much is abbreviated, such as, AM-FM-TV, meaning Amplitude Modulation, Frequency Modulation and Television. B.J. never was afraid to attempt a new idea, try any new method or technique as long as it was consistent within the preview of the ultimate objective. If things got side-tracked into other avenues, onto other paths or went into tangents involving contradictory and antipodal principles and practices, he was against it. But when B.J. introduced radio, it was because it was modern, quicker and a more capable method of advertising Chiropractic.

In those early days there existed only A.M. radio. Later came "Facsimile" which was a method of printing a newspaper in your home via radio. This took place between midnight and 6 A.M. when everything is off the air.

B.J. thinks that "Facsimile" still has great growth potential, but it needs more developing before he will adopt it. The Palmer radio station WHO, Des Moines, Iowa, was one of the first to secure a permit to test and conduct Facsimile presentations.

Following A.M. came F.M. B.J. was among the first to contact Mr. Armstrong, the inventor of the F.M. process on which he has a patent. As soon as it was practical, both WHO and WOC went F.M. B.J. was still not satisfied; he continued to search for undeveloped factors which would make radio a better and bigger offering to the public.

TV was being developed in a crude way. Millions of dollars had been sunk into television trying to make it work. By frequent trips east, B.J. kept his fingers on the pulse to see what was going on. When he felt that T.V. was beyond the playboy stage and a reality of commercial value, he secured two C.P.'s (construction permits) from the Federal Communications Commission and placed his contracts and secured equipment.

To look at T.V. today, realizing how it has changed the American home life, it is almost impossible to believe that at one time newspapermen were afraid of it. Not only were they afraid of T.V., they felt the lifetime of radio was short. It reminded B.J. of railroad men who scoffed at airplanes and said they could never replace rail in freight, passenger or express business. The coming of the aeroplane did force railroad men to improve service with streamlined trains to expedite service. T.V. eventually came into its own to change the minds of newspapermen and millions of others.

One of the biggest thrills B.J. ever received from radio was on one of his trips to N.Y. on the Pennsylvania lines. Across the New Jersey swamp meadows, he saw a huge bill-board about 40′ long and 15′ high. All it said was "GET DAVENPORT TONIGHT." It was not necessary for Philco to suggest that people use their sets as it was the only set which could receive programs at so great a distance.

Back in the days when B.J. decided to try T.V., radio men were afraid of it. Finally, in 1947, NBC who pioneered in the development of T.V., began building and broadcasting shows to the eastern seaboard. These shows took like wild fire. People installed living room T.V. sets and spent hours watching it and exclaiming over it.

Today T.V. is an established necessity for radio men, much as sound is a necessity for the movie industry. At one time, movies were wonderful things with sight without sound. Then came Al Jolson with "Sonny Boy." Here sound was meshed with sight. This sensation brought Warner Bros. from bankruptcy to lead in the movie industry. Radio at one time was sound without sight. Then came sight added to synchronize this revolutionized radio.

Following T.V. came color, which WOC and WHO broadcasts twice daily. Desiring to be another first, in April, 1958, WOC made an experimental test on Stereophonic. In some ways there was a duplication of the same show broadcast simultaneously over T.V., F.M., and A.M.

Time will tell whether this becomes a regular method of broadcasting.

Why anyone should have feared T.V. was a cause of bewilderment to B.J. Anyone who picks up magazines such as Saturday Evening Post, Look, Fortune or any newspaper and looks over the advertisements can see that advertisements are more pictures than words. Advertisements employ the use of two-thirds pictures and one-third words attractively displayed to catch the eye. Some of these pages cost over $15,000 per issue. B.J. knew that advertising men did not throw their money away, and this is what he told those who argued with him against going into television.

"One picture is worth a thousand words," he said. "Can anyone, no matter how great his vocabulary, how vocal his imagination, how perfect his enunciation, transmit what he sees for you to see? Could you do it? Can you describe in words over the air to those listening so that they will picture what you see? You can describe it, but that doesn't mean people will picture it. Oh, sure, they can imagine it via words, but can you carry a mental picture which you see with words to those who can't see it? No! Can an announcer portray football games, wrestling, boxing matches, horse or boat races as he sees them? You can close your eyes and imagine them, but do you really see them?

"T.V. supplies that missing link between what actually happens and your eye to your mind. Supplemented by words, you get full visual action and satisfaction. As T.V. is received in a home, the person watching it actually sees better than if he were on the gridiron, in the garden or with any other large crowd in the bleachers, grandstand or circus tent.

"Why? Because in crowds there are heads in the way and he is too far away from the action. The television telephoto lens is closer to the act, ball or performance than the closest person. Telephoto lenses bring your eye closer via the screen in your home. Yes, gentlemen, I tell you there is a grand and glorious future for T.V.

"Why do people go to see football games and go to the theatre? Is it not because they want to see and hear and gain pleasure from doing this?"

"But B.J.," one man said, "people will leave their houses anyway to go see these things. People like to be part of an enthusiastic and screaming crowd. T.V. can't give them direct contact."

"Ah, but there are still those to whom staying at home is preferable. There are still those who cannot find baby-sitters or feel unwell, or who like the comfort of an uncrowded living room.

"More people are travelling on planes today because advertising stimulated their desire to travel. Competition awakens more people to the value of each. We either grow out of one thing into another or we stand still. We must train ourselves to adjust to shifting scenes. Conditions change faster than most of us think they will. Many times we must keep our lives fluid and elastic to meet changing tides and times. The automobile made going rough for buggy builders, harness makers, horse breeders and livery stable operators. The world survived . . . but mainly it was a world for the far-sighted, flexible people.

"Radio came and displaced phonograph record makers. Record makers came back to make more records than ever before. Television and no doubt countless other innovations yet unforeseen will change the pattern for innumerable people. The world will survive, the people will survive.

"I am not saying that we should uproot ourselves from firm foundations, I am saying we should be flexible and go along with factual, practical, and workable solutions to world problems.

"Because patterns won't stay put is no reason why we cannot make a new pattern and perhaps a better one. Twenty years ago, movies flickered and produced eyestrain . . . not so today. Television, too, can be a great thing."

The men around B.J. decided that B.J. and his enterprises should go into television. His speech convinced them that television might someday be something.

And so it is. In millions of homes all over the world, T.V. is watched all day long with immense enjoyment. Audio radio took youngsters off the streets by giving them a reason to keep them at home; video radio will get even more youngsters off the streets and into the home. The most enthusiastic video enthusiasts are kids, teenagers, and kids up to 80 years old.

B.J. feels that T.V. helps to educate and mold the present child. He has built a building which now houses his AM, FM and TV facilities across from his home on the east of Brady St. hill. PSC on the top of Brady St. hill consists of 4 city blocks.

In the early days of AM radio, the sponsor through his advertising agencies thought it was vital to crowd and squeeze all the commercial words he could into every 15, 30 minute, or one hour show. In a 15 minute show, it was common to have 500 word commercials, which ran eight to ten minutes. On a 30 minute show, the commercials ran twice that long—1000 words. Shakespeare said "The show's the thing," but the sponsors forgot this. The constant hammering away by commercial announcers for so long a time, got boring and listeners would shut off their radios. The listening audience was now past the novelty period. They were disgusted with long-winded, repetitious, noisy commercials. Audiences refused to buy the sponsor's product; hence, radio did not pay off. Cancellations of contracts occurred right and left. Radio stations were hard hit.

Network organizations suffered greatly. Regional and local stations were in the red. What to do? The sponsor demanded sales. He thought the way to get them was to have 500 word commercials. The agencies deplored this and denied its value, but they were afraid to fight the sponsors.

B.J. realized that unless the listening audience bought the sponsors' product, radio was doomed. To save the industry, B.J. came out with a small pamphlet which he sent to radio stations everywhere. It contained, among many other suggestions, this advice: "Eliminate the negatives, and accentuate the positives. Cut your commercials down to 1 minute messages, read twice on a 15 minute show. Use a maximum of 4 minutes on a 30 minute show. Cut your copy, make each word a sales word, and state your message in the positive." This pamphlet was rapidly followed by follow-up, enlarged pamphlets which were sent out free to all stations and advertising agencies.

B.J. then travelled to New York, Toronto, Quebec, Chicago, Winnepeg and Hollywood, putting on radio schools and inviting all executives of all local stations. Each meeting was held in a ball room in a local hotel. The usual audience consisted of from 200 to 400 people.

Between the pamphlets and the first-hand education of radio men, advertising agencies and sponsors on why it was not only advisable, but necessary, to keep the copy brief, B.J. was able to change radio thinking on commercials. People began listening to radios again. People began to buy the product advertised, and radio advertising began to pay big dividends.

B.J. then published the sixth edition of RADIO SALESMANSHIP. This was a big book, about several hundred pages long, and gave examples of how to do the things he advocated. This book is now used as a text in 128 schools, colleges and universities in U.S., Canada, New Zealand, Australia and Great Britain.

It was B.J. through his educational campaign, who saved the radio industry from going to the wall.

As gigantic as many of the sponsors were, as huge as the nets were, as experienced as so many station executives were, they lacked the knowledge to save their industry. Who was this one lone wolf in Davenport to change all their thinking, and introduce such radical ideas? He was simply the man who knew what the people wanted and how to give it to them. This was the most important thing the tycoons of the broadcasting industry had to learn.

When B.J. first put T.V. on the air, it was natural to try it on the 1949 pre-Lyceum and Lyceum homecoming. B.J. used it to teach Chiropractic techniques in the auditorium and bring speakers right up to those in the tent at Lyceum. Even to those in the rear, 120 feet away. B.J. distributed T.V. sets throughout the tent so they could see and hear. This solved some Lyceum difficulties.

Referring to Lyceum difficulties, B.J. has had them. Each year his problem has been where to find a tent for the 5000 visiting Chiropractors. What kind of a tent could he get? How large a tent could he secure? What condition would it be in? Would it be fireproof? The people who asked these questions usually waited long enough so that it seemed impossible for him to answer according to the law . . . which prevented him from putting the tent up for Lyceum.

In 1948, B.J. decided to attend to all things as far in advance as possible.

He rented a tent large enough to meet with all requirements months before Lyceum. The week before, it was used at the Wisconsin State Fair in Milwaukee. A violent storm came up and the wind ripped the tent to pieces. He was not informed of the condition of the tent until a few days before Lyceum. He had to start a wild search for one and he wasn't sure if he would have it. The one he finally secured was too small.

This incident taught him a lesson. He decided to have his own tent made to fit the lot on his property. He bought it and ended his tent problems. It is 120 feet long, 100 feet wide, has a 40 foot roof, with 10 feet walls and is guaranteed flameproof. PSC is the one Chiropractic school that owns its own tent.

PSC was the first Chiropractic school to introduce television instructions of their latest scientific research at its pre-Lyceum school and Lyceum Homecoming.

WOC was the first T.V. station to go on the air with television in Iowa. This makes another first for B.J. The first was WOC being short by only 5 months of being the first radio station to go on the air in the U.S.

B.J. admits readily that when he first started in radio, some 40 years ago, he knew nothing about it. Innate told him some day radio would be a great service in entertainment, education, sports and world affairs. He knew that he would be able to talk to millions of people everywhere. It was through radio, which had a tremendous future, that B.J. could help shape the destinies of mankind.

WHO has had many well-known guest speakers. Among these was Harry Truman. Tom Dewey had been asked to speak first, but refused. (Both were running for the presidency in 1948.) This was Truman's first major talk on his long western tour. His talk was directed to the farmers of America and reached over 120,000 farmers in front of him.

A few incidents happened on this speaking tour of President Truman that are worth telling. His 11 to 12 morning talk to 120,000 farmers, with WHO as the net-key station, fell completely flat. President Truman asked B.J. what was wrong. B.J. asked WHO farm Editor Herb Plambeck who said: "Your talk was written for the network. It was not written for the local farmers of Iowa and the farmers from surrounding states who were here." It was suggested that Truman go back after lunch and give another ad-lib talk. He did speak ad-lib, concentrating on farm problems. His talk was so effective, it turned the political tide in Iowa.

At the luncheon, which was served in a tent by the wives of the farmers, it was extremely hot. B.J., who sat directly opposite President Truman, said to the President: "Mr. President, any man who wears a coat here today has a dirty shirt." This took the President by surprise, but he was quick to catch the hint. He got up and took his coat off. Then all the rest of the men followed suit.

It has been said in political circles that this visit of President Truman to WHO changed the political complexion of Iowa from a normally Republican one to a presidential Democratic state. It has been said the farmer vote of Iowa is what changed it. B.J. felt it was a social courtesy to ride in the President's special train from Davenport to Dexter, Iowa. He disclams any credit for the turning of the Iowa political tide.

As for Ronald Reagan, who was a sports announcer for WHO, when he graduated from college, B.J. says, "He was a nice boy with a nice voice. I doubt if WHO really had anything to do with getting him where he is now. I'm glad he was associated with WHO, but if it hadn't been WHO, it would have been another radio station."

Today, these two stations are in AM, FM and TV. And what does B.J. think he knows about T.V.?

"Less than nothing," he said, frankly.

But Innate has been televising for millions of years. Innate knows and Innate will tell him what to do, how to do it and who to get to help him to do it.

Whether it was Innate or whether it was B.J.'s common sense, it makes no difference. B.J. took a chance on the new field of Chiropractic; it flourished. B.J. took a chance on radio; it flourished. B.J. decided that T.V. could be accepted by millions very easily. . . . He took a chance and was in on the wild fire which spread as the public pasted their eyes on the T.V. screen.

B.J. took more than one chance and each of them paid off with dividends . . . dividends of satisfaction as well as monetary dividends. Not many men have a chance to say that they took a chance and won. B.J. can say he took many chances and won each time.

29

---◆---

MANY FACETS

B.J. IS MUCH LIKE A DIAMOND—he has many facets to his thinking and activities. As a boy, when the circus came to town, he was up at 4 to see them unload. He watched them erect the Big Top. He carried water for the elephants.

Later, with his Palmergrams, he was to issue hundreds of letters to circus folks. In this way he began a life-long friendship with circus people. The Ringlings, Beatties, Christiani family, Canastrelli family, Zack and Estralita Terrell, Art Concello, Pat Valdo and Emmet Kelly were among the great circus friends that B.J. made.

At the Iowa state Fair Grounds, in the Exposition Building, WHO had a large studio where broadcasting took place day and night during the fair season. This building also housed The Old Trouper—The Famous Two Hemispheres Band Chariot Wagon, made for P. T. Barnum at a cost of $40,000. It was pulled through the streets with a 40 horse hitch. It weighed 10½ tons empty. Merle Evans and other band leaders rode it in parades. Many interesting stories are told about this Old Timer.

The Ringling family bought it from Barnum & Bailey. From then on, it changed hands often and finally wound up here in the Fair Grounds Exposition Building.

During the war, the Army Air Corps took over the fair grounds, and

146

put the wagon outside. The summer heat, winter frost and constant rain ruined the wagon until it became almost a total wreck.

B.J. used to hang around WHO studios in the Fair Grounds. He was shocked at what had happened to this finest, largest and most beautiful of all band wagons. He found out that it was owned by Zack Terrill of Cole Brothers Circus. He asked for it and Terrill turned it over to him. He had it brought to Davenport where he turned out blacksmiths, carpenters, cabinet makers and painters, to work on it. It was completely rebuilt at a cost of $13,000. More than $6,000 worth of 23 carat gold went into its carvings.

In 1952 B.J. had a winter home at Sarasota, Florida, which is the Circus City of the world. Circus folks winter here and many active as well as retired circus people own homes in the town. B.J. bought his home in Sarasota so he might renew old friendships.

One winter, a man named John L. Sullivan (no relation to the boxer) had a dream about creating a Circus Museum which would include all things pertaining to the history of circuses from the days of early Rome down to date. He and B.J. decided to suggest the project together. It finally was incorporated, stock was sold, and buildings were erected. They were known as "THE CIRCUS HALL OF FAME." B.J. presented to the Hall of Fame, with no strings attached, THE TWO HEMI-SPHERES BAND WAGON. This Old Trouper has the spot-light, center stage, down front in the Hall of Fame. The Bandwagon has had all its old glory restored.

All the greats and near greats of the circus gather at B.J.'s home in Sarasota during the winter months. They come, they hang around, they talk about old-time and modern days.

This is just another facet of this much misunderstood man.

30

OPERATION 75

"A MAN," B.J. BELIEVES, "may have numerous business activities, but he still needs a family and its love. Money cannot buy that."

Not too long ago, the Chiropractic profession donated money into a fund called "Operation 75." This was to commemorate B.J.'s 75th birthday and the celebration was held at Lyceum. They presented him with the keys to a new air-conditioned, gold-colored Cadillac and a bronze bust of B.J.'s hands. This was done on the family rostrum while thousands watched and applauded the grand old man of Chiropractic.

There were more than 3,000 congratulatory cards, wires, cables and letters with over 280 tributes, pledges, honors, citations of many kinds and other ways of saying, "We remember you, B.J.; thanks for all you have done. We appreciate it." (All of these are housed and displayed in large wall show cases on the walls outside and above on the walls of B.J.'s Trophy Room in the Research Clinic.)

A check in the amount of thousands of dollars was also presented to him.

B.J.'s 75th birthday was a happy one. His first Innate flash was to publish another book and dedicate it to his many thoughtful and kind professional friends. He used the large part of his check as part payment for the production of his Vol. XXXV.

B.J.'s closing words in this book were:

"To get, give. To have friends, be one. The love you keep, is the love you give away."

This year, B.J. will be 78 years old. His last 58 years have been devoted to loving and nurturing Chiropractic. He started out hoping to make Chiropractic a recognized science. He succeeded. He started out hoping to benefit Man. He succeeded.

B. J. Palmer has friends all over the world. How many friends he has is too hard to find out; they are too numerous. Therefore, he has proved himself a friend. He is loved and the object of devotion. Therefore, he has given unto the world freely of his love.

If you were to ask B.J. if he is sorry that he never took time out to enjoy himself more, he would say:

"What more can a man ask for? I think I have done all the enjoying it is possible for a man to do. I have seen something grow from a seed to a great field. I worked hard cultivating it and it has lasted.

"I am one of the few lucky men in the world who has lived to see all I have seen, meet all the people I have met, accomplish all that I have.

"I have but one complaint . . . that in nature, age must make one old."

31

A BRIEF TESTIMONIAL

When D. D. Palmer discovered Chiropractic, done by hand, people scoffed. Some, whose sufferings were beyond endurance, did go to D.D. and were surprised that they were helped where medicine had failed.

B. J. Palmer, the son, took over the developing of Chiropractic and the core that his father had started. He fought, built, protected the profession. He trained men to carry on the work. (*When Bart was 17 years old, he suggested to D.D. that a school of Chiropractics be started. His father at first was furious.*

"It's a family secret," he said.

"You believe in your work and so do I," his son said. "But we cannot hope to adjust all the vertebral misalignments in all the sick people in all the world. There must be others to help us cure the sick."

D.D. finally agreed and started the first known Chiropractic school. It was known as the Palmer Infirmary and Chiropractic Institute. In the first graduating class, there were only four. Now, there are many thousands of graduates from Palmer's school and there are many other schools throughout the nation.

B. J. Palmer went into court to help defend his science. He hired lawyers and won his cases. B.J., when only 20, worked night and day to keep Chiropractic going and to keep it growing.

Since Chiropractic was an unknown science, it was feared by the public. B.J. felt there had to be a way to let the world know about the science so that they could try it.

He went into radio, an undeveloped field, hoping to build up radio which would lead to the educating of the layman to Chiropractic and the good it could do.

But still the scoffers created trouble for Chiropractic. B.J. raised money for whomever it was who was being persecuted and dragged into court. The law suits and court trials against practitioners became bothersome; they caused B.J. and others to neglect their own businesses—the furthering of Chiropractic—to make sure that they were not being knocked down a peg.

B.J. and his associates were aware of the dangers of other instances where Chiropractors would be taken to court without able counsel and perhaps be convicted. *It could exterminate the individual Chiropractors. It would wipe out Chiropractic. Years of struggle would be defeated by prejudice and ignorance.*

To prevent this from happening, B.J. organized the Universal Chiropractors Association which became a hallmark in the development and evolution of the science of Chiropractic.

B.J. was the secretary-treasurer of the new organization. Morris and Hartwell, famous political figures, became the organization's national counsel.

The organization was independent of the Palmer School of Chiropractic. Its board of directors consisted of five members, all Chiropractors, who were practicing in various sections of the country. In later years, the constitution was amended so that not more than two members of the board came from the same Chiropractic school.

Now, still later, there are many such organizations to protect Chiropractics. But it was due to UCA that the firm of Morris and Hartwell made it possible for Chiropractors in 45 states in America, parts of Canada and Europe, to practice legally.

Today, Chiropractic principles are accepted as a science by the most eminent scientists. There are few who scoff.

During the 1800's, medicine had been practiced in this country in various forms since the first early settlers had arrived. But only a few of the early medical practitioners had attended a medical college or a tax-supported university.

Long after the Civil War the knowledge of medicine was gained by most practitioners by serving a term of apprenticeship with some local M.D. Many of them gained their knowledge of medicine while sweeping out offices, cleaning the M.D.'s stalls and currying his horses, or driving the M.D. around the countryside on his house calls.

D.D. started his learning of the body as a child when he collected bones of animals which had perished during the winter. He learned which way bones were supposed to be knit by practicing on animals that had been incapacitated. The bones always healed.

Few M.D.'s knew the internal structure of the human body; few could boast of the background, practice and study that went into D.D.'s education and few had the interest to search for new methods of curing the sick.

D.D. attacked problems of human sickness with a zest and zeal that knew no bounds. When he tired and stopped searching, his son took over, to advance further and find out more.

Pill . . . potions . . . blood-letting . . . prayers . . . herbs . . . symbols and signs . . . alcohol . . . fancy-named medicines; THIS they called medicine; this is how the people were deluded.

"Well, the yellow stuff didn't help . . . neither did the green one; maybe the blue medicine will turn the trick . . ."

And then D.D. managed to help a man regain his hearing after 17 years of silence.

Chiropractic progressed and gained acclaim by leaps and bounds. But a man who is fighting for something does not let well enough alone. B.J. and his associates started a world famous clinic.

Throughout the years the men in the Chiropractic field put a constant demand on B.J. to build a personal clinic that would explore the problem cases and correlate the information gained. Then this information would be used in a scientific research program.

B.J. certainly was the man to turn to. He was a leader and his school had on hand all the latest scientific knowledge necessary to deal with stubborn cases.

B.J. invested $1,000,000 to build the B. J. Palmer Chiropractic Research Clinic.

The Chiropractors in the field sent their problem cases to the clinic. Upon entering, the patient was examined by the medical staff who used ail the latest medical scientific instruments. This information was recorded and turned over to B.J. Then B.J. examined the patient with all the scientific instruments that the Chiropractic profession had discovered.

When the patient completed his Chiropractic adjustments and health service, the same medical staff re-examined the patient. Their new findings were correlated with the Chiropractic findings to determine how much help the patient received through Chiropractic.

When the patient was discharged from the clinic, he was sent back to his Chiropractor, along with a complete transcript of the patient's case history and the clinic's findings. With this information the Chiropractor in the field can render better health service to his patient.

The clinic received attention from all quarters.

The clinic became so famous that one of the foremost doctors in the

U.S. came to it for assistance. The doctor's wife had been given up as incurable. The doctor consulted with B.J. and then decided to send his wife as a last resort.

The doctor gave B.J. all his medical findings on his wife's case, which B.J. refused.

"What do I want with your findings?" B.J. told him. "No one knows the findings better than you and you were not able to get her well with them."

The Doctor's wife left the clinic and lived in comparatively good health for many years after.

The effectiveness of the clinic and Chiropractic in general have gained a permanent place in society as a method of helping those who are ill.

There is a great demand for Chiropractors these days. According to the 1940 United States Census, there was one lawyer for every 742 people; 1 nurse for every 371 people; 1 medical doctor to 799 people; 1 dentist to 1878 people and 1 Chiropractor to every 7,000 people.

In the days when B.J. was pioneering for Chiropractic, it was difficult for a Chiropractor to set up practice and find enough people willing to go to him. B.J. realized the difficulties and spent years after he had graduated, traveling around, setting up practices, acquiring patients and then allowing a new graduate to take over the practice. He would then go into another town and start the whole procedure all over again. This way, he managed to build a practice and make things easier for the new graduate who was anxious to use his knowledge to help make people well.

According to one survey made recently, there are about 25,000 Chiropractors in the States attempting to serve approximately 180,000,000 people. In Canada there are 750 Chiropractors to serve a population of approximately 13,500,000 people. In many regions, there is an acute shortage. Some cities do not have even one Chiropractor.

In the early days of Chiropractic, practitioners were dragged into court. In 1913–1915 two states passed laws licensing Chiropractic. Today, in all states, except four—Louisiana, Mississippi, New York and Massachusetts—including Hawaii, Alaska and Puerto Rico as licensing Territories, a Chiropractor may be licensed by taking a state examination.

When Mabel Heath, B.J.'s wife, graduated from the Palmer School, a woman Chiropractor struck B.J. as odd. Today women comprise 18 percent of practicing Chiropractors. This compares to more than 13 percent in medicine, 16 percent more than in dentistry, 8 percent more than in optometry and 15 percent more than in law.

The above facts stand out like a sore thumb . . . B.J. did manage to make something out of Chiropractic. But the going was not easy.

Twice during the days of early Chiropractic B.J. had most of his faculty walk out because they disagreed with him. Both issues concerned introduction of new scientific instruments into the art.

When an x-ray machine was invented, B.J. realized its importance. He made every effort to secure an x-ray machine for research purposes to enable Chiropractic to operate as a more scientific healing method.

But he met with almost insurmountable obstacles. It took him several years before he could buy a machine.

The scientists who were developing the x-ray had realized its value to the medical and surgical profession and attempted to prevent other types of healing from using it. They didn't want it used in drugless branches of the healing arts.

But in 1909, B.J. acquired the first x-ray used in the Chiropractic profession, and in 1910 he built an x-ray laboratory with a library of several hundred glass negatives showing various spinal conditions.

B.J.'s farsightedness was unpopular with some of the members of the faculty at the school. They just could not grasp the possibilities of the x-ray. They threatened to quit the school if B.J. introduced the x-ray into the curriculum.

B.J.'s decision was this: Bow to the whim of men who cannot adapt the new idea, or do what he thought best for the profession and risk losing some of his friends. He did not hesitate; he went ahead with his plans. The men, as they had threatened, left and started a school of their own, a school which was not going to use the x-ray in its curriculum.

B.J. introduced the x-ray and set up a new department in the school, called the Spinograph Department.

This is now considered one of the most important phases of training in all reputable Chiropractic schools.

In 1925, 16 years later, B.J. was again confronted with the problem of losing some of his best faculty and loyal friends because he wished to introduce another instrument into the curriculum.

This time the instrument was the Neurocalometer, patented by the Palmer School, invented by Dossa Evins, a faculty member of PSC. The Neurocalometer's principle function was to locate nerve interference in the spine. After an adjustment, it was again used to recheck the spine and see if the interference had been corrected.

When the Neurocalometer had been proven beyond doubt, he called his faculty together to tell them of the latest step to be made.

The faculty responded by threatening that they would leave if he introduced the instrument. B.J. had a tougher decision than the last to make; he knew that he had some of the finest brains in Chiropractic on his faculty. . . . Could he dare to risk losing them?

With a heavy heart, B.J. decided to introduce the Neurocalometer into the curriculum. He hoped that his faculty would stay on to see the results of employment of the instrument. They did not. They left the Palmer School and started their own school.

Many decisions had to be made for Chiropractic, many decisions were made; each was made with the interests of Chiropractic in mind. A man with less love for the sick and the science that proved itself capable of helping cure might have given up advances to maintain friends.

As was said in the beginning, and was proven, the name Palmer and the word Chiropractic belong together for they are as oxygen is to life.

Daniel David Palmer gave his life to this science and died before it achieved its ultimate.

Bartlett Joshua Palmer is giving his life to this science and will not live to see its ultimate.

The third generation Palmer, Dave, has undertaken the responsibilities to see that the science goes on . . . but he will not see the ultimate.

For Chiropractic, though 63 years old, is far from a finished product. It is after all a science.

Research continues—the search goes on—to find out the new, the unknown. And with each step Chiropractic advances.

There is no end. There can be no end of its advancement until Man knows everything about everything.

Many new people have, and will continue to enter the field. Although their name is not Palmer, they will have great contributions to make. They will follow in the footsteps of the father and son, Heinrich Duerringer and so on down the long list.

And many, the inhibited, the man afraid to think about the new, the undiscovered, will continue to scoff.

But they cannot beat Chiropractic. It is a science that needs further exploration. It is a healing art which is needed by many people.

The book started at the beginning . . . there is no end.

B. J. PALMER

DEVELOPER OF CHIROPRACTIC

— philosopher, scientist, artist, builder —
the bit of a mortal being whom Innate
Intelligence developed

BOOK II

THE PHILOSOPHY AND SCIENCE
OF CHIROPRACTIC

AT THIS POINT you have just completed reading the history of chiropractic, and of B. J. Palmer. It may seem unbelievable to some that one man could accomplish so much in one lifetime. Yet the fact is, Palmer's amazing accomplishments could fill many volumes other than just one book.

The only way your author can explain his feeling for B. J. Palmer is to cite the example of Carl Sandburg and his literary devotion to Abraham Lincoln. Sandburg spent many years studying the life of Lincoln, whose personality and way of life had many facets.

Lincoln worked hard and tirelessly to free this country of slavery.

B. J. Palmer has worked even harder and longer to free mankind of medical slavery.

Not until after Lincoln's death did his life's work become appreciated.

Like Lincoln, B. J. Palmer is destined to go down in history as a great humanitarian.

The remainder of this book is an attempt by the author to simplify, for the layman, some of B. J. Palmer's lectures and writings on the Philosophy, Science and Art of Chiropractic. The author deliberately referred to Dr. Palmer's writings of approximately fifty years ago to show that Palmer's thinking was many years ahead of the accepted doctrines of that era. Much of what Palmer taught then is being substantiated in medical research today.

"Some portions of this book have some words in regulation spelling; other portions have same words in phonetic spelling. Just as Chiropractic is a new subject, so are some writers, authors, and publishers introducing some phonetic spelling in books, magazines, and newspapers. We hope our readers will not be prejudiced because of this."

Joseph E. Maynard, D.C.

1

UNIVERSAL INTELLIGENCE

IN ORDER TO MAKE A COMPLETE study of Chiropractic philosophy we must study life in its entirety, in its integrity. There is life, therefore there must be a source of life. Now, we do not care what this source of life be called, but there is, beyond the question of doubt, a source. The very foundation of Chiropractic philosophy is the knowledge of an intelligence which exists everywhere. In all ages men have tried, by all manner of systems of philosophy, to solve the phenomenon of life. Everywhere we meet the fact that there must be a cause before there can be an effect. The motto of Physical Science is "there must be an adequate cause for every phenomenon of nature." Common sense teaches us that there can be no effect without a cause. Electricity is unseen, yet men do not deny its existence, for everywhere its manifestation is observed.

We see on every hand the expression of life. We see all about us effects, and the natural question is, "from whence." The fundamental principle of Chiropractic philosophy is the fact of the intelligent expression of life. This intelligence is unseen, but the expression or manifestation is seen everywhere in the Universe, and it is folly to deny the existence of such an intelligence. We propose to take what we find of truth in other philosophies and make use of it; it is not necessary for

Chiropractic to reject all that may have been said previously on the subject of the first cause.

The two systems of reasoning—the a priori, which infers effects from known causes, and the a posteriori, which infers causes from observed effects—have been in use a long time; but, while the systems are right, the procedures have been wrong and have not led the investigators to the cause of incoordination in the body. Why these mistakes should be made with respect to pathological conditions in the body when they have not been made in considerations outside the body, we cannot tell.

When we find an abnormal condition (an effect) in the body, our procedure in Chiropractic is from cause to effect, and so we are led back to the causative subluxation in the spinal column.

There are certain laws at work in the universe, but there is apparently more at work than the laws of chemistry and physics. We might say at this point that there are certain truths which we perceive intuitively and which cannot be perceived in any other way. To illustrate: The infinity of space we perceive by intuition, we accept the fact because of our inability to do otherwise; it is impossible for the finite mind to conceive of any limits to space; we cannot think of a place where space does not exist; therefore we believe in the infinity of space because we cannot disbelieve it. The same is true with time; we cannot conceive of a condition where time will not be a factor. Neither of these facts can be demonstrated by any scientific tests; they are, however, everywhere accepted as self-evident and necessary truths. It is equally impossible for us to imagine any change or effect without a cause producing it. This is not only "evident" but "self-evident," and in reality, there is nothing we are absolutely certain of except those things which are based on self-evident and necessary truths.

We cannot think of law but as the outcome of Intelligence, and we see Intelligence manifest in every law. Tendency is the very nature of law, and tendency always looks toward an end, and this end shows the previous existence of Intelligence. We are not considering this form of moral standpoint or in any way whatsoever from a religious standpoint, but merely from the standpoint of the intelligent expression of life all about us, which evidences an Intelligence in the Universe.

This Intelligence has received many appellations in different ages by different races of people. Some speak of the First Cause as "Nature." The Mohammedans refer to this power as "Allah"; the Indians as "Manitou"; the Hebrews as "Jehovah." The term "I am" is used in the Bible; among the Christians the term "God" is used. It matters not what term is used. This does not change the entity; such an Intelligence does exist. Wherever this entity or Deity, if you please, is expressed we always see it expressed in an Intelligent way, therefore there must be intelligence. We find no place in the universe where intelligence is not expressed, therefore we would say it is universal; so it is the most natural thing that the term Universal Intelligence should be applied to this very apparent force in the Universe, and this is the name given by B. J. Palmer, and it is what we use Chiropractically, we cannot think of a term that would be more appropriate and comprehensive.

Now let us return to our original premise, that "for every effect there must be an adequate cause." We believe an adequate cause in this case would be an intelligent cause, and since the cause is manifest everywhere in the universe it is in reality a universal cause. Then there is only one conclusion that we can reach and that is, that this first cause is a Universal Intelligence. All life is, then, the expression of Universal Intelligence. Then to make a study of life we must start at the beginning; therefore, our first step in the normal complete cycle is Universal Intelligence.

2

INNATE INTELLIGENCE

IN OUR CONSIDERATION OF Innate Intelligence it is as unnecessary for us to endeavor to define life as it is for those who study physics to fully explain and define matter. We cannot define electricity, but we recognize the fact that there is such a thing as electricity, for we see its manifestation and study it through its manifestations.

We likewise study "life" as we see it operating through matter. Psychology makes a study of the phenomenon of mind, but Chiropractic Philosophy studies the complete manifestation of life, as well as going back of the expression to a study of that which is expressing itself, considering, what might be termed the "essence" as well as "attributes" of the Innate Intelligence.

In the study of this subject, we find it necessary to define the terms that we use. We will begin by defining the term "Innate." Innate— "Existing in, belonging to, inborn, native, natural, belonging to the essential nature of." Essential—"Of or pertaining to essence." Essence—"That by which a thing is what it is."

Innate Intelligence is the term applied to the life within the body. We might say it is that which constitutes "You." We are unable to define "Life"; so is Innate Intelligence beyond the scope of definitions. Philosophically man is a duality. Anatomically no such division exists. Chiropractically we have an Innate man and an educated man; we divide Innate Intelligence into innate mind and educated mind, which subjects will be considered in a separate article. Innate Intelligence is ruler supreme in the body. Universal Intelligence being the source of life, we still consider only our relationship with this intelligence on the plane of the expression of life in the physical. *We can best illustrate the relation between innate intelligence and universal intelligence by the use of an illustration given by B. J. Palmer where he refers to Universal Intelligence as the sun, Innate Intelligence as the sunbeam.* The sunbeam is not a part of the sun, neither is it a part from the sun. We cannot think of the sun without sunbeams and there could be no sunbeams without the sun. We cannot think of Universal Intelligence without Innate Intelligence. There would be no Innate Intelligence if there was no Universal Intelligence. The Universal Intelligence would not be what it is, without Innate. The sun is the source; the sunbeam, semi-source. Universal Intelligence is source; Innate, semi-source. The brain becomes the medium through which the Innate Intelligence is expressed, in other words the educated brain becomes the mirror and the education is the reflection. Now, if the mirror be imperfect the reflection will be imperfect and it would be folly to try to patch up the reflection by substitution, stimulation, etc.; but we find as soon as we repair the mirror the reflection will be changed accordingly. Innate Intelligence is sometimes spoken of as a segment of Universal Intelligence; also as an endowment from Universal Intelligence. Theology teaches that "God breathed into man the breath of life and he became a living soul." Hence this "breath of life," being God's breath, the life in man would answer in kind to that of the divine. The Innate Intelligence being an endowment from Universal Intelligence is of necessity, in kind, the same as Universal Intelligence. In other words, the Innate Intelligence (the life within the body) is perfect. We would not speak of an imperfect sunbeam. A reflection might be imperfect, due to an imperfect reflector. The expression of Innate might be imperfect, due to the imperfections of the material through which expression takes place. The expression of Innate Intelligence through the innate functions of the body is always perfect when the path of the cycle is unobstructed and environmental conditions are right. No amount of education will enable Innate to more perfectly carry on the metabolism of the body. The organs of the new-born child functionate as perfectly as do the organs of the adult; the stomach digests the food, the blood carries the oxygen, the liver secretes the bile, the excretory organs work regularly without the aid of the educated mind. These functions are called involuntary functions; they are involuntary to educated mind but voluntary to Innate Intelligence. Educated mind has to do with the so-called voluntary functions of the body and has control over only a small portion of the body compared with what Innate controls. It is through that portion of the brain known as "educated brain" that we become consciously cognizant of things external. Educationally we do not appreciate the greatness of Innate Intelligence. We would find it profitable to study more carefully this intelligence that is expressing itself through the body; and, as B. J. Palmer suggests, we would find it profitable to "council with your other self." And this inner self is, we believe, endeavoring to transmit greater thoughts to the educated mind, if we were educationally capable of receiving them. Is it not true that you have at times seen some great something standing as it were in the eyes of some silent man, and it seemed as though some intellect back of the individual was revealing, in a single flash, what the tongue could not speak in a lifetime; and haven't you even at times in your own experience seemed to get hold of ideas that you could not express in words, and at such times seemed to get an intellectual uplift? "While the world is asleep at midnight the nightingale sings its sweetest song." Even so do our deepest aspirations unfold only when in meditation or, we might say, when we are in "council with the other half of self." Educationally we cannot influence Innate in the work of the body except by obstructing the path of the cycle. The innate functions are performed regardless of our educated intelligence and when we do interfere with the expression of Innate by obstructing the cycle, she is not slow in letting us know. Very early in life we learn that Innate's voice, is indeed, a "still, small voice," and that she continues to quietly whisper regardless of the thundering of education. Hunger and fatigue are warnings against overtaxing the body and the call for nutrition, and if this warning is not heeded, great damage is done to the tissue cells. Thirst is the call of Innate for water for the tissue cell. Pain is Innate calling for help because of some abnormal condition existing in the tissue cell. The same immutable law governing the expression of life in the human body is found working wherever we have life expressed. We see life expressed Intelligently in the vegetable kingdom. The innate of the acorn rends away the shell and proclaims its oakhood. In the rosebud, concealed beneath many velvety coverings, innate bursts its wrappings and proclaims its scarlet secrets. Man plants an unknown seed, but the sharp thorns proclaim the thistle. The innate of the plant never makes a mistake in its expression and grows cocoanuts on an apple tree. The grain of corn placed in the proper environment always grows a stalk of corn and never an oak tree. So in the body the expression of life is directed by immutable law. We find the expression always an intelligent expression; therefore, the expression of life must be under the direction of an Intelligence. We cannot go through our osteological studio without having this idea confirmed by examining the specimens there. A blind law could not accomplish the things we see here in the mending of fractures, the building of braces and bridges; the strengthening of weak parts of exostosis and ankylosis. They are all under the control of Innate Intelligence.

3

THE EMBRYO

"WHAT IS THE EMBRYO?" (em, in, bryo, to swell.) It is that expansion of germinal cells into a physical form which is taking place within the uterus. We will commence at fundamental, in our imagination, and create a mental and physical human being.

The child is the evolution of generations. When this process started we don't know. We shall aim, therefore, to confine our remarks to that portion of this progression that we have before us. A male and female must exist in specie to propagate their kind. In the human family the male produces a spermatozoon, which is characteristic in shape of a tadpole. It has an enlarged head with a tail. The female gives forth her proportionate share—ovum—viz., virility and quantity considered. The male may eject 66 percent and be weak and the balance, or 33 percent, would be strong and more than compensate for the excess of its opposite. The sex, then is determined by the excess of sex elements, considering quantity comparative with virility. This is round in its shape. The male is the giver and the female the receiver. At the time the spermatozoon is ejected the female brings to the front an ovum from the ovary. Some claim that they meet in the Fallopian Tubes, others the vagina, but it is more reasonable to believe they would unite where they intend to stay— the fundus of the uterus. The majority of authorities concur with the latter. After contact, the walls of the ovum, at one spot, fabricate;

fibres split; to make an opening for the reception of the spermatozoon. Here is where the tail is of service. Acting as a propeller, it works through the fibres into the ovum. Immediately after the frayed edges close and heal. The product is a microscopical unit, one-half residing within the other half externally. Under the action of normally increased heat, the next process is one of fusion, so that the two sex elements blend into the future characteristic child. At this stage the spermatozoon and ovum lose their identities and that of the third party becomes a reality—the embryo.

The first noticeable change is the "swelling" of germinal, embryonic cells into the blastoderm, which expands into two, between which, at a later period, is created the center. This outer wall is termed the epiblast; the center one, mesoblast; and the most internal one, the hypoblast. Let us see why a "blast." It is that which takes a character and transforms the same substance into different form. But embryological research into the gradual appearance and the formation of this important system of organs yields the most astounding and significant results.

The embryo as it exists, after fusion, represents the future adult. We want you to know that the embryo and foetus are, when expanded, the future individual. The process which we shall portray is of simple cellular expansion. Each layer in performing this action blasts its individual structure. The hypoblast expands into the epithelium of the alimentary and respiratory tracts, also the cellular structure in digestive glands. The epiblast makes the epidermis and nervous system, the mesoblast forming the remainder or the bulk between the two. It is impossible, in studying physiology of the embryo or foetus to demonstrate where one tissue breaks and another begins. The process of development is one of interblending; the intermixture of one into the other. The physiology of these tissues, as we shall study it, is very delicate when individualized.

How does each blast of condensed germinal cells expand to be the superficial skin of a mortal when it is the size of a pinhead in the first or blastodermic state? How can they expand into a full adult? This epiblast has within its walls an intercellular tissue. Within this are many germinal vesicles. What is a germinal vesicle? It is that enclosed tissue containing multitudinous germs. It has a nucleus and its center is a nucleolus; divide this and we have many nucleoli. Each nucleolus is a germinal spot. If you can imagine that each germinal vesicle contains millions of germs and each in turn pursues the expansion process, you can vaguely grasp some knowledge of how the child matures to an adult. Its process is slow and steady; no one day or hour marks the difference between embryo and foetus; foetus to infant; infant to child; child to boy; boy to young man; or young man to manhood.

Then starts expressed life with an allotted number of germinal cells. The expansive process begins and continues until all germs have been expanded and utilized. Granted that a person could live without subluxations, pressure upon nerves or the hindrance of the transmission of currents, he would live the "natural" life and die the "natural" death, which would be when all cells have been brot forth from the reserve stock and utilized. Many a person dies of "old age" minus any pathological conditions.

He gradually expands into the various attitudes before the world. We will allow, as it were, a germinal cell to expand in your imagination. It is now confined within well defined cellular walls, but it has an individuality, expresses thots. It will progress to a centrosome or center of attraction at the periphery. The walls break to permit freedom to show its makeup and discriminating quality. As it enlarges to and outside of this surface, it is proportionately adding liquid particles and, like a sponge, the more it absorbs the larger in size and the sooner it is a matured cell. The reticulum expansion creates a space filled with serum, thus this process increases size and weight and changes form.

What does a cell look like? A tissue cell, whether bone or other constituency, has for general structure a network of tissue called protoplasm, the interstices of which are now filled with serum. What was formerly in collapsed form is now enlarged. Contained within each vesicle—remembering that each blast has many vesicles—are millions of germs. When each has expanded, we have the completed epidermis of the infant. True, the process is slow, but so long as there is a reserve stock of germinal cells to replace the utilized ones, life exists. When the retained store is spent, death is the result. B. J. Palmer was the first in Chiropractic Philosophy to voice this principle.

As the epiblastic germs are enlarging, the same process is taking place within the other blasts. As each matures it is placed according to character and function. The expansion is not alone in size but quality and character. There are tissue discriminations and with a harmonic process of expansion, discrimination and appropriate deposition we have in the period of 280 days, or, as generally known, nine months, the completed normal object—the coveted child.

What is behind this embryo that makes it expand? Do these actions happen, come haphazardly? Do they appear at random and the product of luck? To say "Reflex Action" or that of a "Sympathetic Nervous System" is incomprehensible and not scientific. This body, physically, has not within itself the property of self-government. Let us find a satisfactory answer to them. The child is a product of what? Certainly of an intelligence which is—cause and effect. Is it the product of mother's education up to the time of birth, be she 18 or 40? You will agree, the youthful mother can deliver as perfect, handsome, cheerful, healthy and intelligent baby as her older sisters. Is the mother, with her limited education, who perhaps never attended school, the creator of her child? Did she direct the deposition of these various tissues and place them where they are? Could she determine and demand the sex desired? No! We must look to an intelligence greater than that possessed by the educated mother even tho she be a university graduate. At this point the science of human evolution has a direct and profound bearing on the foundations of philosophy. Our bodily structure and its life, our embryonic development and our evolution as a species, teach us that the same laws of nature rule in the life of man as in the rest of the universe. For this reason, if for no others, it is desirable, no, indispensable, that every man who wishes to form a serious and philosophic view of life and above all, the expert philosopher should acquaint himself with the chief facts of this branch of science.

"At the same time we must admit that our knowledge of the evolution of functions is very far from being complete as our acquaintance with the evoluton of structures. One might say, in fact, that the whole science of evolution hardly exists even in name.* * * It is so intricate that most men still look upon the mind as something supernatural and that cannot be explained on mechanical principles.

"They throw light first of all on the 'natural history of creation,' then on psychology, or the 'science of the soul' and through this on the whole of philosophy. And as the general results of every branch of inquiry are summed up in philosophy, all the sciences come in turn to be touched and influenced more or less by the study of the evolution of man."

What is the first organ built? We say built because the body is the finest mechanism. Nothing is "built," created or made without a guiding hand. The incipient expansion of the blastoderm and the first from that, the three blasts from which is expanded the first organ—the embryonic brain and the nervous system. From this period on it is a constant, direct communication between the mother Innate to what will, at birth, be the Innate brain of the child. It is this guiding mentality that matures the form of the physical child—the embryo to foetus and foetus to birth. It is, as it were, the expanding or unfolding process of the bud to the most beautiful rose. This embryonic brain, at birth, becomes the Innate brain.

The foetus has a life but it is based upon what is termed stationary life, that is the same life as is found in a corpse, alive and yet not alive in the sense of the circulation of intellectual currents. Again we wish to contradict this, while the foetus has a circulatory current of intellectual units but they come from the mother and are dependent upon her for them. At birth the child becomes a unit, that is, becomes an independent factory and manufactures its own currents and circulates them accordingly. When with the mother it was dependent, after birth it becomes independent. In the former the mother brain manufactures the currents for the child, after birth the child makes its own. Now is when this inherent power takes possession and proceeds to live within. He or she is as capable, complete and will direct the functions of that infant as thoroly then as in adult life. It is called instinct, oftentimes, for want of a better knowledge. Chiropractors supply the missing link; definitely elucidate its mysteries and demonstrate its existence.

How great and intelligent such a controlling mind must be that can command and execute millions of cells to expand in proper form, shape and discriminate between them in texture, function and then have the ability to place each where it must be. This distinction continues until we have one arm, its mate, then a foot and its opposite, in like manner the process simultaneously continues thru the three blasts, expanding the embryo proportionately in all directions, hence the future child advances no one place more than another, after the embryonic brain is in action.

As you know, after birth, nothing is added; if you should have a hand or arm cut off, another would not grow out again. The process of growing a hand goes on in the uterus of the mother—a process which cannot be changed in any way after the child is born, and yet before birth the insignificant thing which you call "instinct" did all this. "Great things come from insignificant sources!" (??) doesn't look reasonable. It is a great study to watch the development of this really great thinker which is doing things. This great thinker is the thing you would humble by dubbing it "Reflex action." Do reason and compare. As great as educated intelligence is—he thinks he can conquer anything, but he can't add a finger nail to the finger already created. This insignificant power creates not only one fingernail but twenty of them, at the same time growing 100,000 hairs on your head, perhaps mending two or three broken bones, attending to the reparatory work of the body, etc., all at one time. Compare this with your intelligence and see whether you can begin to do one portion of the work that your better self is doing. Innate works 24 hours in the day, and if educated works 12 hours a day you are all in.

Man tries to find how sex is determined; what is the secret that produces male and female? Where is he who has an infallible rule?

Cells continue taking their places until the matured normal form has been reached. The mother Innate has completed her labors; she places her thots into expression; the quickening process is started and maintained until the child is expelled.

You ask the question, which precedes, life or breath? Life is necessary to make breath possible, again, it was dead matter until breath took place. We don't know. A child is, on the outside, an independent unit.

The process of birth is the maturing to shape. That follows the maintaining or keeping to a normal the form as given before birth. By accident you remove a large portion of a member; the arm will never return in form but the stump and sore will be healed. "Healed," yes, but how and what is understood by that? A physician uses many names he is intellectually ignorant of, altho scientific in the use and abuse of terms. Even in the adult we have blasts and germinal cells and at the immediate time that injury took place there are germs, in process of expansion being carried to the wound, placed side by side until the external surface is covered by new tissue cells of the same character. As long as Innate can continue to use the brain as a medium for sending mental impulses to germinal cells and can, uninterruptedly, perform this action; life—in its fullest entirety—exists.

Coordination must exist between the mental and brain and brain system. The process of healing will not and cannot take place if there be complete interruption between mental impulses and their conveyors, the nerves. If there be such, then incoordination, a lack of harmony or non-expression of mental impulses, exists.

Chiropractic is philosophy complete. Death is the entire dissolution between mental and physical. What could and would take place if we were to cut or produce pressure upon nerves? A physician would say "degeneration." Some fractured femora heal quickly and others cannot be made to do so. What is the cause? Incoordination, and the physician does not know where. There is only a partial harmony between the mental and physical. Pressure upon nerves restricts the quantity of cellular expansion, thus there can be no healing of the wound. Disease is in proportion to the degree of pressure upon nerves. If 90 percent, it is one-half doing its duty, etc., etc.

Disease is in proportion to the quantity of mental impulses which are hindered in their transmission by the degree of pressure upon nerves. If 90 per cent of pressure exists, 10 per cent of current is hindered in transmission—it is almost, but not quite, death. If there is but 50 per cent of current there, then one-half is and one-half is not doing its duty.

This 100 per cent is subject to fluctuation. When sitting or relaxing we are using 100 per cent of current in all portions of the body, if we are normal. When we get up and walk around, we are still using 100 per cent—always 100 per cent, but the 100 per cent standard fluctuates within its range. We run a mile. (Time is a factor in addition to quantity.) As long as the amount of current, per the same space of time, meets normal adaptation, then it is 100 percent regardless of whether the person is sitting, walking or running. As long as creation and expression meet you have completed a normal cycle, which is equal to a standard of 100 per cent.

We have studied the process necessary to give to a mass of tissue its normal form. Let us briefly look into that which produces abnormal forms or prenatal monstrosities.

Under the subject of the embryological development of the form of the future child, we have studied all of that which goes to make a child normal in form. We have found that we have a normal creation. Again we conclude that the product is normal in form and that there must have been normal creation before transmission and expression. A law is a term used to express a condition which can never be read by man; expresses certain unalterable conditions which are observable by the educated intelligence of man. Then the law is simply the observance of things which do not change; the law of creation is one of these; one of the fixed quantities upon which the world rests.

The law of creation or embryological development is always the same. Sometimes things stand in the way of the fullest expression of that law. That is termed a perversion of the law of expression—not that the law has been in any way interfered with. Because we have a disease of some sort does not follow that Innate Intelligence has in any way been changed —it remains the same, but an obstruction brings about a perversion of the law of expression, so that in studying abnormal forms, which we shall briefly look into, we are studying the actual conditions which result from this perversion.

Were you to ask for a definition of pre-natal monstrosities (postnatal, also) we would say that a prenatal monstrosity is that expression of the perversion of a normal creative type; as creation is normal so must transmission be to the point of interference. From that point on the law remains the same, but the function of the media through which the law is taking effect has been perverted.

The connection, direct, between the mother's Innate and the embryonic physical brain is by means of the umbilicus, thru which, are nerves bearing direct messages. If the mother's spine be examined and there be found no subluxation to produce incoordination, then her generative organs, at this time, will be capable of normal duty. If abnormal, we may find the umbilicus (normal 20-21 inches in length 1/5-½ inches in width) varying in length from 20 to 60 inches and from ½ to 1½ inches in thickness. If the foetus fills the uterine walls to its capacity, what must be the change necessary to accommodate this additional bulky tissue?

The foetus is supposed to be in motion; the fact is this uterine body as an individual, has no independent action. The muscular walls of the uterus are constantly contracting and relaxing to get development and strength and be prepared for expulsion, thus shifting its contents from side to side.

This cord, during the uterine contractions, may convolute itself around the leg, neck or the body; once, twice or thrice, and become tightly drawn. Thus you know why a child is born minus an extremity. We can account for monstrosities which are born abnormal in form; that is a portion enlarged, very small, or abnormal in deposition, viz., the fetal child has a spinal column and is subject to the same law of cause and effect, to a subluxation and consequent pressures thereon, as in adult life. From this are emanating nerves as thorough as in the adult. When the funis is wrapped around the vertebrae and becomes tight enough to produce subluxation, thus creating pressure upon nerves as they emit thru intervertebral foramina, intensify, stimulate or inhibit the functions; thereby increasing, decreasing or wrongly placing the expanded cells. If pressure be great, paralysis of mental impulse is the result and the organ can express but little expansion of cells, therefore minutiae of portions.

"Why is the funis abnormal?" If there be co-ordination (between Innate brain and physical) within the mother, the generative organs could not help but perform these functions in a normal manner. In all such cases, of the above, referred to, close examination reveals lumbar subluxations of the mother. Adjusting such, returning them to normal would allow uninterrupted communication to the embryonic brain. Then and not until would the child resume its normal and cease to be a monstrosity upon birth.

Is the embryo a product of force plus matter, or of intellectual force plus matter? We make a distinction between force as commonly conceived by the physicist, and force as conceived by not only the Chiropractor, but by many of what might be called "new thoughters," or "free thinkers." The physicist leads us to believe that force and matter are inherent and coherent, therefore constantly together and could not be otherwise. We cannot gainsay that statement because true, but it does not carry its truth far enough. The seed is true to an apple, altho but a part, the core might be true and still not be the whole apple.

We cannot conceive of any quantity of matter but that there is a quantity of force in it. We say that the corpse represents a dead man. He is dead only relatively. As we compare him with you, or I, he is dead, but compared with other conditions of death which are inferior to him, he is alive. Could we mentally conceive the actual conditions of the molecules, atoms and electrons of his body, we would find they were in motion, yet the degree that you and I are going through is faster and greater. Relatively he is dead to us, relatively he is alive to something beneath, and, after all, everything we conceive is but a series of comparisons. Force might be greater than the amount of matter to reach a normal standard as we view it, yet that force and matter might be relative, normal to something below our standard.

It seems natural for man to view everything from his own viewpoint, so assume an ideal as the normal from which to judge, and from which we get relative bearings. Therefore, force and matter are inherent and coherent, but that statement has no bearing foundation, breadth or standard, until we add three phases—question of quantity, time and intelligence.

We cannot consider man without time as a factor. How old are you? How long do you live? How long does it take to build a child? How long will it take a nerve to grow? You cut your hair, and cut it again because time intervenes. A patient comes; he is sick; he wants to get well, NOW. He cannot. Time must enter.

Force plus matter is less than one-half of the view-point. Force plus matter is gauged by quantity plus time, equaling the product. Scientifically, we cannot assume a single hypothetical question but what we assume all its elements as—force, matter, time, quantity and intelligence.

The railroad train is a mechanical device. We introduce a certain amount of coal and water, then comes force in burning—forces of heat and steam. All to what end? To move the quantity of matter, gauged by a pressure of steam on the dial. To the end of a mile a minute. Time becomes a factor.

You and I are male and female, we are no exception to this common rule of the necessary elements. We are matter and force; quantity of each and time is necessary. The weight of a certain man shows a certain amount of matter. It takes more force to move an engine weighing 42 tons than one that weighed two tons. It takes more force to move a 320 pound man than a 150 pound one. Suppose our man weighed 300 pounds, he had 100 foruns to move him. He would move in a certain time a specified distance. Suppose, though, he had 200 pounds of matter and 200 foruns, he would move three times as far in the same time, other things being equal. Increase the matter, with the same given force and you move relatively. Decrease the matter with the same amount of force and you increase speed and distance proportionately.

A male is a certain amount of matter. He has working through him a certain amount of force. How much this may be, depends upon the number, degree and location of subluxations in his spine, interfering with the normal quantity of force getting to the quantity of matter. He has enough to be normal at all times, which is judged from the time he is born until he dies. Increase subluxations, decrease the amount of force getting to matter, and the time he lives is shorter. Eradicate the subluxations, let the normal amount of force reach the normal amount of matter, and you increase life to normal. The four attributes work hand in hand, blending as if it were one condition. When those four blend together freely, normally, or freely abnormally induced by subluxations, the man, in either event, issues a certain product.

That product, in a consideration of embryology, is the spermatozoon— the product of the male. How much matter or force he may give, in what time he gives it, depends upon what he represents. You cannot expect a normal product from an abnormal producer. The abnormal machine turns out imperfect work. As the producer, so the product. The same is true of the female. She represents a certain quantity of matter working with a certain degree of speed, proportionate to the amount of force she receives to do it within a certain time. Therefore, her product equals the number of subluxations she may or may not have in her spine, which determines the amount of current which gets to the amount of matter, and the product is the ovum in the female. Here are two products issued by the producers, the status and conditions of which depend upon the four elements working in each, either harmoniously or inharmoniously.

The two products of the male and female, assume a relationship; this in itself is nothing more or less than adding the two products. If they are abnormal, you cannot expect the future product to be normal—assuming the premise that we presumed of the ideal man.

Let us put this thing into figures. We have 100% of force plus 100% of quantity per the unit of time. We have four elements, 100% of each, when they get together we have a product, and that is desired. We are trying to work to the end of having each man or woman issue 100% product, assuming he is a 100% producer. The same is true of the female. That means if we get 100% of each of two products (male and female), the result is that when the two fuse, one combined normal product will be issued.

When we add spermatozoon to ovum, each loses its identity, neither is as it was, the third condition exists—the blastoderm, which begins a process of expansion of only what was in it. Nothing material is added except liquids. What was there will expand. If the elements to make a normal child were not there, the child will, nor cannot be normal. The given amount of force works on the given amount of matter in a given time. We could not increase as a product what we didn't present, neither can we expect the child to be something different than its parents pre-arranged it to be.

This process of expansion, to take place in the blastoderm, is based upon the four elements, because these form the premise upon which natural things grow. The amount of expansion is determined by the amount of force working through the given amount of matter deposited in a given amount of time, which is 280 days, other things being equal. In 280 days it is presumed that a certain amount of expansion has taken place to form a completed natural product, providing the normal amount of matter had been placed and a normal amount of force has worked in a normal amount of time.

This introduces the fifth element, which was necessary from the beginning. We cannot reason any other way, although the physicist says he sees no necessity for the element of intelligence. Intelligence is not concrete, you can buy and sell.

Let us go one step further and weigh relatively that portion of our brain we call educated. It is force going through brain in certain quantities in a certain amount of time also. Here is an idiot. We ask him common questions, his answers are incoherent, far fetched, etc., and you hardly say the word. Here is the element of time. Our boy is working an educated brain with a small amount of force. There is not a sufficient amount of force to answer intelligently. Another has a normal amount of force working normally, therefore gives you answers quickly. Time becomes an element of thought educationally. We say our ideal man is educated because he goes through a certain process. What is it? He goes through an introduction, interpretation, elimination, adds or subtracts, accepts or declines, all of this goes to make the elements upon which we base our conclusion. He tells whether a certain element is hot or cold, good or bad, moral or immoral, whether a certain act is a moral obligation to your neighbors or not. He speaks of height or depth, and makes comparisons. He constructs thoughts, builds ideas, and tears down old ones. Constructs and tears down buildings. He is a constructive and destructive creature. All of this is the process of reasoning or thinking upon things.

The end of all thought is to act. We call this a process of intelligence. We think we concede logically and without question of doubt that every man has an educated intelligence more or less, according to speed, time, comparative with quantity of force acting through matter. We know anatomically and through the process of vivisection that, educationally, we do not use all that matter called brain inside our skull.

It is a question whether the balance is used by the physicist's basis of "force plus matter is inherent and coherent," or there is more of this intelligence or another which resides and does the same things that we do, far better, in higher degrees and specialized work. As force comes through our educated brain it produces thoughts, it is a question whether the balance of this brain does or does not think. The physicist says it does not think, reason, discriminate between hot and cold, good and bad, moral and immoral, height and depth—does not use a process of subtraction and addition. It does go through "sympathy" and that we know is "by means unknown." If they had established a foundation which would stand logic, investigation, and upon which they could assume a premise which would hold, then we would have to meet their conclusion in ours, but they have reached none, other than to say, "by means unknown." They haven't established a means by which this occurs. Co-existent to finding "by means unknown," they have reached the conclusion, that "force and matter are inherent and coherent," and there the hypothesis ends.

We have seen that the spermatozoon and ovum fuse and form the
blastoderm, for 280 days it is expanding its cells. They are opening up
like a flower bud. First it is small, but organ by organ it opens, membrane by membrane is formed, finally we have the full development.
From the beginning there is a placing of bone cells as they develop.
Many go to form the femur; femur cells don't get mixed with those that
form the patella, and here are little bone cells by the million, each helping to form bones, and none get in the wrong pew. Each cell knows
where to go. While these bones are developing, there are tissue cells
making muscles and connective tissue, and they don't get mixed, and
while this is going on, other cells are making ligaments, nerves, hair on
the head and fingernails. There seems a process of discrimination between a muscle, nerve, ligament or blood, and there is something that
directs each cell. There is no confusion, but harmony in the placing of
these cells—millions of them—and all are being rightly placed in the
little child in the short space of 280 days, and yet if one man with hundreds of men employees, and dozens of factories working put up an
eight-story concrete building in one year's time, he thinks he performs a
wonder, when it isn't as the snap of a finger compared with the building
of one child. Not only are these cells placed, but they are of different
sizes. Those which make the extremity of the femur are larger than those
of the shaft. They are differently placed, differently built. Go over
the body, you find they are of different shapes, sizes, colors, densities,
and grow with different speeds. In the child the lumbar centrum is the
last to ossify, and it is the opposite with the spinous processes. Some of
these bones are ossified when we need strength at birth, there are others
which not finished at birth, are finished afterwards. The liver cells are
a different color, size, and condition than those of the heart, etc., and
all of this, it seems, brings to light a process of discrimination. If you
educationally possessed any one of these attributes you would consider
yourself a wise and capable man. You would call that thot, act and accomplishment the acme of intelligence. When a man can build a straight
wall, or put up a chimney 40 feet, so that it will swing with the wind,
he is an artist, because every brick is plumb. A man who doesn't know
how will have a curvature, get it wobbly. If you could place even osseous
cells in that body you would call yourself wise, by the standards by
which we judge education, which is by and through your educated mind.
But here is SOMETHING which places bones, muscles, nerves, ligaments, cartilages, and all other structures, and is doing all simultaneously,
not one mixing or fusing with another. Not only placing them, but regulating size, quantity, position, place and density. You haven't the intelligence to do it with, you are shy the necessary education, and we do not
know of a school teaching it, there is no place to learn it, and if there
was you could not do it, because it is outside of the province of educated

man to do those things. Not only are the attributes we spoke of, "force and matter inherent and coherent," essential, but there is the intellectual phase that adds the burden and, without a murmur, frown, scowl, or protest this "something" assumes the load, goes on quietly, smilingly and does its duty.

In case of an emergency, as a fever, this force takes on added responsibility, carries you through, struggles to see that you do not give up the ghost, and finally you pull through, and then builds you up to apparent normal again. Put your hand on the hot stove, a water blister forms, skin raises, there is a protective sac of water underneath. Cut your skin, a cicatrix forms which protects the new tissue and only a scar is left. Get a fall, produce a fracture. Not only was osseous tissue manufactured to be normal from day to day, but now new tissue united the portions in ten days to two weeks as solid as before. Supposing you get a blow on the skull, a concussion on the spine, there is an attempt to deal with it the best thon can. Suppose you got a dislocation, and it was never set, then this "something" in and behind forms new processes, uses mechanical principles, brings out ideas and movements found in mechanics and utilizes them. Supposing you have a prolapsus of the heart, pressing upon the diaphragm. It is not within the province of this something to correct the prolapsus when there is a subluxation cutting off force, but it can contract the diaphragm and thereby hold the heart up, which is adaptability again. Introduce poisons into the mouth, stomach floods the stomach with mucus and other fluids, to dilute the poisons, to save tissue cells from becoming destroyed, to save life. A bullet enters your body, as in war, it is never found, but in post mortem it is completely encased with cartilagenous tissue cells. This sac is dense, solid; it is like cutting a gristle. Why? To keep rust from getting inside outside. Introduce a splinter in your hand. Give it time and it will heal, after a while the bealing bursts and with the matter comes the splinter. The man who works hard, shoveling, forms a callous on his hands.

If you had the possibilities, with your educated brain, wouldn't you try to do the same? If you had excessive heat, wouldn't you take that man where he was cool? The body cannot cool it with ice, but it causes a perspiration. What do you do when you cut yourself; bring the edges together. The body naturally contracts its muscles and lets the edges come together. What do you do in a case of concussion, educationally? You let the man have rest and quiet. What does the body do? Purposely makes the body unconscious so that he cannot move. In a case of prolapsus, what do you do? Externally you put on a truss. Internally then contracts muscles so it must stay in. In the case of poisons, what do you do? Try to purge, or take a drink of lukewarm water for the purpose of diluting the poison. The body does the same, only naturally. In the case of the bullet, you tried to artificially extract it. From internal sources, there will be a bealing, if the bullet be near the surface, and exude it-self, or it will make this tough casing around it, if internal. In the case of a splinter, what do you do? Artificially you pull it out. Naturally, the tissues would beal, form a blister, and float it out. In heavy work, if your hands are soft, you wear a leather glove. Leather is artificial callous to the soft hand. Naturally, it grows its own leather.

If we, educationally, try to do the same that are done naturally, then compare the relative degrees of perfection in the doing of the same. Educationally, we cannot grow leather, so we put on leather. Innately, the leather is grown. The intent is the same all through the things we would do if we could. Those conditions are adaptations to circumstance. If a man would do these things for a purpose, isn't there something in and behind that is doing the same in a better way? If we reason and think in the putting on of gloves, is it not also reason and thought in the growing of natural skin. If we naturally think, reason and study to drink lukewarm water to purge poison, then, if without your doing that the stomach is flooded and the poison diluted and purges, isn't there reason, thought, study there?

Let us refer back to the child again. We told you it was the product of all the attributes necessary to form it, and isn't it the product of thoughts in and behind the parents, and after it is born isn't it then the product of the thoughts in and behind the brain which we educationally have no control over—the part we cannot use?

The question arises whether there is such an intelligence residing in the other part of the brain over which we have no control, or whether it is simply "force." Let us study briefly the field these people cover. We are told those things, which go on, are controlled by the SUB-conscious mind, without consciousness—an unconscious mind. Consciousness is to be awake, to understand, comprehend. Here is a mind working with-out comprehension, understanding, of what it is doing, it uses no process of discrimination. It doesn't make any difference whether bone cell goes to the place intended for nerve cell or not. It doesn't know the difference between good and bad, hot and cold, moral or immoral, height or depth, or any other attributes. It is without consciousness, it is asleep, dead to the world.

On the other hand, we think any mind or force, which goes to our extremes or placing all those primary tissues in proper place, never fooling itself once, not only that, but going through all the attributes of which we spoke,—size, color, quantity, and kind—that may possibly enter in conscious, but it must have a SUPER-consciousness as com-pared with our educated mind, an idealized brain and understanding. This mind is far above anything we educationally can compare it with. Instead of SUB-conscious, underneath your educated consciousness, by comparison, inferior to you—it is the reverse, for this other mind does everything we cannot, even though we were given the force and matter it uses in a given amount of time. In comparison we should reverse the positions and place the sub-conscious mind as SUPER-conscious mind, instead of looking down, look up to, because it is our superior.

That the original premise that "force and matter are coherent and inherent" if true, if we can add three qualifying conditions, which is that with this force goes an intelligence, that with intelligence is a super-strata.

In all thought we reason from the known to the unknown. Educationally, we know what we think, reason, study, discriminate, compare different quantities of force and matter plus a given amount of time in which done. We know that with this process we issue certain products, those tally with the degree of the producers. Look at the product of the other mind, this child, with which we educationally cannot make a comparison, hold a candle to it, and yet we are presumed to say, from the physicist's and chemist's standpoint, that all this occurs without intelligence,—by means unknown.

By comparison, reasoning from the known to the unknown, a product that is so much better than our product must be produced by an intelligence comparatively greater. We know that the product is only equivalent to the producer. As we think educationally, so do we produce. Look to the product of the Innate, the child. As the child, so must be the Innate, other things being equal, giving her freedom to act. As the height of intelligence we see the product, so must the height of intelligence be in the producer. The more we see in the child, the more we see of the grandeur in the possibilities of the maker of that child, then do we receive an idea of how we should revere and hold in esteem the Innate that made it.

We grow in appreciation of things natural around us as we study and decipher them in their natural relations, and then we are compelled to say that anything that can make that great product must be a great producer. We learn to admire the producer as we see the product. It is natural to presume that we educationally would do as she innately does, if we could. We cannot. We must study them to appreciate ourselves. What we are educationally, is coming from our superior. We can never say that the inferior makes a superior, but superior issues inferiors, and inferiors study and try to equal superiors.

In study, it seems that the physicist's basis that "force and matter are inherent and coherent" and letting the premise rest there, is too narrow, not broad enough nor forcible enough to meet facts as they are. Children are dual things, part educated mind, and part innate, the actions governed educationally are inferior to the innate actions, and the products compare relatively.

4

———◆◆◆———

PHYSIOLOGY

THE STUDY OF FUNCTIONS is the observation of action. When we see this it is life applied, existence expressed, in a physical manner. We must start at definite points and reach final conclusions. Function is action and it is impossible to have known life before execution is perceptible. Life exists, mentally, before its expression physically. Nothing is enacted in the physical, but its mental equivalent must precede it.

Thot is to the brain cell what function is to the tissue cell of the balance of the body. The terms "thot" and "function" are both abstract until we apply them to some action which has taken place in a physical medium.

When we conceive that two brains have passed thru them an unsensed substance, which the brain transforms, we call it function after expression.

We can see this unsensed attribute only after it and the material have been united as one.

The Innate brain, as a part, is the first embryonic organ formed. Life exists around us at all times, but should we wish to take one hundred units of life we could not do it. To measure it in square inches is an impossibility. It has no space limits; exists in unknown quantities and cannot be confined. It is sufficient to know that an individualized portion of this unseen force passes thru the medium of the brain of each plant, animal or human being, and there makes its existence known thru a physical intermediate. Altho of the same consistency and making the individual live, it is, by him, unseen, altho, performing his functions.

The brain function is the first incipient action. What is this? To passively absorb and transform external etherical units of force to an internal physical power. Electricians are aware that a transformer is a convertor; the same exists here. Absorption—sparse transformation-expulsion.

These brains have, combined, a brain cord extending from them which is an elongation of fibres from brain cells.

The next function of spinal cord is to transmit; to conduct that which is transformed. The fibrillae can aptly be compared to electric wires. The wire does not create but transmits; does not interpret nor switch onto some other—it just transmits. The wires do not nor cannot perform the duties of a dynamo. You ask, "By what means does the spinal cord carry, transmit or conduct this force?" Each impulse leaves its brain cell with a cellular contractile impetus, which is sufficient to deposit it at extremities. Altho unlimited around us it can be constricted, confined and estimated in lack or excess of quantities or quality by obstructions at intervertebral foramina, a condition which will never be seen with the microscope. That is why it is not spoken of by M.D.'s "What cannot be seen does not exist." Can the electrician tell how much per minute passes over a wire? The quantity of electricity passing thru a wire is known only as a device is placed at an intersection in the wire, and then as the current passes thru it, it registers the quantity and number of units of energy. These devices are called metres, because they register the given quantity of current being transmitted within a given attribute, which we may be investigating, such as time, speed, quantity or quality.

Yes, by the quantity which is expressed in action in that given time. Can the electrician tell how such passes over a wire? If he knew what electricity was he could, perhaps, describe its transmission. Chiropractic philosophy explains most thoroly, why and how Innate creates and utilizes force.

Mental impulse is that accumulation of immaterial units of intellectual energy which, after having been absorbed, transformed and expelled thru the brain, Innate Intelligence deems of proper quantity and quality to personify specific characteristic functions.

Every function of the body is controlled by mental impulse. D. D. Palmer was the first to claim this theory.

Innate Intelligence is that sum total of individualistic mental impulses each of which is composed of multitudes of intellectual immaterial units of energy, after they have been received at the brain and transformed for the needs of the natural body. It is a name given to the intelligence which exists in transformed form in any object living in definite size and shape.

These brain fibres emit thru the various foramina and after their first division again subdivide and continue this process of separation until each cell or tissue has its fibrallae. Chiropractic philosophy explains how each brain has an intelligence which is capable of stamping, on each impulse, an individuality. With this comprehension we can easily understand why functions are harmonious, but to "turn back" on the supposition that harmony exists because they are "reflex" or "sympathetic" does not meet the comprehension of a person who wants to know why the intelligence expressed.

When we look to the minute dissection of muscles we find that each is made up of muscular fibres and each of these is composed of cells which has its independent brain, nerve and tissue system placing it in direct communication with the mind and subservient to its demands. Each fibre acts as a unit and the multiplicity of actions, guided by Innate, of the many makes a harmonious whole.

Bone, without mental intercourse, has no property to move. Living osseous structure, under a microscope, is gradually changing its consistency. As certain cells are utilized others come. The expansion of germinal osseous cells, from ossific centers, is but the minute action thruout the bony framework, which gives Innate another opportunity to express her mental and physical unity; adapting her power to the circumstances that have been, are present, or are expected.

All nerves are alike. Those coming from the brain are efferent, and express one character, motor. That is, each fibre will carry impulses which, when expressed, produce some individual characteristic action or motion. What kind it will produce depends upon the type of impulse that is given to it at mind. The discrimination, in tissue action between them, is due to the different species of impulse. In general, they are motor, but this takes on many changes. When secretory mental impulses are placed in action, at periphery of brain fibres, it means that that issue will perform a secretory act, creating a juice. Following this must be the excretion.

Nutritive or tropic impulses, when expressed at periphery of fibres, mean that certain kinds of materials and impulses are utilized to perform that function. We have also calorific; that is that character of mental impulse (spark) which, when expressed at peripheral, induce combustion and produce—heat. The disposition of the latter would not be in accordance with secretory or nutritive. When we cut, tear or bruise tissue, reparatory impulses are needed, which have that distinctive, expressive quality, and when placed into action, induce repairing, thus healing the injured portion to its normal condition.

The brain is the generator, maker, transformer or converter of mental impulses, and as there resides within this brain an intelligent mind (Innate), we must admit that to Thon belongs the honor of giving to these impulses their distinctive qualities—not alone for the functions enumerated, but all power that is created.

The generally accepted function of the stomach is "to churn food." The stomach, liver, spleen or any other organ has no function to perform, although each is supposed to express such. "Music is the product of a musical instrument. In other words, the instrument is there to express a function providing it gets or receives a function to express." Every tissue has "a special office" which is sent to it. Therefore, all functions are mentally created and physically expressed. Function is one, but might be divided as: Mental manufacture and physical expression. "Johnnie is a lively fellow." Chiropractors mean that Johnnie is able to put into action a far greater proportion of impulses than the average person. He is more nearly normal.

The stomach is composed of muscular fibres placed during the embryonic of fetal life, and are daily expressing impulses going to them, and will continue so until the nerves are unable to transmit, deposit or place them into action, after which death is the result. As long as there are cells in reserve and they are capable of being expanded, then life—action—can exist in that organ. Take away mental impulses that would ordinarily go to the muscular fibres, so there can be no expansion of cells to replace those utilized, and death of that organ exists; there ceases to be an "instrument" for expression of "function." The physical function of the stomach is to promote contraction of muscular fibres. These produce a wave or rhythmic action and a churning-like movement is present. As long as food is in the stomach Innate will adapt itself, with rhythmic movements, mixing it with splenic fluids.

The movement of the bowels is peristaltic. That is, express a rhythmic-like movement through them always towards the external, gradually working onward fecal matter until it leaves the bowels. This is bowel expressions of life, although mental conception and propagation preceded it.

Study respiration. The lungs contract and expand. It is an Innate or voluntary function, continuing whether asleep or awake. Who is it that guides and directs every impulse as it goes out? Where is this fellow that accommodates himself to the external and internal man? We run and breathe faster, perspiration follows more freely. Can you call those "reflex actions?" An echo is a good example of "reflex action," but we cannot believe that our physical is the expression of an echo. Our wish is to be a reality and explain its existence and actions by such means. To explain by "reflex action" is like hitting echoes. Try to hit it here and find it there; you attempt to bat it there and where is it?

Suppose we fracture the femur. Can you say that the fracture happens to heal? Is that an accommodation that is "just as luck would have it?" If these functions portray deep thought (they do to a Chiropractor) we must place behind them an intelligence greater than man. This gap is well filled by proving that Innate built piers of exostoses and repaired it.

Abnormal brain functions may exemplify many "mental Aberrations." The brain is physical, composed of tissue cells similar to the stomach or bowels. It must be kept to normal in nutrition, calorific, etc. One, two, or any number of combinations of these, in excess or not enough, means—disease—physical disease of the brain—with the inability of Innate to work through it—thus giving rise to what is commonly termed "mental disease," with physical portrayals.

If the brain is not sufficiently nourished, it becomes depleted and acts as a poor medium for ethereal power to pass through. It makes a weak transformer. That person is liable, under conditions, to do many peculiar things, talk faulty; in brief, be slightly or greatly insane.

Function is the expression of mental impulses through an "instrument." If at any time an accident, strain or wrench occurs and produces a vertebral subluxation, this, by occlusion, impinges nerves, as they pass through the intervertebral foramina, that are transmitting mental impulses to that "instrument" at periphery regardless of where located.

Disease, regardless of character or location, is but a loss or exaggeration of one or more specific functions; that is why, in the analysis of disease, at each recitation Chiropractors resolve to "component" functions as well as cause. To simplify is the aim in Chiropractic Philosophy; to make complex, to try and meet competition is oftentimes the aim of improperly equipped minds. Remember, greater movements, all realities of life, are based around simple principles.

Take a case of paralysis which is generally a loss of function—motor power. There was not enough motor brain impulses going to those legs to allow normal action. Calorific and nutritive motor functions were also involved. The hands and feet were cold. His extremities began to deplete themselves for the want of nutritive functioning impulses to maintain the equilibrium under which he has been living. A Chiropractor analyzes symptoms back to various functions and cause of each, thus reaching a definite conclusion the adjustment of which returns normal health. The spine holds the secret.

When summed up every disease is a lack of or excess of function; too much or not enough of mental impulses. There is too much or not enough motion of the stomach; an excess or lack of action of the diaphragm; an evidence of too much or not enough movement of the bowels; supply is too great or too little to the kidneys.

In brain tissues we can have both; find the same in all organs or tissues of the body. The M.D. believes that if there is not enough life, "give something to stimulate and make more." Too much, slow it down (drug). The M.D. has a thousand and one things to try. What would stimulate function in one may not in another. No wonder it is called "practicing"; he is always trying, not doing. After ten years he settles to three or four kinds of medicine (if he is honest,) and many, after twenty-five years' practice, only have two. When there is too much function he has one to deaden, when not enough he uses the opposite to stimulate, and finally (providing he follows the golden rule) he will quit both and tell the patient to try something on his own hook or live quiet until he dies.

To know Chiropractic, by its psychological and metaphysical completeness, gives to man a unity that has never been conceded by medicine.

To sum up, as Chiropractors, we grant that, spawned as it was of the crude concepts inherent in the minds of most of its early practitioners and early research students, medicine has reluctantly been brought up to date in matters of hygiene and sanitation, but they have not yet learned what even a domesticated cat knows about health and health laws. A sick cat cannot be tempted even by cherished delectables until its ability to eat is restored. To this day their favorite reply to questions about disorders such as migraine, arthritis, rheumatic pains, diabetes, common cold, etc. is: "cause unknown." But they go ahead and treat it anyhow, whatever the disease they know nothing about.

Chiropractic, in its short 63 year history, on the other hand, has built its enviable reputation by restoring to useful lives, countless victims of these afflictions. Because the Chiropractor is trained to look for cause where it is more likely to be, and prove it by removing that cause, whenever and wherever possible. Often, a simple adjustment, so bare of glamour and fanfare that so-called great medical neuro-surgeons hide their surprise in scientific shame, corrects a complaint that baffles the best of the best, as "incredible." Sure, it's Chiropractic.

5

———◆———

THE SENSES

THE EDUCATIONALLY KNOWN physical senses are sight, taste, hearing, smelling and feeling. These are received thru physical channels. How many may exist beyond, of the Innate mind, you or I do not know. A few people have some of the latter so highly developed that they become in effect a reality; the actual performance of the function is a declaration. We might refer to clairvoyancy or telepathy, etc. in this chapter. But it is not within the scope, in this chapter, to speak of "Senses" beyond those in common, daily use, which are known physically; if they be not known to our educated, we know they do exist by their responsive expressions externally from Innate. We would not understand that sense exists were it not for their expressions. You nor I could nor would not comprehend what we saw were it not for actions responding. We would not know that music was pleasant if it were not that we acted in a receptive manner to it. We could not realize that foods were tasted if not for the apprehension. There must be a synonymous action with each sense to let its actuality be a reality.

We know that man exists with a dual brain, one in which Innate resides and another thru which Educated takes cognizance of external things. A sense is that impression mentally interpreted, made upon one or the other brain. Place the tips of the finger, peripheral ends of fibres, in contact with a substance and you create an impression, conveyed by afferent fibres to the brain within one five-hundredth of a second. Within this remarkable division of time the mental knows all about it.

You ask what transition impressions must pass thru to be "sense," the brain and its intelligence, residing therein, whether that be Innate or Educated, receive impressions and place upon them the stamp of interpretation. This may be good, bad or indifferent, similar to the television set, which may be sharp, dull, indistinct, or not focused. The fact of having touched the periphera does not mean that we have "sensation." Chiropractors consider everything, from the external going inward, as impressions.

Impressions placed into active forces which cannot be harnesses or measured, which you and I have no control over, and then a physical quantity (nerve) carries that distinctive kind of action, and a physical organization (brain) receives these impressions and place them thru a period of development. After which its demands must be replied to, and that response is the recognition and proof that there is a sense of this, that or the other character. The sense is the external, thru an intermediate, coming in contact with something internally. We see or hear, yet there is no skin to skin contact. There is the continuity of tasting, apposition of substances in feeling which is the coming together of two material bodies; and interpretation at one central point, either brain.

Each brain has its complete number of senses. The Educated mind can see; listen to music; touch and feel; taste anything which is placed within the organs of taste. Therefore, this brain must have fibres to transmit impressions. Every afferent fibre admitting impressions responds thru a motor to the point of origin of the impression. We have a complete circuit by means of the brain.

We do not know how many more than hearing, taste, smelling, sight and feeling there are in the Innate brain.

You can see why two brains, each working with an individual set of sense impression fibres, going into and carrying outwardly the motor responsive impulses, that whatever impression is carried to one brain is also impressing the other, therefore is never lost.

There are many impressions which are interpreted as pleasant and to these we grow receptive. There are those on the reverse, which are repulsive. How is it that a merchant, seeing a well dressed lady entering the door, bearing the prospects of being a good customer, invited her to a chair and talked pleasantly to her? Because she made a pleasant impression on his mind. On the reverse, a beggarly appearing tramp enters. He may have a million in pocket, but he made a poor impression; he calls the clerk and throws him out. Your physical was contractive because he made a poor mental impression.

There are many things which conscience (a sense of the Innate) prompts you not to do, for it is not just, honest; but you can, by force of Educated, perform that act. Then comes pangs of consciousness which cannot be restricted, there still being that intelligence, greater than the Educated, that you cannot get away from. You can domineer and command the Educated to overthrow Innate temporarily, but permanently you cannot. We may be able, in a measure, to dictate to and control the Educated man's ideas and impressions, but there is one being you cannot twist around your finger—Innate.

What is conscience? It is Innate voluntarily expressing and acting in response to voluntary impressions received inward. It is that good or bad, right or wrong interpretation that is placed upon Innate impressions. This fellow is always ready to bore and bother you. Educated may persist in "stealing anyhow," but Innate reminds: "If I could but return those jewels I would do it," remembering Innate only has to do with all that is internal, therefore, cannot utilize nor act with externals. A woman has this "intuition" more. It is an Innate voluntary action more dominant in women; she listens to its reasonings, is more susceptible, and as a medium is more willing.

Conscience is of two characters—Educated and Innate. Conscience is but an ideation following the interpretation of all of the senses of each brain that is doing the interpreting; for instance, the ideation following the intellection of the five senses of the educated mind, thru the educated brain, upon all the impressions being received from some one specific, definite, characteristic function—this is equivalent to the conscience of that mind. As the Educated mind deals only with external conditions, we can say that the scope of the Educated mind is confined to ideations formed of ideas surrounding it.

Innate mind, through the Innate brain, having at least five senses, each of which is better than the opposite in the other brain, and in addition to these many more—how many we do not know, but the interpretations made by the five senses and the additional ones of the Innate mind form the Innate mind ideation; equivalent to an Innate conscience.

How often you merchants, who have a wife in business with you, have noticed similar to the occurrence of where a stranger enters and accosts you with, "Mr. Merchant, I want to borrow one hundred dollars; I am hard up." "What security have you?" He submits something which your educated senses, and as far as the intelligence of that brain knows, can be accepted as good. Upon returning to your office to get the money, your wife says: "I would not do that if I were you. I do not feel just right about it." Every successful person wishes to reason all deals upon a business basis and is loath to accept such "women's foibles." He wants definite facts or logical deductions which could be passed upon by a jury. But to repeat that "his wife did not feel just right" is no excuse and would make of him a laughing stock, altho he runs no risk by not doing it and might have lost by loaning. The wife gave free rein thru her physical to Innate. Her impressions were keener and created a higher degree of interpretation, consequently responding with more force, sufficiently so, to try and save one hundred dollars. Man has an Innate and should allow this to be developed the same as a woman. That is why, "Let your Innate sway your entire internal and as much of the external as you can," and you will not lose. The Innate knows a thousand times more than you and I ever will. Follow the appetite and inward desires and you cannot go wrong.

Each sense starts into action different characteristics. Impression is carried by way of an individual fibre, thru spinal cord and to an individual lobe of the brain. It is there interpreted, for instance, as one demanding heat. Immediately that lobe which interprets impressions communicates with the calorific. "We need more impulses, calorific in character, in the pelvis." There is an Immediate response and heat is the product, providing there be no interferences with these messengers from the time of leaving brain until expressed at tissue cell.

Another fibre might convey impressions which, when interpreted, might have the deductions that the ossum innominatum is broken and force must be directed to repair it. The Innate mind thinks, reasons, and immediately responds with impulses. Cells are expanded from an ossific center, sent to, and are accurately placed to make a correction according to some mechanical principle. Fusation proceeds until the fragments are welded with the new material. This can take place whether the pieces are placed in apposition, or never set, which is found so frequently in animals, domestic or wild.

Again we call your attention to the intelligence behind all this, which tells each cell where to go and what to do. Whatever an impulse does, it is motor; that is, it gives vent to action—function—life. When we cease to have life in whole, there is death; if a particle of life—function —is impeded, death exists in proportionate degrees. The different degrees are named according to what kind of death inaction is portrayed. We can say all impulses are motor, but we subdivide each into a type. Call it calorific; reparatory or creative (as in organs of reproduction) it is motor.

You are asked educationally to sense by interpretations what the membrane of the bowels feels like. Can you educationally do it? No. Why? Because you have no educated afferent and efferent fibres leading from the educated brain to that membrane, yet should anything go wrong (excessive heat) there would be impressions made which would travel afferently through the Innate fibres, passing to the Innate brain, when the Innate mind interprets them, and then by a series of connections passing always from the Innate brain as products of the educated brain (the receiver); so much so that the educated brain would say there is something wrong in my bowels, because of the thought having been worked out in the Innate brain and then given to the educated brain. The educated brain has no known means of communicating at will with the Innate brain, in a manner similar to the Innate brain communicating constantly with the educated.

We know that you may think that this is wrong because of the many psychological phenomena. Any distress in the stomach (or disturbance) is always Innate mind at work through the Innate body. At such times the educated mind is a blank. When the educated brain is asleep, or doing no work of its own, it becomes an absolute, complete and responsive medium for thoughts and ideas coming from the Innate mind.

It is the Innate mind, through the Innate brain, communicating with the educated mind and educated brain—there is no intermingling of thoughts at that point, but they all come from the superior source thru the inferior—the educated mind in the educated brain does NOT communicate with Innate mind in the Innate brain.

The following illustration is simple and practical to all. Those having constipation will recognize the reasoning: The bowels are ready to move. You go to the bathroom and wait, wait and wait. Bowels do not move, are not working, and you reason that "Nature must be off duty." Anyone with normal Innate voluntary function ought to have a movement of the bowels and not know when such begins or is thru with. We do not know when food in the stomach is digested. We are not aware when food has passed into the small intestine. If the stomach and bowels are doing their duty, why should we need to know it? It is not necessary for the Educated mind to keep tabs on those functions which its superior (Innate) senses and controls by the law of adaptation. This person has been waiting for Innate to do his duty, but owing to the impingement upon those fibres they are unable to convey mental impulses which could perform that action. Then is when Educated senses the inability of Innate to perform his work and concerted action follows. The bowels cannot get their normal supply of mental force, therefore cannot maintain a normal equilibrium—are paralyzed in action. No matter how many impressions went to the mind, there was an inability to respond. Fecal matter gathers without any prospect of being evacuated. In another moment an appeal for help is made to the Educated mind, in the form of impressions traveling to this brain, hence Educated responses follow. The forces of both brains combined are occasionally sufficient to produce the requisite action.

The Educated and Innate mentalities do not talk these things over within the skull. Each is composed of many lobes—Innate brain has comparatively more. It is these that intercommunicate with each other in that brain but not with its mate in the other brain. All lobes in Educated participate and the various lobes in the Innate brain hold communion, but there is no crossing or telephone system from one lobe of Educated to another in the Innate brain, although every Innate lobe is in constant communication with every Educated lobe. This is one instance where we believe we have no reciprocal action. Each brain is independent of the other, yet each is dependent upon all the lobes within that one. Both receive the same power from a superior source—Innate.

Innate controls the two brains, the physical for the purpose of running bodily functions, which is done perfectly if not hindered by derangements of the osseous tissues which would interfere with the transmission of mental current. Innate starts the physical body, knowing all about how to conduct the physical functions, but knows nothing of the external. During life Innate learns of external things and is educated accordingly. At death Innate lets go of the physical but retains all that has been learned during each physical life. Innate has used the physical brain and body to perform the various functions to maintain expression for the purpose of education—self preservation—adaptation.

In dealing with the senses, what they are and where, we cannot help but consider diseases of them. Each may be affected by excess or a lack of the normal responsive function. These are most commonly sight and hearing. Why is one or the other minus? To have normal sight means the coordination of impressions, their interpretation and motor impulses to respond accordingly. Any one of these acting below or above the standard means incoordination. This condition can take place in the optic set of Innate or Educated brains, for each has its combination to sense external objects with. We have seen individuals who had a normal eye, so far as physical examination was possible, but could not see. Somewhere along the circular path was a circuit breaker, and that switched impressions which never reached the brain. Some individuals have Innate sight and no Educated. When you study and appreciate such ideas it clears a multitude of secrets, explains many mysteries and "phenomena" which have never been previously intelligently answered.

You will realize how much greater is the ability of Innate over Educated by studying the expressions of both. The former is capable of placing a greater degree of interpretation upon impressions. If you desire to realize how great the labor of sensing and responding is, take upon your Educated brain the duty of every organ and muscle necessary to control the body for one day, and we will guarantee you will be glad when one hour has passed around. Could you, for one day, take an arm alone and control its every sense? Would you try the experiment of keeping up its wear and tear? When you know that Innate controls the entire body with its innumerable duties, will repair portions if fractured (the normal alone proving to be an enormous task for the Educated); but Innate adds many another step, with the utmost ease, without bluster or horns or trumpet, but, as a powerful force will adapt its powers to the conditions that are constantly changing according to climate, age, sex, etc., etc., thus showing itself to be the only master. It can truly be called a master mechanic when examples of its work, accomplished thru the physical body, have been studied.

There is thought in this paragraph for comparison. Where have we any master? We talk of "masters" of art, literature, sculpture, etc., but are they masters? They are simply expressing things. Anything you might want to compare with the work of Innate is not possible. Everything man wants to do is a duplicate of something already existing. We can take marble which Innate made and chisel it in concrete resemblance to a human body; we can take ideas and put them into concrete; we can make chairs, tables, etc.—all concrete things. As yet we have not shown ourselves to be masters; we can put on canvas the characteristics that make the tree or the animal, produce the color of the sky, etc., but still we are not the master. We are but duplicating on canvas something which exists in life, so that everything man does is but duplicating something that already exists.

With all this as a sample, can you not see how great your Innate is, how noble are these senses? And then to think that many of you, relatively little, insignificant people, will try to place your 40-year-old intelligence in competition with that which cannot anywhere near be equalled by the production of Innate man. Man's every action was, thru Innate, first made a possibility. So fearfully, wonderfully and philosophically is the human body made that scientists are beginning to realize that all inventions are but infringements on Innate's patent office. Trouble and worry in the past could have been avoided and inventors made a careful study of the devices employed in making these human bodies. The principles of the block and pulley or the tackle could have been discovered ages before had our bodies been studied as a psychological unit; from cause to effect, or vice versa. There are several complete pulleys in the body, notably the movement of the eyeball inward toward the nose.

Engineers made exhaustive tests and experiments before they discovered that a hollow shaft or rod of iron or steel is twice as strong as a solid one. Yet Innate had patented this device in our bones. Every important bone is constructed on this principle. The ball and socket of the hip bones were the forerunners of the modern ball bearings, and it was the first self-feeding, oiling machine in the world. The value of air pressure and a vacuum was unknown to man until the last century, but every one carried the secret in the airtight hip joint which Innate Intelligence had designed to lessen muscular effort to hold our legs upright.

Engineers have made wonderful progress in developing compound suction and circular pumps, but all of these principles are found in the heart, and this little pumping machine is still without a rival in the mechanical world. Innate has and will have had patented every device which has been or will be registered at Washington, D. C.

The principles of the safety valve for steam engines are not new. Our bodies carry the first safety valves ever designed. There are upward of two and a half million of them. They are sweat glands. Each has a valve which lets off heat from the body when it gets beyond a safe temperature. We cannot stand a rise of more than 8 to 10 degrees and live. If, therefore, the two and a half million safety valves were closed for twenty-four hours, death would supervene.

In the ear there is a little device which is the original of our modern compressed air inventions. The delicate drum of the ear must have an equal pressure from the outside and inside to receive and transmit the sound vibrations. To make this possible the Eustachian tube was devised. Its function is to regulate the air pressure.

Very few things of worth devised by man can be found which have not in their fundamental principles been copied from nature, and in marine architecture the likeness is most clearly defined. As an instance of natural buoyancy in water a better example could not be cited than the fish, which, by means of the swimming bladder, is enabled to descend by ejecting the air contained in the bladder and ascend by refilling it. The submarine is patterned after this principle, with the exception that the air is always present in the air compartments and regained by pumping it out.

The fish which are the swiftest swimmers have pointed snouts, small fins and more or less cigar-shaped bodies, and smooth skins. This is well exemplified in the dolphin and shark, which are among the fastest swimmers in the fish tribe. The ordinary torpedoes and submarines have a general resemblance to these fish, as the illustration points out.

During the construction of the Thames tunnel early in the nineteenth century, Brunnel, the celebrated engineer, found great difficulty in boring through the soft clay formation without running a terrible risk of an inrush of water. While examining a piece of timber honeycombed by the burrows of the ship worm, or teredo, he conceived the idea of a boring shield in several sections. This type of shield is now in use, thus adding another to the innumerable inventions conceived by watching nature.

No sensitive electrical device is more carefully protected than the spinal cord in its movable frame of vertebrae. Innate has adjusted it with more precision than the movements of the best watch.

A whole line of important patents could be evolved from a philosophical study of Innate. In the splicing of broken bones Innate can give the best surgeon pointers. When a bone is broken the splintered ends are surrounded with osseous cells until firmly held in position. Then gradually a layer of bone is placed between them and soldered together. All the physician can do is to bring the two ends together so that the joint will be, in a measure, smooth and even. Innate does the rest.

Chiropractors deal with impressions and that which interrupts their expressions. It may be that an insane person is able to sense normally, but interpretation or expression is insane. It may be that an insane person sees, but that alone does not make normal interpretation, which is insanity or diseased brain.

What is to be done in insanity? Go back to cause? Adjust that and return the brain to its normal capacity and capability. Interpretation then will be normal and expression follows likewise, then what have you? Coordination—health, in all that the word implies.

If impression be given full power to deposit itself in the brain, normal interpretation follows and Innate brain can and does send forth responsive impulses and these are given an uninterrupted channel and are allowed to deposit themselves in tissue and are expressed; then coordination—health—exists. It positively cannot be otherwise. The circle is made from tissue to brain cell and reverse, a circuit unbroken. Action must follow.

6

<hr>

BRAIN SYSTEM COMPARED
WITH NERVOUS SYSTEM

TWO NERVOUS SYSTEMS are commonly accepted. They are the cerebro-spinal and the sympathetic of the present-day anatomies. They define cerebro-spinal system, in ways not clearly understood, not definitely taught anatomically, nor comprehended physiologically, a myth as a system which in some way, far fetched, tied up with theories, connects itself with the body and controls some of it. When we thought, we moved the hand, hence there was a connection some sort of a way. The brain controlled the hand; one material thing dominates another of like kind.

In the sympathetic nervous system you have 129 brains variously distributed, a small portion inside the skull, the most of it up and down the outside of the spine, the rest distributed through the body, one great brain known as the belly brain in the abdomen, and some of these brains in the legs, arms; then there is a heterogeneous "tag,—you-are-it" system running around these 129 brains, and 121st tags and 61st, and there is a running around which is controlled by "sympathy," which, we are told, is "by means unknown." In no way does the sympathetic nervous system definitely connect itself with the brain. It is presumed that fibres enter a ganglion on the side of the spinal column. Another fibre starting there runs up two or three inches and ends, or seven or eight inches and ends, and eventually it is presumed that an impression which starts at the fingertip, goes to the first ganglion and there is plunged into a whirlpool, swirled around, and then sent on to the next whirlpool where it is whirled some more, and after going through an endless system of whirlpools it is presumed to get back to a finger tip. Scientifically, there is no system; physiologically, it is not definitely connected; neurologically it is a superstition. Thus we find ourselves trying to find something definite, specific, tangible, real, and we are surprised that all ends in a complexity out of which we cannot unravel a single knot. Now you are looking at man from an accepted standpoint. We find he is composed of knots within knots, whirlpools within whirlpools, and cesspools within cesspools, and we don't know where we are, after a long space of time and study. Contradicting that, we look at the average man as he is, and as you and I, with our average sense, observe him. He doesn't present to us such a seemingly complex arrangement. His actions seem to be definite: discriminating, selective, awarely conscious, and more or less articulate.

This appraisal represents a system quite specific, definite, exact, scientific, logical, practical, and simple; and then we try to appraise his Potential.

Man is man, the same man you observe is the same fellow we look at; the one we study is no different than the object others investigate; therefore we must be agreed as to what is the individual to whom we look. We do not deny the existence of the system that has been studied, written, pictured and portrayed by anatomies, notwithstanding that we have been frequently quoted in that sense. We deny such as a "sympathetic" nervous system, only so far as it is a SYMPATHETIC system, the nervous system we concede, but as for the physiological explanation of sympathy we cannot see. Laboratorical findings we grant, the deductions made thereon for the purposes of physiological study we severely question. The system of nerves erroneously called "sympathetic" is a laboratory finding, hence we admit as a fact, but the abstract deduction that it is "sympathy" that goes thru them and regulates function is, to all purposes, malicious in application. It is the title and study thereof, to which we direct thot, not to anatomy. We trust that this will clear this point.

As we have already shown, from a sympathetic nervous system standpoint, we cannot tell and we do not know of anybody that can, where this system begins or ends. It really has no beginning or ending, at least not anatomically, no one teaches that it has a beginning or ending. Its boundaries are without limit, because of no beginning or ending, or no point where we may start and work toward an end. It is a boundless circle, space void of space, if we can conceive of such, if their physiological explanation be true.

The function of the sympathetic nervous system is to regulate functions by sympathy. The functions of the cerebro-spinal nervous system is in its way to link the brain with the spine so that the spine can link itself to the body in general. That is the common concept of what it is presumed to do. Its limitations are to regulate the so-called voluntary functions. Brain System . . . Consciously, we pull a cord to ring a bell. The thought impulse alerts the entire body, but specifically directs only certain parts of the body to perform particular, coordinated movements that result in the ringing of a bell (if there is a bell to be rung).

We are not voluntarily digesting peanuts. We presume this is an involuntary act because we are not directing and controlling that process. This is also a voluntary act. As soon as the peanuts got into the stomach, there was an impression which followed an afferent nerve to the brain. There, Innate Intelligence interpreted the impression which was as follows: There are peanuts in the stomach. They must be digested; we will proceed to act upon them. The brain consciously directs the processing of the ingested peanuts, employing the structures that are constructed and developed to perform their functions.

To the Innate Intelligence, there is no such thing as involuntary action, whether it be to heal a fracture, weld a cut, coagulate blood, grow hair or fingernails. These are all voluntary actions, as directed by a higher power whose plan we do not understand, but whose work we recognize as being ingenious, intelligent, and readily adaptable to environmental influences.

This brings to mind the idea conclusively broad that there are two kinds of acts in our body. If Innate were to speak, it is a question whether she would not say one. We have a voluntary act wherein the brain is in connection thruout with the balance of your body in its functions. Thus man is classified into two. There are two divisions of brain, naturally there must be two divisions of nerves, two divisions of the material part of the body. If it were possible to divide, there would be an Educated and Innate man, but the two are blended so that each works with the other if we have sufficient of each to harmonize. There are two systems wherein the brains are connected with all that is below or beneath them. To make both understood and properly titled, we would say the proper term is "brain system."

If you were to speak of a sympathetic nervous system you get an idea that here is a system of nerves which are being regulated, as a system, by sympathy, and all three words contradict each other. You cannot have sympathy regulated by system; you cannot have a system regulated by sympathy; you cannot have nerves organized into a system being run or managed by sympathy, because sympathy is "by means unknown." Anything which runs by means unknown cannot be classified or organized into system.

We speak of the cerebro-spinal nervous system. In this sense we are practically saying a brain is one part and a spinal cord another, and we are classifying portions as if each were a total. In other words, the separation avoids their continuity and interdependence.

To make all clear and broad, we introduce a new idea. If we were to pose an innate problem, like the production of a child, we find that the first thing she makes is the brain. Were you to watch the process, you would find that from each brain cell there is a prolongation superiorly and another inferiorly. The superior prolongation is short, and the lower, or inferior prolongation becomes long. The brain cell extends itself, stretches and elongates and when many brain cells are doing that, these fibres, extensions, or prolongations congregate and a sheath is wrapped around them, the sum total being called a spinal cord; from that begins a process of lateral branchings going into every organ, so in reality this thing called a nerve is a portion of the brain cell, because it starts from there.

Let us give a natural comparison. An acorn becomes an oak tree. It is all there, the trunk, branches, leaves, and future acorns. To prove this, we put the acorn in the ground, watch it. In time it splits its shell; up comes a sprout. Later a branch comes, then another and another; they are coming from the acorn, and finally the entire tree is formed, and all the fibres we see cut in the branch, when traced clear down come from the acorn.

All fibres in the body, spinal cord, or organs come from the brain in the skull and are prolongations from it, therefore the proper name "brain system." In this application we refer to the brain system in the sense that the brain cell blends into the fibre. The efferent fibre blends into the tissue cell, the tissue cell blends into the afferent nerve fibre. There are no endings or beginnings. At what particular fraction of a second is daybreak? There is no way to classify. The night blends into day and day into night. The astronomers set a moment which they say is sunrise. But there has been considerable light in the sky before the exact minute they set. There is no place in Nature where thot draws lines, it is a whole and blends into all. In this sense, these brain systems weave, in, thru and between each other and have associated thots, functions, impressions and interpretations, and one big associated purpose, and that is what we all aim to elucidate.

Could you remove all other systems, such as blood, muscular, osseous and serous, and leave complete the brain system where the two blend into one, we would have a complete organic man. He would be a man because he would have every brain and tissue cell connected. It would include the meninges, scalp, all tissue cells, making a network, consequently you would still have the man, you could not remove all other systems, you could remove only the liquids which were not directly connected with tissue structure, such as blood and various excretions.

We want you to picture an average tree,—pine, oak, walnut, mahogany or hickory. Go below the ground, trace to the extremities of the roots; there are small fibrili, so small that they lose their identity in dirt. Trace them up and they lead to a larger fibre, then this larger fibre joins with another of similar size to make a still larger, until at last we are led into the tap root, which leads us to the core or tree's brain. Come on up and there is a ground line. Trace up the massive trunk, it divides into two, and the two making four, four into eight, eight into sixteen, etc., until you get to the leaves, and even there is one main fibre which sends off branches into smaller fibrili until they cannot be seen, by the eye, but under the microscope they branch until they get too fine for the microscope to detect.

We said the trunk divided into two trunks. Could you take the diameter of the two they would equal the diameter of one, the diameter of four would equal two, diameter of eight would equal four, and so on, with the exception that as anything divided, it becomes larger, not because of more matter or a greater number of fibres, could you count them, on the combined total of every leaf, than there is in the trunk of the tree. The sum total of all branches of the tree would not be in excess of that of the trunk, other things being equal, and permitting compressibility.

Man is the same. Take a brain cell, look to the superior portion and you find little fibres. Some run over to other portions of the brain to connect with other lobes, in this way we get association of ideas. If you could add all superior brain fibres you would not have a greater number than leaves the foramen magnum, which corresponds to the trunk of the tree. The only difference is, the tree stands on its base and we stand upside down. Any horticulturist will tell that a stationary tree has a brain, thinks, reasons, studies, schemes and circumvents ideas the same as movable man. The brain of the tree is near the root where superior and inferior fibres congregate.

In your observation as a Chiropractor, you reach the conclusion that every viewpoint, thot, condition, pathological change, adjustment, whether good or bad, to what degree and character this brain system and the force behind, work to the end of what you want to accomplish. Unless you put that final interpretation you lose, you are not going to comprehend or understand the object or appreciate what you do to your patient. Whether you study anatomy, physiology, microscopy, embryology, philosophy, science or art, place upon it the interpretation of Innate force and Innate brain. Complete the Educated and Innate cycles to the brain. Link these and make one and that represents life as it is. If you place that interpretation upon studies, then you are a Chiropractor. Limit yourself to any portion short of that, then you are not a Chiropractor in the broadest sense.

7

———◆———

A VIEWPOINT ON THE

NERVOUS SYSTEM

MAN HAS ONLY one brain, there is only one mass of matter that performs the function of being an absorber, condenser or acts in the capacity of a sponge to this force which we gather and which becomes the "I" of you or me. That place and that matter is within the skull or the cranium; is surrounded by meninges; and should there be a continuation of the matter of the brain, that elongation does not act in the same capacity that the brain does.

This brain, anatomically speaking, is divided into two halves, a left and a right hemisphere; each is divided into convolutions, gyrations, lobules and lobes, etc., until eventually, anatomically speaking, we reach the brain cell. Our position calls for an explanation of the division of this brain functionally or philosophically speaking. Function is what a particular portion of matter does and how. The brain, functionally speaking, is divided into two portions—Educated brain and Innate brain. These are not Educated and Innate brains; they are two divisions of brain to which we apply a title as we view the kind, quality or quantity of function that goes through each. We have a brain through which an Educated mind works; we have another through which the Innate mind works; or, we have a portion of the brain through which Innate intelligence acts and another portion through which Educated Intelligence acts. Consequently, giving each portion of a brain a name appropriate to the kind, quality or quantity of intelligences that act through it.

We make a distinction between the Educated and Innate brain because it is only the kind or quantity of thought that gives to it the attribute of quality. Innate is a name the same as Educated, but there is a distinction between; Educated being inferior, Innate superior; Educated being smaller, Innate larger; Educated being raw, Innate refined, thus giving the aspects of kind, quantity and quality.

We take that viewpoint because anything the Educated thinks has never been thought in kind, quantity or quality that Innate would place upon the same, did she receive from the same source. We think of generation or reproduction of life; Educationally and Innately we think upon sex organs; Educationally we could not, nor have not been able to produce a single generative organ, we have never so thought in quantity, kind nor quality sufficient to make a generative tissue cell, let alone an organ or a set thereof, not considering the functioning generative organs, but Innately the mind has thought kind, quantity and quality sufficient to not only make one generative tissue cell but millions, form, position, functionate and reproduce them—all of which Educationally we could not do. Here is an instance of where two intelligences, residing within one unity have both thought upon the same issue, yet one makes and remakes, the other cannot even conceive. That shows there is a distinction to be made.

Man is two men, he is Educated and Innate. There are dual personalities in each and all. We are here together. But we, as educated people, are ninety-nine percent Educated fools. We have been taught that whatever we know Educationally—that was all; whatever was Educationally taught and whatever we accepted as Education, that was the height of knowledge, and that there was nothing greater or higher; that was the summum bonum of Intellectual aspirations. Consequently, it is conceded that he who goes to school, colleges or universities the most; gets most from books, who has the largest vocabulary of words; can string the greatest number of thoughts into ideas—that man is the best Educated man, that man stands higher in the viewpoint of the mass of people.

Innate has been observing a long space of time. This intellection is a part of the entirety of the accumulation of thoughts. How old it may be we do not know, so much so that it has been turning over man's matter, to such an extent that it represents to our Educated minds almost perfection, so that he who gives the greatest play to his Innate Intelligence in acting through the Education is the best knowledge condenser of facts known and of many facts unknown Educationally.

Man Educationally knows little: Innately much. Education is but a reflection of what you possess, Innately; because everything you know

Educationally, is, was, and will be first conceded, first known by your Innate, then handed to you to be Educationally thought upon, from which you will deduce a fact which might be in line with the known Innate knowledge fact.

You should counsel with your innerself; with the other half of self. We make the term "other half" because it is necessary to divide ourselves into two to be a totality.

We, on the reverse of most persons, believe that the animal, which, perhaps has no Education, is our superior on the common ground that we steal Educationally from Innate is not to our credit, whereas the animal, which does not steal anything is a better Innate knowledge acting animal than we.

Man is dual. This is true functionally, for by Educated volition, we cause our arm to move; certain thoughts; we might walk, run, jump, swim, etc. Then there is another line of functioning over which Educationally we have no control.

For instance, a bone is fractured. We have no control over that fracture, Educationally. It is Innate that comes to the fracture, expands osseous cells, makes ossific material necessary, deposits it in the right place, right quantity, unites segments, heals and causes it again to assume normal condition. It is Innate which heats or cools, causes secretions and excretions, controls all the essential nine primary functions which Educationally we could not control one impulse of let alone making the impulse in the right quantity, quality and right kind or deposit it at the right place at the proper time. Thus, we are dual on first concept.

Psychologically, functionally or physiologically speaking, we are divided; therefore—those statements being true—we are philosophically dual. Anatomically, you will not find this division. Anatomically, a muscle is a muscle regardless of whether it pulls up or down, whether on the anterior or posterior of the arm, forearm or upper portions, upper leg or in the thigh, in the abdomen or upon the scalp. Regardless of location, muscle is muscle, bone is bone, nerve is nerve; but functionally speaking there are two kinds of muscles, nerves, men. There is that Educated man who Educationally thinks in an Educated brain, has Educated nerves to transmit those thoughts, Educated muscles to execute them, Educated afferent nerves to carry impressions, an Educated mind to reason upon them and an Educated process of adaptation.

Then, again, there is the Innate mind working through the Innate brain, which has Innate efferent nerves to transmit Innate efferent impulses to the Innate set of muscles which give origin to the impressions, and those impressions travel back to the Innate brain, where Innate mind thinks upon, interprets, and brings into play this high qualitative adaptive Innate Intellect. Thus man is divided into two—an Innate man and an Educated man.

Each of these divides into subdivisions. Here is a left and a right Educated mind the same as there is a left and right Educated brain; then there is a left and right Innate mind, the same as there is a left and right Innate brain.

Individuals are deaf in only one ear; blind in only one eye; have a headache in only one-half of the brain and not in the other; or a well-marked headache in fore-brain, or Educated brain, and not in the rear or Innate brain.

By marked contrast, take the generative organs during the "periodical term," when the female has a known periodic headache. This is never in the fore brain, but always at the base. If the individual has a pro-lapsus of right ovary, that individual has a drawing heavy pain upon the left hind brain only—the left ovary involved, upon the right hind brain.

Show a case of hemiplegia where the individual is suffering from paralysis of one-half of the body, whether it be crossed or straight—by "crossed" means affecting the right face and the left body or the left face and the right body—or if it be a complete case, one entire lateral half without crossing—and the organ commonly known phrenologically as the "Organ of Hope," situated on top of the skull is soft, there will be an adaptation in that part of the brain, tender to the touch; the individual is despondent. Scratch the organ of hope or stimulate it, the patient brightens temporarily. We speak by way of showing that the "Organ of Hope" has a certain function and is involved in hemiplegia. A case of paraplegia has other places which are tender; a case of monoplegia always has its marked place in the skull.

Man is divided into the divisions outlined. When you study brain anatomically you must not lose the value of divisions of that brain functionally, carry that constant connection that exists between a portion of that brain and steps through which it may go in carrying out its functions.

The "Brain System" includes the brain or brains, function or functions, Education or Educations, names, locations, spinal cord and its tributary nerves, aspect of their functions, where they go; also this anatomical brain in action. When you view matter, view what it does; what makes it act, how, where actions go, and how they are transferred from place to place, if you take that viewpoint, "Brain System" will be of practical value.

8

SYMPATHETIC NERVOUS SYSTEM

IN THE STUDY OF CHIROPRACTIC there is possibly no one point upon which we so radically differ, from all preceding schools, as in eliminating the so-called sympathetic nervous system. We shall endeavor, by quoting authorities, to show how much they are in the dark as regards the origin of "involuntary functions," and by so doing supplant it with a superior teaching of Chiropractic. The most interesting will be to enlarge upon the two direct systems, as taught by B. J. Palmer, then quote what the sympathetic nervous system is as considered by medical schools.

You are aware that the child suckles at the mother's breast; the bowels move and the kidneys of that infant act; it is nourished by the milk eaten; you even realize that "involuntary functions" are performed as thoroughly in the child, at birth, as in the adult, but have you ever studied the why, beyond the "nature" aspect?

The educated Brain is undeveloped, therefore cannot answer. The study of words is the study of how the educated mind can express its thoughts. The Innate Mind does not need words. It transmits its thoughts direct without the intervention of words to express them. Words combined in sentences and paragraphs never equal the clearness of the thought, no matter how carefully worded your language may be—it never quite says all that you have thought upon that particular subject, therefore some value is lost between creating a thought in one mind and giving thought to another mind by words. Innate mind loses nothing in transmission; thoughts are transferred exactly as they are created from one mind to another, therefore the second mind receives exactly all that the first mind thought.

That is why B.J. says, that the Innate mind is perfectly capable of thinking the highest type and form of thoughts at birth and is able to transfer those thoughts from the infant Innate Mind to the adult Innate Mind of the mother or father, so that there is a so-called material intuitive understanding between them and the child, but the educated mind must progress to the point where it begins to say common words first, such as "mamma" and "papa," which are words of a natural language. The chatter of monkeys and language of all animals is natural. Man has an educated language.

The educated mind forms words to express its thoughts. Innate Mind at birth is capable of expressing thoughts, but the Educated Mind is not.

From each brain emanates efferent fibres necessary to convey impulses to tissue cells which regulate the functions of the body and all afferent fibres which conduct impressions from the periphery to the brain.

The educated brain is as yet undeveloped, therefore cannot answer. This is but one of the conspicuous differences between the two brains. The Innate brain is proportionately larger and has comparatively many more lobes than the educated. The latter controls all functions that come in contact with the world, the Innate all that pertains to internal man: its scope, therefore, is greater.

Each generative organ is composed of many lobes, as it were, and has its special function to perform. The lobe which issues calorific impulses will not propagate motor actions, nor will the excretive accomplish what is intended for secretive. They are confined and cannot compete with another. Each lobe issues its bundles. The many bundles of the Innate and Educated brains join at a common meeting place, internal to the magnum foramen—which cable is covered with three sheaths when it is commonly named "the spinal cord," although we prefer "Brain cord." This proceeds downward, representing the entire "nervous" system as it issues from both brains, through the spinal canal of the vertebrae. If there be such a thing as "twelve cranial nerves" they are but distant branches of divisions from the original 31 pairs as they divorce. We do not deny the existence of "12 cranial nerves," but we will give to the same a new path to travel. Instead of proceeding direct from brain to the organ, within the cranium, we will follow their path, outward, through the magnum foramen and then through some intervertebral foramina, proceeding thence to its organ, within the skull by a direct and well defined path, according to nerve tracing which has many a time deduced those tender filaments from the spinal exit to the periphery where the affection exists. These are facts and are substantiated by results.

Superior to the atlas we have the first pair of branches, one to the left and its counter on the right. One pair divided between each two contiguous vertebrae from above downward. Although the cord proper ceases at the space between the second and third lumbar, yet branches continue to emit through the sacrum and between the sacrum and coccyx. The process from this point outward is one of division, separation, and again segregation into nerves and they into fibres, fibres to fibrillae, which eventually terminate within some characteristic tissue substance. Generation commences at brain cell, which is then passed to an individual fibrilla, passes thence to the cable, through the foramen magnum, down through the spinal cord, emitting at its intervertebral foramina, thence through the same direct channel to its tissue cell. Retracing the path would be to start at tissue cell, proceeding until it reaches the spinal cord, continuing its character as an individual fibre until it reaches brain cell. Each fibre connects brain cell to tissue cell, or vice versa.

We have reasons why it is impossible to have a sympathetic nervous system. Let us allude to the last *Dunglison's Medical Dictionary,* which is standard in every college. In speaking of this system he says "Sympathetic, depending on sympathy. Sympathetic affections of the organs are those morbid phenomena that supervene without any morbific cause." Can you or I imagine anything existing without a cause? Is it possible that "morbid phenomena" live or die without a cause? We cannot conceive, as wild as our imagination may seem, anything which may exist without a cause, and yet Dunglison gives such as a basis for his definition.

In speaking of "Sympathy," Dunglison (23rd Edition, p. 1082) says: "Sympathy. Connection existing between the action of two or more organs more or less distant from each other, so that affection of the first is transmitted secondarily to the others, or to one of the others, by means unknown." "By means unknown" takes, from under the M.D. the very props which they were supposed to be upheld by. When a Chiropractor has intelligent deductions of where, how and what those "unknown means" are, it fails to be a "Sympathetic Nervous System." Traceable knowledge of the Innate independent and direct nervous system fails, in all involuntary functions, to bear the slightest resemblance to a "sympathy basis." The M.D.'s have been wearisomely toiling, for centuries, trying to build a super-structure that could shed common sense arguments; trying to account for involuntary functions upon a basis which has failed to demonstrate a result sufficient to make any honest doctor cling to it. Think of taking a "by means unknown" basis and from that work out a "sympathy" racket that a simple child would get confused on, let alone the many sincere men who have gone to their graves in despair that have failed to be any nearer to the solution at death than birth. And Chiropractic is the first school that scientifically connects, by nerve tracing, that gap between "mental and physical phenomena"; accounting for every act, voluntary or involuntary, from an intelligent basis. He need not say "by means unknown" to cover up his mistakes whether buried or living.

Dunglison in his dictionary says "The great sympathetic is a distinct nervous system, supplying the organs of involuntary motion; for although communicating with both brain and spinal marrow, it does not seem to be immediately under the influence of either. Its special functions are not yet well understood." Dr. Dunglison does not state what this nervous system supplies to "the organs of involuntary motion," although we suppose it does do a something, but just what this thing is is "unknown," because "its special functions are not yet well understood."

Cunningham's *Text Book of Anatomy,* p. 702, in speaking of the "Sympathetic Nervous System," says: "The sympathetic nervous system consists of a pair of elongated cords, extending from the base of the skull to the coccyx; connected on the one hand by a series of branches to the spinal nervous system, and on the other hand giving off an irregulated series of branches to the viscera. . . . The distinction is not absolute. . . . The non-medullated fibres in the sympathetic system are derived from the axons of the sympathetic ganglion cells. Some fibres appear to contribute to the formation of the comisural cord.

"The Morphology of the Sympathetic System. From a consideration of its structure, functions and development, there appear to be two separate structures represented in the sympathetic nervous system—the spinal and the sympathetic elements—it is certain that the cells and fibres of the sympathetic system possess a vital activity apart from their connection with the central nervous system. The phylogenetic relation of the sympathetic and cerebro-spinal elements in the system is impossible to determine. It may be that the sympathetic system is representative of an ancient architecture independent of the cerebro-spinal nervous system, the materials of which are utilized for a modern nervous system, examined in every light, it possesses features which effectually differentiate it from the cerebro-spinal system."

Dr. Cunningham knows that functions are accomplished. He realizes they are not under the control of the will, but, like his predecessors, they start and end "by means unknown" and "no foundation, no castle." He strives to tell where this system starts and ends and we are still pondering. What its functions are we are to reason "by means unknown." Isn't that logical, deductive reasoning? How long would such arguments exist if applied to the financial or commercial world? How long would it take to topple the greatest business if based upon "by means unknown"?

Morris' *Human Anatomy, Third Edition,* p. 879, says: "The Sympathetic System. It was formerly believed (showing that they change in theoretical anatomy as much as the physician in practice, according to fashion; if it was a fact or truth it could not be garbled) that the sympathetic and cerebro-spinal portions of the nervous system were distinct from each other, the sympathetic system being endowed with the supervision and control of the more vegetative functions of the body, whilst the control of the more animal functions were allotted to the cerebro-spinal system. It is now known that the two systems are but parts of one continuous whole and that the central terminations of both systems lie in the brain (why did he not stop here?) and spinal cord; but though this close association is incontestable, it must be clearly recognized that the fibres of the cerebro-spinal nerves are more particularly associated with the voluntary muscles, the sensory areas of the surface of the body, and the lining membranes of the joints, whilst the sympathetic nerves and the cells to which they belong are concerned chiefly or entirely with the involuntary muscles of the viscera, the blood vessels, and the hairs, and with the secretory cells of the various glands."

After carefully studying Morris the mysteries are unsolved. He does come almost, but not quite, to it and then slides off. It is easy to see that Morris is an original thinker. But, to go too far would mean to be "churched," a thing no M.D. pleads for. Fear has greater terrors than starvation and ostracism that is bestowed upon the original thinker or doer.

Dutton's *Anatomy,* p. 327, says: "The sympathetic nerves control the circulation of the blood, respiration, nutrition, and all the various vital processes. They are the involuntary nerves, not directly under the control of the human will." In his six pages upon this subject he does not state where it starts or goes to. If we would supplant "the sympathetic nerves" with the "Innate brain and fibre system" through its intelligent energy; and "they are voluntary to the commands of the Innate will at all times," it would make of the above quoted paragraph a Chiropractic thought.

Eckley's "Dissection and Practical Anatomy," p. 355, says: "Function. To innervate viscera, glands, unstripped muscle fibre, bones, cartilages, fasciae, and conduits generally not under control of the will." The "will" here referred to is the voluntary one. The Innate voluntary will is not known to the anatomical world, therefore, it cannot be talked or written about. Innate voluntary functions are known of, but nothing further than that they are "reflex actions" performed through a "sympathetic"—"by means unknown" nervous system. Isn't that a brilliant basis to account for Innate voluntary functions—the greatest intelligence which rules, creates and guides you and me—the greatest mechanical

machine made? How stupendous—is—ignorance! Dismissing the knowledge of an Innate will and the "sympathetic nervous system" is not
under the control of such, and that such a non-existing (to them) will
does nothing to such a nervous system, what does such a system do is
answered by "it reflects." If, as Eckley says, "To innervate" what? What
is this "innervate"? How can this be performed without a guiding control? According to Dunglison, "Innervation" is "the nervous influence
necessary for the maintenance of life and the various functions." "Influence. To control or move by hidden, but efficacious power, physical or
normal." Webster. Can you fancy such a crude state of "innervation"
without a general or commander? Imagine a battlefield with no officers
whatsoever, each man shooting heterogeneously because he but reflects
the actions of another distantly or remotely reflectedly noticed across the
field, and then you can conceive of what a glorious old time this sympathetic nervous system is having within us for it has no head nor feet,
comes and goes without any restrictions or bars whatsoever. No parents
to guide it, no restraining or advancing control, for it is "not under the
control of the will," and acts as a "connection existing between two or
more—'men'—more or less distant from each other, so that the affection
of the first"—perhaps the D. T.—"is transmitted—to the others—by
means unknown."

Werner Spalteholtz's "Hand Atlas of Human Anatomy," Vol. 3, p.
763 says: "Systema Nervorum Sympathicum is formed: 1. By a chain
of ganglia on each side of the spinal column, the ganglia being united
with one another by verticle bundles of nerves fibres to form a longitu-
dinal cord," and as yet we have no head nor tail. A ganglion is a knot-
like enlargement upon the course of a nerve and each is supposed to be
an independent center for the formation and dispensation of nerve power.
"Ganglion they have been regarded as small brains, or centers of nervous
action, independent of the encephalon, and intended exclusively for
organic life. Ganglia are chiefly composed of vesicular neurine, and appear to be concerned in the formation and dispensation of nerve-power."
Dunglison. Upon each "spinal nerve" is one of these and at many remote
points are many "centers." Center—"A collection of nerve cells to which
external impressions are carried and whence impulses are sent out."

Reflex Center—"A part of gray nervous matter which transforms into
a motor impulse a sensory impulse it has received." Dunglison, 23rd
Edition.

The anastomoses of nerves is referred to in Dunglison's dictionary,
23rd Edition, p. 754. "They extend from the nervous centers to every
part of the body, communicating with each other; forming plexus and
occasionally ganglia."

What a confusion 62 or more generals would have on one battlefield.
It would remind the observer of the pit of a New York Board of Trade.

Common sense reasoning would unlimber such joints and determine that this would not be practical, that behind each movement must exist one intelligent brain to determine the character, quality and quantity of impulses necessary to guide and restrict distant functions.

Gray's *Anatomy,* Fifteenth Edition, p. 798, says: "The sympathetic Nervous System is (1) a series of ganglia, connected together by intervening cords, extending from the base of the skull to the coccyx, one on each side of the middle line of the body, partly in front and partly on each side of the vertebral column"; but as yet we do not know where it starts from and ends. We are told it innervates involuntary functions, yet where this "innervating" force comes from, its guiding power; the how, what, where and which we are left to decipher as best we can. M.D.'s have not dared to think; to grope with this weird material or challenge its existence, but try to demonstrate a different kind of an action by pleading to the internal with treatments on the external and thus fail to give relief to suffering humanity that so badly needs it. Will and can you?

Sabotta-McMurrich say in their "Atlas and Text-Book of Human Anatomy," page 238:

"The sympathetic nervous system presents a distinct contrast to the cranial and spinal nerve, as well as to the whole central nervous system, in that it included mainly the visceral and vascular nerves, and although it has manifold communications with the cerebro-spinal system, it represents, to a certain extent, an independent system. It is composed of a number of independent centers which form a chain on either side of the vertebral column, the successive centers being united by short nerve cords. The structure so formed is known as the sympathetic trunk and the ganglia inserted in its course are the ganglia of the sympathetic trunk.

"The ganglia of the sympathetic trunk are connected with the neighboring cerebro-spinal nerves by rami communicants, through which the cerebro-spinal nerves receive sympathetic fibres, and conversely, cerebro-spinal fibres enter the sympathetic nervous system, there being thus a mutual anastomosis. The white rami fibres do not necessarily terminate in connection with the cells of the trunk ganglion with which they first come into connection, but may pass these and terminate in a higher or lower ganglion, or even in one of the ganglia of the sympathetic plexuses.

"From the ganglia of the sympathetic trunk the branches of the sympathetic nervous system arise. They differ from those of the cerebro-spinal system in many respects, being in the first place of a grayish-white color, not pure white like the latter, since they consist mainly of non-medullated nerve fibres, and furthermore, they rarely have a straight course and they form long branches. Much oftener, almost without exception, they form sympathetic plexuses which, especially in the region of the head, extend along the blood vessels, and especially the arteries, cerebro-spinal fibres having a part in the formation of the plexuses, intended for the viscera of the thorax and abdomen. Imbedded in these sympathetic plexuses, especially the visceral ones, are numerous ganglia, some of which are very large and others microscopically small; they are known as ganglia of the sympathetic plexus and again give rise to sympathetic fibres. Many small microscopic ganglia may also be found in the organs themselves (heart, eye, intestines).

"The sympathetic fibres, like those of the cerebro-spinal system, are partly motor and partly sensory, and the system supplies practically the entire nonstriated musclature of the body.

"The sympathetic trunk is a paired structure resting upon the anterior (ventral) surface of the vertebral column, almost parallel to the median plane. Each trunk consists of a number of ganglia arranged at rather regular intervals, and united into a chain by usually short connecting cords."

McClellan, in his "Regional Anatomy," Vol. 2, p. 200, is as clear and comes as near to Chiropractic thoughts as any are aware of. This work is out of print because its author dared to be independent of the "Code of Ethics," as worshipped by men who think more of money than shattering idols.

In "The Region of the Back" we find "the very complicated courses of the nerve-fibres of the spinal cord to and from the medulla oblongata and thence to the brain have been most laboriously studied, and there is yet much to be determined regarding them. From delicate and careful dissection, from experiment and from observation of pathological changes, a great deal has been learned, and the following description is now generally accepted by histologists, but will doubtless be modified by future researches.

"Spinal localization is naturally fraught with great difficulty, and, like cerebral localization, requires a most exact knowledge of anatomy. Much has been determined, much is inferred, but there is also much to be ascertained. It has been said by one of the ablest of modern investigators (Mills) that the value of a study in spinal localization depends upon the exactness with which phenomena are differentiated."

The latter paragraph tells much of the truth of all investigation. It has been made from and upon a sympathetic "by means unknown" suppositions base. It will be noticed that all authors refer to function as a "phenomena."

"Phenomenon. An extraordinary and unexpected event." Dunglison.

"Phenomenon. That which strikes one as strange, unusual, or unaccountable; an extraordinary or very remarkable person, thing, or occurrence." Webster.

There is no doubt but what all involuntary functions are "phenomena" to M.D.'s because they have no knowledge of the origin of power or the starting point of nerves that carry such, therefore, every movement is "by means unknown."

Every function, expressed, ceases to be a "phenomenon" to Chiropractic philosophy students. Mental impulses must be carried direct from brain to tissue. Let us stamp these with intelligence in preference to "by means unknown."

Consider digestion. You are hungry. Certain foods are delicious and, if you are like us, you will make a meal of those. Follow your appetite and you will but comply with what Innate Intelligence sees is needed for the body's good. Food enters the mouth; passes into and down the throat. What moves it? There is an excretion from the mucous lining, and an oil that mixes in and around, creating of your food a bolus, and being covered with this substance, allows it to slide into the stomach without resistance. Do you produce this oil? Can you, then, churn the food in the stomach or does something else do it? We know it is churned, after which it passes to the three divisions of the small intestine for further digestion, the excrements being involuntarily carried out. Do you do it? No! Behind functions is another intelligence. To call it "Sympathetic" might pass with an M.D., under normal conditions, but it does not meet the comprehension nor account for the cause of all accommodating diseased conditions, for does not Dunglison say: "Sympathetic affections of an organ are those morbific phenomena that supervene without any morbific cause?" How to account for "morbific phenomena" without "morbific cause" is what has been echoing for centuries and still they hit the vibration. Chiropractic has started right. It has built a foundation that is impregnable, has stood investigation by the best in the last sixty-three years. Why? It has for its foundation the knowledge of the M.D.'s "by means unknown."

Water may be swallowed. Do you follow it through all its intricate processes, until it leaves your kidneys? No. You do not and could not if you wanted to, guide the every action necessary to make of it a food and lubricator. This nourishment, after made, must be properly issued. Can you do it?

Suppose the radius bone is fractured. Do you concentrate your brain thots upon it, for fourteen days, until it knits? You do not, nor could you if you wished, control the impulses necessary to heal it.

Where is the child, woman, student, or philosopher, who can, if we give him all the various tissues necessary, put them together and make a child? Can he properly place them, saying nothing of the creating and making the tissues? Where is the man who could build a tree or put together the substances sufficient to resemble the form of a living object? Supposing men could place the various cells, could he impart to the voluntary created child that which is crudely known as "the spark of life"? Can he give to a corpse, life at command?

Here exists the trunk with its roots, at the bottom, and branches at the top, the ground line being between. The lower extremities are supping inward the requisite liquid nourishment to keep the cells expanding. Suppose we were to support the theory that the tree, as it stands, was incomplete—insufficient to live, that it is not able to and cannot maintain an existence. There is something lacking which it must have to sustain life. You say "may be, but what is lacking?" We reply. "The sympathetic nervous system of innervation, so that morbific causes can exist 'by means unknown.'" Suppose we should say, "It needs the sympathetic system so that reflex actions have a place to play hide-and-seek, peek-a-boo, I see you, or you're it, in." We further argue that it requires a chain of ganglia on each side of the spinal column, to make such possible. True, we cannot establish where it comes from or where it ends, but it "does come" and "they must be there" for the "means unknown" to continue to play their games in, and about the time we demand that every living organism must have such. But, when we lead you to the body and tell you that very condition is supposed to exist, then you see the ridiculousness of the situation. We have driven our theorist to a corner by a little common sense (anything can reach such a scientific elevation that it loses its practicability), and he offers the consolation that "we don't know different, we don't dare to think outside of the 'Code of Ethics' so we must hold fast to the past, right or wrong, until the other fellows, that we have placed in jails for independent thinking, have forced us to recognize something better."

You ask: "What are his reasons for this system?" Looking back even into Chinese history, thousands of dynasties before the birth of Christ, we find it was the custom, when sickness prevailed, to give the physical man medicine, the treating of effects. We have, from those times till today, always had two extremists. The allopathic, homeopathic, eclectric or osteopathic physician treats man as a physical character. The mesmerist, hypnotist, metaphysician or Christian Scientist, etc., claim if anything is wrong it is because of the mental sins. If you can clear your mind from such thots you will be all right. Your Innate mind is not capable of running its business, therefore you must dictate to it. We have in this chapter, an intellectual knowledge of the workings of a physical system in all its functions.

We cannot but reason that these are controlled by a mind greater than voluntary man. To say that they are the result of "sympathy," and you know, according to Dunglison, it is "by means unknown" expresses ignorance.

Suppose a nursery man should approach you and say, "Every tree must have a sympathetic system to live." What would you say and think of his sanity? That is what we think of the M.D. He has to find something which would in a measure, try to supply his lack of knowledge of functions of the body and he thinks he has furnished it and perhaps has (until a free thinker lights the match), and then where is it? Vanished, only to exist as an imaginary ghost. It will take time to convince him, that what he thot he saw was practically nothing. The M.D. is trying to account for "phenomena" thru physical "sympathy"; the Chiropractor proves his thots by showing (nerve tracing in the living and pathological-osteological specimens after death) the great intelligence of an Innate which works thru a brain.

A person says, "I feel sick in my stomach and have a sick headache." The M.D. would say, "The head is in sympathy with your stomach." Let me show you how nicely the Chiropractor analyzes this case. At a certain dorsal vertebra, upon the left, goes forth a nerve which reaches the stomach; upon the right fibres run to the throat and head. Suppose there is a subluxation at a superior vertebra. If the intervertebral foramina are occluded on left and right sides, the head and stomach will both be abnormal in mental impulse expression. Not that they are in "sympathy," "by means unknown" because each has its direct connection with the base of supply. A new student, in adjusting, in the clinic, might have thrown the subluxation a trifle too much to one side or the other; the patient will return saying, "You fixed my headache, but my stomach is on a tear," and by aiming to correct this he may adjust too far to opposite, and again the patient will come back explaining "You fixed my stomach, but my head was on rampage." By placing to normal that vertebra, the patient will, the third time, say it was all right. In this one instance, one or the other or both could be bad. With medical men this would be a good illustration of the sympathy between stomach and head, because he does not know the real cause.

Starting from somewhere and going to nowhere definitely, we are supposed to have a conglomerate chain on each side. We do not know, and cannot find, in ten leading anatomists today, the starting or stopping point of this chain. The fibres of it, so they say, run into and come from ganglions and where they are supposed to insert is enough to make the M.D.'s continue to guess at "morbid phenomena, that supervene without any morbific cause." We cannot pursue any study unless its premises are common sense, reasonable, practical and exact. We must be able to start at rock bottom and go to the top. In the Sympathetic Nervous System, we fail to find any antecedent other than "sympathy" is something accomplished "by means unknown." Inasmuch as this philosophy holds to practical facts and B.J.'s aim is to teach specific, pure and unadulterated Chiropractic, he cannot pursue a "by means unknown" study in like manner.

When we apprehend "sympathy," it does not convey a presentable reason for the intelligence expressed. To uphold that you grow because we grow; that you eat because we do does not give me the reason why. Can you say it is "sympathy" that makes your glands secrete juices because mine do? Can you argue that because the liver secretes so does the spleen, that it is "sympathy" that does it? Can you argue that one dozen men, all going into business, to do each other, that they are in "sympathy" with each other? The more you embrace "sympathy" is to cling to a raft of air bubbles.

Shall we continue to concede to a sympathetic nervous system; reflex action and reflecting of one function to another "by means unknown" the control of such a great piece of mechanism as we represent? Will you give to some illogical system, whose origin or termination has never been definitely settled, a control of the body? Can we say this universe is controlled upon a sympathetic basis?

How long would your or our business continue if we allowed our sympathies to run it? Think of functions, representing the greatest development of intelligence for you or I could begin to guide one, let alone hundreds and will you then tell me they are based upon "sympathy, means unknown"?

If you were to study Chiropractic physiology-function and how performed—philosophically—you would see it is impossible to convey such thru a meaningless set of nerve fibres. As previously stated, the M.D. had to have some sort of a talking basis. He did not know of the relation between mind and body. His nearest comprehension was "nature." By stimulating any one of your abnormal functions, he could and did make you feel better. But it is not stimulation Chiropractors work for. By returning the occluded foramina to normal size, cyclic currents are restored, the mental is connected with the physical, and in this way, account intelligently for so-called "phenomena." Instead of existing as something "unaccountable"—supernatural, haphazard, maybe, or "extraordinary," he explains how every function is conceived, conveyed from brain cell, thru nerve fibres to tissue cell. He does not need to say "an impulse comes up to a certain segment, ganglion or center, and reflects down to some distant tissue." Sympathetic fibres may arise anywhere. They run very indefinitely. It is not a system because it has been built "by means unknown." When you have pain in the right toe and left knee, the where, why and how of such definite reflections, in the spinal cord, are indefinitely understood by M.D. Definite effects produced by indefinite cause.

They teach that spinal cord segments control all involuntary actions of the legs, the generative organs, the control of the liquids in the bladder, urethra, etc. They will say, according to Sympathetic System, that an impression from the leg goes to the segment and if it is normally supplied with blood it will then innervate the sympathetic fibres, starting from there, and it is as liable to reflect to the liver as into any portion of the leg. Isn't that specific from a scientific aspect? Can you explain, by such random methods, the intelligence behind these actions?

Patient has rheumatism in right knee and left ankle. Nerves branch from the lumbar and pass to affected areas. If pressure be upon a stated proportion of this bundle, just that many mental impulses will express their transmission abnormally at peripheral ending in cellular structure. Some fibres to the knee are under impingement, consequently the patient complains of muscular incoordination—rheumatism—in that region. The Chiropractor will adjust the vertebral subluxation, taking not to exceed one-half minute, to release this pressure on both sides and the party realizes the benefit. How often a patient says "My rheumatism is switching about." It is because of the different degrees of pressure at different places. There is no "sympathy" about that. Is there sympathy between the two legs that makes them pain at different places at different times? Chiropractic is direct, simple and does specific work. If we find a specific subluxation, use specific adjustment and have prompt, permanent results, it ceases to be complexed.

Let us consider the individual that says "I have indigestion, bloating of the stomach and that causes my heart to palpitate." B.J. in his clinic has demonstrated many a case of bloated stomach and heart performing normal, and vice versa. Does the sympathetic nervous system account for such facts? If so, how? The Chiropractor would say "The mental impulses of such fibrilla are distinct and separate. The nerves emitting in the spine, are impinged and the lack of currents causes heart trouble. The stomach has its specific subluxation. Each is separate and does not involve the other. Nerves going to this organ express their functions definitely, in excess or not enough and we have an accumulation of gases. One disease need not exist with the other. Each has a separate cause."

Referring to "Cranial Nerves" we take serious exception to the correctness of what has been previously supposed to be reliable authority. We do object to the nerves that are now known by the various names being so called because they do not convey, coming or going, those impulses which terminate into those functions. We find this note in Dunglison's Dictionary. "The Encephalic nerves arise from the encephalon or are inserted into it (according as we consider the brain the origin or termination of the nerves) and make their exit by foramina at the base of the skull. They are 12 in number." In Gray we find "The cranial nerves arise from some part of the cerebro-spinal center, and are transmitted through foramina in the base of the cranium. The nerves, after emerging from the brain at their apparent origin pass through foramina or tubular prolongations in the dura mater, leave the skull through foramina in its base, and pass to their final destination." We have yet to find a single nerve involving any function to which these fibres have received the various names, leave the base of the skull but on the contrary have traced them all to some intervertebral foramina.

For the benefit of scientific differences we shall not quote the origins and point of emergence "at the base of the skull" of the "cranial nerve" and state where each leaves the spinal column as a contradistinction because B. J. Palmer has proven them times innumerable after tracing the nerves, affected in diseases of those functions from which those "cranial nerves" have been erroneously named.

The paths which convey those characteristic mental impulses, to each of these localities (eye, ear, nose, etc.), emanate from the spine at an entirely different locality than heretofore known. The method of determining these differences is worthy of more than passing interest. On one—dissection—the body is dead, lifeless, has no feeling, in fact the individual does not know that the nerves being dissected are the ones that were abnormal before death. In Chiropractic nerve-tracing, the body has life, it feels, it uses discrimination in saying this nerve has feeling and that one has not, it responds with intelligent answers, that patient has a voicing in the proceedings therefore accurate and precise knowledge can be gained from the individual affected in unity with the work of the Chiropractor.

The first "cranial nerve" has to do with the "olfactory" function. Perhaps innervation or nerve nutrition would be the term used to express that quantity. Much study does not give us a clear insight into just what the physician thinks that this work has accomplished.

For all organs wherein the olfactory function is concerned the Chiropractor will begin to trace at any portion of the nose, lead directly to the cheek, running over that tissue, above or below the ear on that side to the foramina between the cervical on that side. If smell has been affected in any manner a subluxation will be found to exist at one of those places which is producing pressures upon those nerves interfering with the transmission of impulses to the nose (one side or both), hence disease wherein the olfactory function is abnormal. In such a case the M.D. does not get results and the Chiropractor does. One does not get the nerve that is involved and the other does. In such a case the M.D. does not realize what he has missed because he does not see, anatomically, that he has missed anything, yet physiologically he has missed everything—results. The Chiropractor has the anatomical and physiological proofs to prove both his contentions. He adjusts the subluxation, releases pressures upon an entirely different set of nerves and function is restored.

Nerve tracing is a study which proves much that previously existed as wrong in the second "cranial nerve" or the optic nerve. To localize any affections of that sense the Chiropractor would again fall back upon his standby—nerve tracing—and see where the paths do go to. The optic nerve has its periphery in the retina, but the nearest point at which we can detect its external presence at the circumference of the eye-ball; from thence it passes some of its fibres up and over the skull, over the scalp and back to a cervical subluxation. Or in some few cases another prominent branch has been found passing from below the eye, passing thru the cheek to a cervical subluxation by way of the interior to the ear. This nerve, with at least two branches, has been so often traced that when impinged at its subluxation interferes with the transmission of function impulses going to the eye or interfering with conductivity of impressions from the eye to the brain.

In disease of the eye, where sight is involved, the physician cannot do a thing to stop the progress of any given disease of this organ. He can relieve conditions with medicines and oculists can operate and opticians can apply glasses and the conditions gradually get worse regardless of what treatments are applied. The Chiropractor adjusts the cervical subluxation and the patient gets well, sight is restored and other functions therein restored to normal.

With the third "Cranial Nerve" a similar condition is also found. It is supposed to leave the base of the skull, but we have traced its exit many times to an intervertebral foramina lower down. This nerve has at least two branches, but each has one common point of segregation from the spine, altho the path from that varies. With a case of motor paralysis of any one or more or combination of the muscles of the eye-ball, the Chiropractor will trace fibres therefrom over the scalp and following the length of the spine until it reaches the sixth dorsal, where it obliquely runs inward. In still another case the outer fibres will be found following, over the cheek, posterior to the ear, following inferiorly down the neck, again passing forward over the right or left chest, running under the axilla of either side back to stomach place, where a subluxation will be found. Correction of a subluxation with consequent releasing of pressure upon nerves and consequently the restoration of currents means a return of functions to the muscles of the eye in any one or set thereof.

The fourth or Trochlear Nerve, "eight or Auditory." The physician is at a loss to know what to do with diseases of the ear. He has what he supposes is an exact knowledge of the origin and insertion of this nerve, but its abnormalities are so varied and his science so inaccurate that he is unable to correct a single difficulty other than what he can doctor from the outside. With nerve tracing the Chiropractor can locate such conditions as readily as the physician and he will find them at the same place—the ear—but the cause will be a subluxation at Atlas, where there is pressure upon those nerves emanating from the superior of that vertebra or between that and the Axis. Such conclusions only have been reached thru nerve tracing. Results—which only the Chiropractor gets by adjusting cause—certainly are the proof of the pudding.

"The Trifacial Nerve" always has been an enigma to the physician and it has even been attempted to perform surgical operations by cutting out portions of this nerve to relieve conditions therein. By this means the surgeon has been enabled to somewhat inaccurately locate the peripheries of this nerve. The Chiropractor takes its three branches and traces every fine periphery point by point until he can tell where it starts and where it will enter the spinal column. If the left side be affected, then pressure will be only on that side, or vice versa; or, if both sides, then pressures will exist on both sides. Adjustment at that place relieves all pain permanently.

We have but mentioned these first few "Cranial Nerves" to show how inaccurate dissection is when dealing with pathological conditions in the living person.

It is impossible to gauge an abnormal condition by the anatomical features from which the physician tries to gauge all persons. Even in nerve tracing we cannot lay down one set rule for the paths of the same nerve in any two people, for they somewhat vary, altho pursue a main course. The Chiropractor prefers tracing out the paths upon the fellow that feels and knows. The paths of these nerves are different in many people, yet as a whole have directions in common.

We could give an endless number of reasons why "Cranial Nerves" cannot be relied upon when dealing, philosophically, with the live subject, but we feel that the above proves our contention without doubt. The man who gets the results is undoubtedly following the correct system and without correct foundation all else must go wrong. Therefore we logically conclude that the man who is always going wrong, and working without satisfactory results has a wrong system.

Pressure upon brain fibres means lack of ability to convey impulse. The only place where pressure (constraining force) can be placed upon nerves where they are entirely surrounded by an osseous structure (the only restraining material) is at the spinal column as they pass outward thru intervertebral foramina. That which is the cause of all disease exists at these vital places, from Atlas to and including the sacrum. We do not need a sympathetic nervous system to explain functions. If the fundamental principles of Chiropractic (pressure upon nerves as they pass thru intervertebral foramina, caused by a vertebral subluxation obstructing the transmission of currents, is the cause of all disease, then Chiropractors have nothing in common to do with the supposed to be sympathetic nervous system. Such exist only in the ganglia external to the foramina; therefore not subject to pressure.

If the "twelve cranial nerves" originate within the brain and go direct to their organ, without passing other than thru the base of the skull, there ought never to be a disease of these functions, because they cannot be subject to pressure unless due to fracture or concussion of the skull. Today there are millions of people with diseases of these functions.

Why? Have they all had fractures of the skull? Those "twelve cranial nerves" are but distinct branches of the original "31 pairs." They emanate thru the foramen magnum and are subject to the same pressures at the intervertebral foramina. Chiropractors have traced them; adjusted the vertebral subluxation and returned the normal function, which is proof of its correctness. For the inaccuracy of our fore-runners we have but to look upon the highways and find millions of deaf and blind, etc. Who is correct; the one who treats effects with "sympathy" oil, "by means unknown," or he who has a direct definite system and applies it in the same manner and proves specific results?

Do you see where it leads us? If the sympathetic nervous system is correct, then man ought to be healthy, for there could be no derangement. D. D. Palmer was the first that said that the adjustment of vertebrae restores all functions. The M.D. does not do it.

We feel some of you are thinking the quesion: "How do we prove the existence of a nerve from the sixth dorsal on right to the head?" Chiropractors are peculiar, if you will, in the manner in which they study the human body. M.D.'s have been dissecting millions of bodies of all sexes, colors and nationalities for hundreds of years, and not one has located the cause of a single disease. If you think he has, prove it. When he begins to trace, in the dead body, he follows that sympathetic nerve up to a center and if possible thru to a ganglion which he supposes was the nerve that caused the trouble before death. Let us illustrate with a case of sciatica. They dissect the nerve that they think has created the mischief, and even if it were possible to thus trace it, they have never found that which interfered with its functions; therefore they are still in darkness regarding the cause of sciatica. The Chiropractor traces upon the living subject, a person who feels and ought to know if we get it right, and with that unique study, nerve tracing, we follow its exact course. We are taught by anatomists that "the great sciatic nerve passes out of the pelvis thru the great sacrosciatic foramen. It descends between the trochanter major and tuberosity of the ischium, along the back part of the thigh, to about its lower third, where it divides into two large branches. When the division occurs at the plexus the two nerves descend together side by side, or they may be separated at their commencement by the interposition of part of the whole of the Pyriformis muscle." (Gray, pp. 793 and 794, 15th Edition.) How does he know? Because he has cut it out after death. Let that living case pronounced sciatica go to a Chiropractor. Trace he will, starting perhaps upon the front, inside or outside of the leg. Inch by inch he will carefully and slowly trace that feeling nerve. Oftentimes, while pressing on its path, the pain will be felt at peripheral, which has the same feeling and character as sciatic rheumatism. If we vary the slightest from one side to another we miss that tenderness. Thus we proceed, inch by inch, and trace the exact nerve over the hips to the second or third lumbar. We have now traced out a nerve that no anatomy gives.

Take an example like the given case of stomach trouble and headaches and start at one or the other and trace, from effect to cause and cause to effect, the nerves involved, because it has the same feeling all the way. Upon the right of stomach place, we trace a nerve direct to and under the right axilla, around chest to throat or ear. Whenever touched along its path it creates a sharp expression of pain. That is another nerve that no anatomy teaches. It is but a sample of our work upon the live body. To prove the correctness of Chiropractic philosophy is but to adjust the subluxation; the head and stomach return to normal. The M.D. cannot do likewise, because he is dealing with "nature" by "means unknown." The Chiropractor knows what power he has to deal with, where it comes from, and goes to and by what means; he adjusts the cause of interference. Which is scientific "sympathy" or "knowledge"? The M.D.'s have been trying to get results thru a sympathetic nervous system "by means unknown," and we have adjusted cause that made incoordination between the innate mind and our physical organs.

Take a bad case of enlarged thyroid-goitre. Left side nerves examined and found quite tender. Upon inquiry to the patient; "Do you ever have pains in the left breast?" "I frequently do," was the reply. That fibre leads to the breast and we wanted to ultimately reach the throat. We did, down deep, find our fibre, on the right side, and it was exceedingly tender. We traced the fibre thru to the thyroid.

We shall relate an amusing instance. B.J. had another patient with an enlarged thyroid. Although having taken adjustments for several weeks, he did not know it. She had never called his attention to it and he was surprised when she said yesterday: "I can feel my throat is getting smaller." In adjusting on right side both nerves were impinged. One went to the head and the other to the throat. B.J. was relieving for the head and in doing so was reducing the enlarged thyroid.

Nerve tracing is a most unique, pleasant study. There are some things we cannot answer. The perplexities of today will be provided for tomorrow.

Summary: Are the above conditions the result of a sympathetic nervous system or an Innate Intelligence expressed thru a definite, exact and specific nervous system? Is function "sympathy" or mental impulse?

9

---•◆•---

NERVOUS SYSTEM

CHIROPRACTICALLY CONSIDERED

IN DISCUSSING THE NERVOUS SYSTEM we have a question that is unlimited, but we shall outline its subdivisions in point of order: First, the embryonic nervous system; second, its development; third, location; fourth, function; fifth, how function is performed.

In studying the embryonic nervous system we must consider what a child consists of. We are aware of what the embryo consists. The embryo is that expansion of cells that takes place in the uterus. The spermatozoon consists of the male constituents of a human being. The ovum consists of the necessary female elements. The fusion of the two makes our future unit. Neither alone has all the ingredients. The two amalgamated make the child.

The brain, as a whole, is the first organic enlargement after consolidation of these elements. From this is expanded, at a specific inferior point, a minute filament or cord, which elongation is in proportion with the brain. The unfolding of the one is equivalent to the extension of the other.

That which enlarges first eventually proves to be the brain system (brain, spinal cord and peripheral fibrillae). We wish to carry "The Nervous System" a step farther than is considered by medical anatomists of today. None speak of brain as the organ from which all nerves have their origin. Gray, as the standard anatomy, and the nervous system

224

that it gives, is that external portion from the base of the skull outward. "The brain is a thinking organ and is used with voluntary movements. All others are sympathetic or reflex from the spinal cord, solar plexus outward."

We shall speak of the physical brain and spinal cord, which can be seen or sensed, united with the mental. We will explain the function of the nervous system, considering the same from a philosophical and physical standpoint.

A great many think philosophy a science beyond their reach. It is not. It is comprehensible for the light thinker and unlimited for a philosopher.

The M.D. considers your body upon the physical plane. He studies physical diseases, treating them with physical medicines, expecting to stimulate or inhibit physical organs. He does not know about nor look for assistance outside of the physical.

If impression be given full power to deposit itself in the brain, normal interpretation follows and Innate brain can and does send forth responsive impulses and these are given an uninterrupted channel and are allowed to deposit themselves in tissue and are expressed; then coordination-health-exists. It positively cannot be otherwise. The circle is made from tissue to brain cell and reverse, a circuit unbroken. Action must follow.

We shall endeavor to put our thoughts into illustrated form. This process impresses a more elaborate and practical intelligence.

In considering the embryonic state of the brain, let us consider one (Nervous System) germinal vesicle, which is a microscopical vessel of germinal cells. The term "germ" is considered here as collapsed cells of microscopic size. A process of evolution takes place—development. Each progressively swells and, leaving its vesicular bars, takes up a residence upon the outside. Many germs continuing the same process soon form a definite membrane, which, according to texture, quality, capacity, shape, deposition and character, is called a brain. Let us suppose that each brain has one million expanded cells. As they assume maturity in form each must have a prolongation—the nerve fibrilla. This process fulfilled, we have a brain system, brain, spinal cord and peripheral fibres complete. The spinal cord, with fibres, is but a continuation of the brain until each function terminates in a tissue cell. If the brain consists of one million brain cells, an equal quantity of fibrillae must be the result; consequently there will be one million tissue cells.

This formative process is accomplished during the fetal life of the child. At birth it is thoroughly formed and the expansion taking place after birth is necessary to keep the form to normal.

To pursue this study we must know that the Innate or body building brain has thoroughly expanded at birth—reached its normal in form. Its location, within the skull and the continuation of it by fibres passing, as a bundle, through the spinal canal and the branches to organs, will be considered briefly but broadly.

Suppose the stomach has two hundred brain fibres running to it. Could we start at this organ and so minutely trace each, or the 200 collectively, thru tissue, past or between arteries and veins, thru muscular fibres, they would eventually go thru the intervertebral foramina into the spinal cord. Could we still pursue the same fibres we would find them continuing their identity thru the spinal cord, each landing at an individual brain cell. To weigh the idea further, judge a tree. If the trunk could be exactly dissected, its "grain" would be found to consist of millions of fibres, some large, others small. If the trunk consists of 2,000,000 fibres, its expansion above into foilage must correspond. For instance, the first branching divides into two, one containing two-thirds and the other one-third of the original number. Division and subdivision continues until every leaf has its stem, consisting of seven or eight fibres. Could we take any one of these, as small as they are, trace it thru the leaf, into the stem, to a branch, from that into a larger one, to the trunk and thru that, it would be found ending in the ground as individual fibres. This brings to notice a cell to cell expansion philosophy, connection being made by the intermediate—grainy fibre. Brain cell (in ground) manufactures impulse, its expansion fibre—acts as a direct conductor to superior tissue cells. The same comparison can be made in any vegetation or animal.

Without wishing to detail proofs or authorities it is sufficient to state that brain cell to tissue cell connection, by means of individual fibres, is demonstrated on all cases of vivisectional experiments that are made upon the brain. We are not in favor of vivisection to prove these points, for Chiropractic work has been reasoned from living actions, without vivisection, yet we refer to these to substantiate what a cruel torturing method has also proven. To stimulate any small portion of a brain by electricity means to increase the functions in a definite portion of the body, which always corresponds with location in the brain in all animals or humans alike, showing a systematic arrangement between organs. To change the position of the stimulating electrical needle is to change the scene of action. These experiments can be performed in a like manner as often as desired with always the same results. To turn a heavy current is to reach the same conclusions, the action being deadened. To pith the brain or utilize other means of increasing or decreasing the functions of the brain is to always prove the exactness of localizing the place from which distant functions have their origin.

Before birth the child has two brains built. Both are at work; one is being worked thru and the other with. After birth two brains are being worked thru. There can be only one conception of this statement; one analysis. Chiropractic has named these two brains Innate and Educated.

Innate, that is, the intellectual power, that precedes creation, transmission and expression; which formed the child, which is there previous to, and after birth; the most prominent, indisputable, subdivisional character of this faculty being the educated mind. Innate Intelligence is capable of governing or directing all circulatory functions at any period in which it is present in this composite form.

That Innate Intelligence is capable of directing the child's functions, how to suckle the breast, mixing milk with saliva, juices of the stomach and intestines; creating nutriment, making fecal matter from the remainder and expelling it from the body; controlling the kidneys in proper action; directing serous and blood circulations, and yet that child may not be one day old. There represents an intelligence greater than man can place in comparison. This Innate Intelligence directs all the functions of the body at birth, during life, and ceases to live, in the same volume in a physical body, at death.

Death, as we ordinarily think of it, is a term that cannot be applied. Nothing is dead. Death expresses only an equivalent stage, the same as disease does. For illustration, let us say that normality is equivalent to 2,000,000 cycles per minute and 1,500,000 is equivalent to disease; when the volume of Innate impulses is reduced down to 2,000 vibrations per minute, we have not death, but a state of comparative death when placed beside the greater quantity. We have different degrees of life and many phases of death. When we speak of volume we always speak of action. We would not know volume without having the power in connection with a material thing. We would not know whether there was 2,500,000 or 2,000 impulses unless we observed the thing materially. There must be at all times a union of material with immaterial.

On the reverse we have an educated intelligence. This begins life as an organ to be expanded according to the whims and fancies of each individual, gradually unfolding until death.

Someone advanced the thought of four nervous systems in the body, but we would say this is according to what interpretation you place upon the word "system." It is really improper to say the "secretory system" because it could not be excretory unless it has something to excrete, therefore, we have to have an intaking system, and one would not exist without the other, therefore the "system" should include everything that is necessary to make it complete in its expression of function. We would not call that portion of the nervous system which has its origin at the periphery and its ending in the brain a system—it is only one-half of a system, but this added to that portion of the nervous system which has its origin in the brain and its termination in the tissue cell (the other half of the system) would complete the cycle and we would have a system. So we still maintain that man has two complete nervous systems.

We shall, in a condensed manner, illustrate Innate. We know there is something that exists in and all around us, sometimes called an unknown power. What is this? Religious people call it God; persons who do not know call it Nature; another would name it subconscious mind; more call it intuition. It has a variety of names, but we shall give, what is to Chiropractors as taught by B. J. Palmer. This "power" is an intelligence, expresses individual characteristics. What is it, why and how expressed, the latter especially is a practical branch of Chiropractic philosophy. Our Innate intelligence is not God, but for want of better we shall refer to it as an emanation. This supply of superior force is being supplied constantly, but it is not Innate in us until it passes thru transition. This sunbeam, as it were, must pass thru a sieve called mental. What remains passes onward; thru the mind. Each step brings it nearer to a physical utilizable level. Having passed thru the two ethereal processes, let us now make of it a practical substance by proceeding thru the brain, converting it to a reality—mental impulse—physical power—life.

Let us consider relative sizes and values of these brains. The two brains, the superior delineating the Innate Intelligence; the lower one the Educated Intelligence. Innate guides two-thirds (if not more) of our body; Educated the remaining one-third. Innate mental impulses control all functions which exist within the physical being.

We have for some time made the division two-thirds to one-third. This has always been hypothetical—it might be seven-eights to one-eighth, or one-fourth to three-fourths, as regards weight on a scale or as regards size in measurement, but in point of value and quality and the portions of the physical body over which it has dominant control, there is no question but what it is in the largest majority of the human body—whether it be two-thirds or not, that question we cannot answer.

Innate Intelligence has control over every tissue cell in the human body. Educated Intelligence has control over just a very small portion of the external muscular system—Innate guides the rest, every tissue cell in eight and sometimes nine functions.

Educated has to do only with that which is external. When we wish to see it is with our Educated; when we talk, the same is used. Voluntary movements are managed by impulses from the latter brain, but we do not digest our food with it. The kidneys or bowels do not act at command, neither is innervative nutrition carried on by it. The majority of you, not knowing specific, pure and unadulterated philosophical Chiropractic, try to and voluntarily aim to guide Innate in running the body. When there is a lack of pepsin in the stomach, because something is wrong, you, educationally, say, "We will artificially supply that chemical." You have been educated to do that. A Chiropractor says, "Are you insignificant people, living thirty, forty or fifty years, capable of dictating to Innate how to run the body? Can you tell a mother how her newly conceived child must be made? Can you direct and utilize the forces necessary to make the son or daughter?"

Can you direct a force to remake something that made the force of which that thought was a product? Can you conquer, subdue or compel the source of your own origin to be changed?- *. * * Remember, when studying Innate you investigate that power which has always existed and always will.

The educated brain represents that expansion of material tissue cells that takes place between birth and death, but which is expressing the quantity of thoughts according to the degree and volume of normal cellular expansions of mental impulses coming from the Innate brain. The educated brain, then, in its quality, as well as quantity of thought, is something insignificant compared with the other.

Let us observe the divisions of the functions of each. We have roughly mapped the two brains, their relative significations. Each brain is divisible into many lobes. Each is, in turn, composed of abundant cells. Each has its fibrilla; every lobe its multitudinous fibres; each brain its cable—both cables joined, is the spinal cord before inferior division takes place.

Separation into lobes gives to each the property of being a medium through which a different range of creation of impulses can be placed which, by its peripheral expression, proves it to be a specific function separate, different and apart from the range of motion indicative of another function. No. 1 permits the output of mental impulses which when expressed are calorific in function. No. 2 is contractility. We shall name the 3rd, reparatory; 4th is nutrition; 5th, excretion; 6th, secretion; 7th, reproduction; 8th, expansion; 9th, sensory, almost indefinitely into the number of Innate functions which are involuntary to Educated. The heart action, for instance, is beyond educated mental control, yet but one of the many mental servants of the Innate mind. From lobe No. 1 issues hypothetically fifty thousand fibres.

These go from that portion of the brain to a common center (external to the foramen magnum), there meeting the bundles of other lobes, all passing externally to meet the large cable from the other brain, then pass outward as one to begin an almost endless branching to every organ and tissue throughout the body.

When lobe No. 1 sends forth a continuous stream or current of 50,000 mental calorific foruns, unceasingly and unhindered, you have a normal calorific expression known as heat thruout the body.

That lobe, and that alone, has the function of conversion of power into calorific impulses.

Let us take the next. From this comes impulses which when expressed are (to B. J. Palmer) involuntary motor. We will here state the difference between voluntary and involuntary motor. At will, we can and do pick up the eraser. Suppose it was a hot stove and accidentally our finger touched it. "Unconsciously it was jerked from the stove"; "Intuitively or reflexly it was removed." This action was repeated so quickly following the reception of the impression that was interpreted and adapted to, that it proves itself to be an (innate) voluntary intellectual impulse. There was a voluntary intellectual impulse; one that showed reason, thought, discernment, discrimination; that came from the Innate brain before we educationally, had detected that our finger was on a stove, hot or cold.

Our dinner is in our stomach; that is, we believe so, tho it may have passed into the bowel. We cannot say to our stomach, "You are working too fast—go slower—because we educationally, have no way of directly knowing that such is a fact. We do not know what is or is not present, what is going on there; whether secretions are lacking or in excess; whether quantity and quality are normal; therefore it would be folly to pass judgment upon something which we have no means of determining. The actions that are produced there are Innate voluntary motor impulses, therefore such actions are not within the range of control, direction or transmission of the educated foruns.

The third is sensory. When our finger, not intentionally, touched the stove, there was an impression that traveled in 1/500 of a second to our Innate brain, from where there responded an intelligent impulse, which when placed into action, at the periphery of an efferent nerve or nerves, took our finger from it.

Life—functions; Health—normal functions; Disease—deranged functions; Death—no functions.

A live nerve, like a "live wire," is made so by the current sent thru it (thru the wire from the dynamo, and thru the nerve from the brain); each may be said to have functions.

A subluxation that pinches, or presses upon, a nerve, may be likened to a rheostat in a live wire. The rheostat interferes with the current that passes, or would pass through the wire, it resists, keeps back the current, changes the functions of the wire, also the motor or lamps on that wire. While in the case of the rheostat it is supposed to regulate the current by the resistance, it may interfere with or derange functions of the wire, also the motor and lamp, putting both motor and lamp out of service.

When a dynamo is burned out (dead) it can no longer gather or propel the current through the wires and the wires cease to have functions to perform as before, and the rheostat that once kept back, or resisted, changed or deranged the functions of the wire, no longer interferes with or has any effect on the functions of the wire, as the wire has ceased to have functions, therefore the presence or absence of the rheostat does not change the system, or any part of it, and in such a case it could be removed and then put back again without affecting the motor or lamps that were once active, but are then dead (have no functions).

Should there be a corpse that had subluxated vertebrae pressing upon nerves, in that case there would be no functions interfered with, as there would be no life current to be sent (the generator or generating force being absent in the human body), and the presence or absence of a subluxation would make no change in nerve function, without being changed they could not be deranged, therefore there would be no disease nor life expressed.

In referring to animal life, disease, death—death does not come until disease is finished. Disease, when it is finished, brings death. Disease is but deranged functions,—no function (death) does not come until deranged functions (disease) is finished. Deranged functions, when finished brings no function (death). Therefore, deranged functions (disease) is the product of subluxations—displacements—and death is the product of deranged functions (disease).

No function (death) will not be further commented on in this, but deranged functions can be made normal in the human body by Chiropractic adjusting. A Chiropractor replaces the displaced vertebra, increasing the caliber and capacity for transmission through the impinged nerve, so the nerve function can become normal. With normal nerve functions, we may be said to be in health.

The brain is the instrument of the mind—is the generator of the nervous system. The so-called "nerve supply" is in reality but a mental current sent thru the nerves by the brain and is the real life current; the life of the body, and it is thus carried to every organ of the body.

This generative force, sending the life current, causes the nerves to have work to do—functions to perform. Also the current is carried to the organs of the body, causing them to do work—to perform functions. Thus it is that all functions of the body are made and controlled by the Intelligent mentalities of man.

Any interference with the normal action of the nerves in carrying the life current deranges their functions, and thereby deranges the function of the organs to which they carry the life current. Deranged functions are diseases, and are caused by displaced vertebrae impinging the nerves. Deranged functions can only be made normal by having the displacements replaced, giving free and normal carrying capacity to nerves.

Live things alone are sensitive, the nerves are filled with life which they are carrying to the various organs of the body, and they also carry impressions to the brain, where they are interpreted as sensations when the intellectual mind has, thru the medium of the brain, interpreted them.

This same process may be carried indefinitely throughout. Each body has many glands, the liver, thyroid, spleen, each secreting an oil and chemical; as it is secreted it is sent out by the excretory. Each ingredient requires right tissues and substances and power to produce it. All are actions of Innate voluntary motor, differently located.

Many other functions come from distinctive lobes of that brain. If you hold in your hand a human brain, you have no life. Give to that brain, properly placed, its Innate, then it has life. Connect with the brain nerves, and you have transmission of life. Place at peripheral endings of these nerves, tissue cells, and you have an outlet or proper substance for the expression of that which is distantly manufactured. Do you begin to grasp what life is?

"Life—The state of being which begins with generation, birth or germination, and ends with death; also, the time during which this state continues; that state of an animal or plant in which all or part if its organs are capable of performing all or any of their functions.

"Of human beings—The union of the soul and body; also, the duration of the creature having an immortal life.

"Philosophical—The potential principle, or force, by which the organs of animals and plants are created and continued in the performance of their several and cooperative functions; the vital force, whether regarded as physical or spiritual."—Webster.

The scope of the Educated brain is limited. It is confined to those organs which are necessary when coping with the external world. Our eyes have an Educated voluntary and Innate voluntary optic nerve; the ear has the similar two sets of nerves. Each sense has its two sets. Our extremities have voluntary nerves. We have a few voluntary respiratory. The scope of this brain, is comparatively, as one-third is to two-thirds. The function of this brain is to first convert, second to give impetus to voluntary impulse from brain to tissue cell, regardless of whether a muscle, finger, back, stomach, the thigh or any other portion of the body is to be moved. Do you doubt the supreme value of nerves —conductors-conveyors of impulsed from brain to tissue cells?

Take a skeleton. Let us study him as he was. In that skull was a brain. From that went downward and thru the spinal foramen, a spinal cord. If you will notice closely, we have small openings. Chiropractic is the first science to give utterance to these ideas in the rough; the first science and D. D. Palmer, the first man that made these famous by calling special attention to them, for at that point is the cause of all disease. Nerves branch from the spinal cord inside of the spinal foramen. Brain nerves emit through the intervertebral foramina. Immediately they divide and divide, sub-divide and sub-divide again, until every tissue cell, small as it is, has its fibres ending at or into its structure. We have before us four individual Innate voluntary brain cells, one from calorific, the second from nutritive, the third is contractility and this from the reparatory lobe. Back of them exists an Innate Intelligence which gives power, unlimited, so that they can give impetus to nerve fibrillae and if connection be unhindered, normal expression will be the result. In our next illustration there are four fibres enter one tissue cell, each of which must have heat, action, nutrition, and can be repaired if injured. What is life? As long as brain cell No. 1 can transform and give the nerve these impulses, and the nerve can and does convey these calorific impulses uninterruptedly, will not this cell always be warm? Can it be other than normally heated? Suppose that midway between brain and tissue cell we pinch (just enough decrease) that nerve—slightly impinge it, what will take place at its peripheral? Excessive heat—too much heat. The M.D. would say "Fever." The latter expresses nothing. Excessive heat tells something. We shall produce heavy pressure on No. 4. A heavy pressure paralyzes; slight pressure stimulates. The resultant symptoms are, no more nutritious impulses pass beyond the point of pressure, hence decomposition at the peripheral—tissue cell. With excessive heat it decomposes quicker than if heat was normal. In addition to the foregoing we shall place pressure upon the reparatory fibre which cannot now conduct reparatory brain impulses. What happens? Death. We have the combination of symptoms necessary to produce it. There is no nutrition or reparation; hence, excessive heat makes it much faster.

Suppose we should make another combination and slightly press upon this fibre conveying motor impulses. We have motor paralysis yet reparatory may be in perfect order. This is, in a measure, depleting tissue, but reparative and nutritive fibres are undisturbed, therefore will repair it. Life will continue to be partially expressed, only laboring under difficulties. This is why "We don't feel sick, but we are not well. We are at the store or doing our work, but we do not put the pleasure or vim in it that we should like." They are not bedfast, but are working under difficulties, trying to maintain a 100 per cent normal when but 60 or 75 per cent of impulses are possible. To a person who has health hard work should be the greatest pleasure and life worth living.

Mental impulses of right character, quality and quantity is a necessity to make functional-health, and if Innate Intelligence can interpret incoming impressions accurately and convert the external—into impulses, then there is only one thing that can make disease—the hindrance or obstruction to mental impulses from point of manufacture to that of expression, with the impulse conveyor and nervous system.

The M.D. steps to the bedside. "Johnnie is sick! Put this under your tongue, please. Temperature 103! How have your bowels been?" "Constipated." "Have you any pains?" etc., etc. "Mother, every hour mark on this card his temperature." Tomorrow he calls. "Let me see the chart, please. Johnnie has not been eating much?" "Just a little milk." "Here

is another chart. Keep a record today." Day after day this is repeated,
finally saying, "The fever is running higher. I don't know what to call
it yet. It has not taken a definite form. Meanwhile I will make out a
prescription; give one teaspoonful every two hours." After seven to ten
days he tells the mother, "We will have a long siege, for this is typhoid
fever. I don't know whether he will pull through or not." The M.D.
continues from 21 days to 16 weeks to call once a day at $10 a call.
He has a perfect vocabulary of symptoms, but when it comes to the
most common sense deductions of life and the cause of disease he is
found groping with superstitions. Chiropractors will take a back step
for none of them; we don't care who they are, what college or university
they are from, or their position in life. The M.D., in entering the sick-
room, only senses the physical. This is all he knows or cares to investigate. He does not consider sickness as incoordination to life. Suppose
that child should die; there would be an absence of life—death. The
typhoid child is but giving vent to abnormal quantity of life giving impulses, therefore is partially alive or dead. Why not study life; what it
is, and how it expresses itself. And if there be disease, what causes it?
You say, "The physician is studying the cause." Where? Outside of
man. The Chiropractor confines his research, for each specific cause, inside the body. The M.D. drags foul marshes, sieves the air, digs into
the bowels of the earth, examines water, hoping to find something which
makes man sick.

The human or animal body represents the actions of three laws
("Law—Nature. The regular method or sequence by which certain
phenomena or effects follow certain conditions or causes—the uniform methods or relations according to which material and mental forces
act in producing effects, or are manifested."), spiritual, mechanical, or chemical united as one triune, the first equaling the other two in
point of control or as a regulator. As long as there is perfect union of
these there is perfect health. Just as much as the first assumes an approximate proximity towards perfection it is just that much not normal. This
machine, like all others, is run by power, called mental impulses, made
in and thru the brain, which is connected with the body by a system
of nerves thru which this force passes in currents; inducing the highest
exemplification of the intellectual power. Functions are names given
to discriminate between these actions. Any interference to the passage
of these vitalizing currents produces abnormal functions—disease. In
speaking of "spiritual" as above we wish to confine our thought to
Webster's definition, which is "Spirit-Life, or living substance, considered independently of corporeal existence; an intelligence conceived
or apart from any physical organization or embodiment; vital essence,
force, energy, as distinct from matter. The intelligent, immaterial, and
immortal part of man."

Let us find a condition, in man, that impedes mental impulses, then we will have located exactly what causes a partial depression of life. The spinal column is composed of vertebrae, one above the other. Each is capable of limited movement. The body is not changed in any direction but that you move each vertebra slightly. There are ligaments, muscles and tendons attached to them. Suppose, in the ordinary pursuits of work, you would receive a jar, a concussion, or a wrench to your body or back, one vertebra should, by such a "mere trifle," slip beyond its normal confinement. Then we have a subluxation of vertebra. This is not misplacement or dislocation, but a partial luxation; enough of a displacement to produce pressure upon brain extensional fibres as they emit between the intervertebral or movable foramina, producing slight pressure. This hinders the conducting ability of brain nerves to convey mental impulses to tissue for expression.

What name to give this or that disease depends upon the degree of pressure, and what combination of functional nerves are involved. The combination of functions differ, and can be studied endlessly because no two people have the same.

There are two sides to every question. The M.D. sees no further than symptoms—the effects or results. What are you going to do with your patient? "You need a general tonic or stimulating manipulations to strengthen these organs." "Where are you going to give me this general tonic?" "In the stomach." Suppose the pain is in the foot. "Put it in the stomach." If it was in the bowels? "Put it in the stomach." What is put into the stomach never gets where it was intended. This man, after being drugged for months or years, still has the same trouble. That is one way—to treat effects.

What does the Chiropractor do? Personally, if the patient would say, "My stomach is not right today," we would explain his case as regards to cause and nothing more. Were we to take that stand, in general practice, ninety-nine of one hundred cases would say, "He pays no attention to my case." It would be of more value to him and the world to allow a Chiropractor to spend one minute in studying cause than for him to talk four hours about his symptoms, but it, apparently, does the patient good to tell his troubles to someone and he evidently thinks that that is what the Chiropractor compensated for.

We are getting thirsty; what shall we do? We had to think voluntarily before we could put into execution the act to pour water from the pitcher. Do you realize that thoughts must precede manifestation? Suppose there had been something wrong so that the thought, in the form of mental impulse, could not pass thru that nerve and express itself in that arm? That would be inharmony between that arm and mental impulse. We want the water, but the arm cannot be utilized as a medium to obey the brain—incoordination. The physician agrees there is something wrong in the arm, but doesn't know just what and where. The Chiropractor has definite knowledge and a specific adjustment, not to exceed one-half a minute, which as soon as corrected must, without question, return function.

We have aimed to confine our remarks in this chapter to two systems of nerves, the Innate and Educated.

Innate is a master mechanic, such as you and I cannot duplicate. The workings that it has accomplished under abnormal conditions are wonderful masterpieces of intellectual reasoning. Where there is a fractured bone it may build a scaffold, followed by a rigid bridge, from one fragment to the other to strengthen and build it to normal. It can and has made pivot or spindle joints where formerly there were none. It will burrow an opening thru bones for the passage of nerves.

10

CRANIAL NERVES

THE QUESTION IS TO KNOW whether we believe our senses or not, conclude that we know what we know or whether we do not know what we think we do, or we may know what we might not know, or we really know more than we think we do. Of course, to get such an idea is to doubt yourself, to doubt your conclusions, and whether the idea of today is right and the idea of yesterday wrong.

Anatomy gives a sufficient knowledge of the twelve cranial nerves; it tells their origin, paths, insertion and functions. B.J. is not going to dwell in this except to name, locate and give function in this chapter, then pass to the question:

NAME	FUNCTION
1. Olfactory	Sense of smell.
2. Optic	Sense of sight.
3. Motor oculi	Moves around the eyeball.
4. Trochlear	Draws the eyeball inward.
5. Trifacial	Divides into three branches, one going to the eye, another going to the superior maxillary, and the third or lower going to the inferior maxillary.

237

NAME	FUNCTION

6. Abducens .... Draws the eyeball outward.
7. Facial .... Going to the teeth and those muscles having mostly to do with mastication; principally the muscles involved in tetanus or lock-jaw.
8. Auditory .... Sense of hearing.
9. Glosso-pharyngeal ... Which takes in the oesophagus, stomach, lungs, diaphragm, liver, trachea, bronchii; in fact, the entire respiratory tract.
10. Par Vogum .... To muscles of neck, chest and abdomen.
11. Spinal Accessory .... Going to the muscles of the spine and other tissues.
12. Hypo-glossal .... Going to the muscles that move the tongue.

Anatomy tells us that some of these have their exit through foramina at the base of the skull; anatomy does not tell us that any have their exit through the foramen magnum or other path through and into the spinal cord, and have their exit through any intervertebral foramina; it does not give such a path for any of the cranial nerves. Should we presume, on our first premise, that the functions which these twelve nerves are said to manifest have their pathway through the intervertebral foramina, we begin to digress from the known facts of anatomy. If anatomy is correct as to the origin, paths, and exits of the twelve cranial nerves that have paths and exits through the cranial foramina, and these are solid, fixed; then if the Chiropractic principle be true that we have a diminution of the size and circumference of the nerve so as to diminish the amount of current going through that nerve to make disease, and the premises of anatomy and Chiropractic both be correct, then there would never be any possible disorder of the functions mentioned, such as smelling, seeing, movements of the eye-balls, teeth, etc., it would be impossible to have abscess, decomposition, decaying of gums, sordes; tetanus, hearing affected; anything wrong with the pharynx, tongue, oesophagus, stomach, lungs, diaphragm, liver, trachea, bronchii, respiration; because it would be impossible to produce pressure upon these nerves. Man would be comparatively well if his twelve cranial nerves were doing their duty according to anatomy.

But we find that man's hearing, sight, breathing, respiration, teeth, etc., are involved. Nobody is exempt from these common diseases. As a premise, Chiropractic must be wrong or anatomy is only partly known; both cannot be right. If the premise of Chiropractic that a nerve must be under impingement to produce a disease be correct, and if anatomy is correct that these nerves are so located that they could not be under such a form of pressure, then one or the other must change or enlarge its view-point to correspond.

The question arises, are those nerves where anatomy says they are? To ask such is ridiculous, foolish. Haven't they dissected and found them? Didn't the same type say the world was square and stood on four pillars before Columbus, and because of this they were right? Columbus said they were wrong; he went to the corners, fell into endless space, and came back with Indians, and found there was another side to the corner—he was right.

How did anatomy reach the conclusion those nerves were there? They certainly did not hypothetically assume something as imaginary. They have seen, graphically portrayed, photographed, reproduced, furnished their form; in reality they are there. No disputing the concrete fact. There are nerves where they say. Dissection must be proof of the existence of nerves.

In what way did they prove the physiology, the function that went through these nerves? It would be impossible to prove such in a dead cat, dog, horse, or man. They could not prove the existence of a function when there wasn't any. In what way is vivisection performed? With and without anaesthetic. The knowledge of anaesthetics is of recent origin; consequently they use it to relieve tortured animals. Previous to that they cut and got at these various sensitive nerves. They stimulated without anaesthetics; they found that they led to a certain place, and by stimulating a nerve under specified conditions, certain actions occurred; that was proof that this nerve was optic, because the eyeball moved whenever that nerve was touched. They also found while working on a certain nerve that every muscle moved from the torture that it was going through. They could as conclusively have said that this nerve went to the bowels, because they evacuated after this pain, as to have said that it went to the eyeballs, because they rolled with agony. Modern vivisectors cannot rely upon the conclusions reached, because torture makes all nerves twitch and jerk.

What accuracy is there in the use of anaesthetic to vivisection? Our animal is under ether; he is dead to the world; his body is stifled in action, feeling is paralyzed; that is the object of an anaesthetic—to paralyze function and feeling; and proportionately as feeling is dead, proportionately is responsive function absent. Here is the animal, with its functions and feeling gone; yet that is the animal under test to see whether this particular nerve has a particular feeling, function or responsive action, or not. That hardly seems a conclusive test to demonstrate the function, etc., of a nerve. These animals cannot speak, hear; they bark with pain, jerk from agony, and that is all they can do. No matter how much an animal is under anaesthetics, they contract muscles more or less, squirm the body, the same as a person does under an

operation. That pleases the vivisectionist, because he watches for movement. Nothing definite can be reached under that phase of work, although
they do form conclusions, establish and teach physiology accordingly.

"If we take as a foundation either the different sensations which are
aroused in us by external provocations, these also differing in their
nature and mode of action, or the motor phenomena which are most
directly associated with these sensations, we may divide innervation into
five great systematizations, or principal categories, which will be: visual
innervation, auditory innervation, tactile innervation, olfactory innervation, gustatory innervation.

"Sensation is, in fact, the quality which is most characteristic of the
nervous system; this latter being, of all the tissues, that which displays
it in the highest degree, and which, on account of its complexity and its
organization, confers on it its highest value. This first conception is a
matter of ordinary knowledge. On the other hand, all sensation is in-
timately connected with motor actions, which may affect areas of the
nervous system at the same time various and distant, but of which
some are immediately dependent on these sensations, and, as such, are
characteristic of them. Each sensory system is a sensitive-motor apparatus, which, in a certain measure, is not isolated from the others, but
capable of being so isolated; that is to say, is complete in itself.
Functional links exist between these partial systems, so as to insure the
unity of the nervous system, and by it the unity of the living being.
This second conception, which sanctions the intimate connection between
sensation and motion, has begun to be generally adopted. Finally,
sensation allows of an infinity of degrees and of graduations, from those
which have their fullest expansion in the superior senses, down to those
quite obscure ones which interpret our most elementary requirements.
In writing a complete history of the nervous system, it becomes necessary
to connect these subconscious (sometimes called unconscious) sensations, with the motor acts related to them, to the distinct sensations
of the superior senses, according to their functional affinities. This idea
of an obscure consciousness governing all living actions, even those
which appear quite mechanical and automatic, is the most modern of all
those we have passed in review, and daily gains more adherents.

"Specific Activities.—The nervous system is an assemblage of partial
systems, each, in an isolated manner, presiding over some function of
a determinate nature. None of these can replace any of the others or be
replaced by them. This partition stands out very clearly when the
nerve system is considered at its periphery, either at the point of arrival
or of departure of the stimuli by which it is traversed; it becomes more
and more obscure in proportion as we penetrate the depths of the
system—of this statement the question of cerebral localizations is the
proof. We shall then start from the extremities of the nerves, ascending

nearer and nearer to the brain, tracing in this way, according to their kind, the great divisions and subdivisions of the nervous functions. The sensory field is particularly favorable for the determination of this kind of division.

"Sensory field; its divisions.—The sensory field is divisible at the periphery into five parts, corresponding to the five senses. . . . Out of the infinitely varied movements by which it is surrounded, our organization has chosen five particular orders; those are the source of all our knowledge. . . .

"It must be observed that, among the undulatory movements of the air, as of the ether, our organization is not restricted to, or has not succeeded in adapting itself to, all, but only to a small number amongst them: to those for the ear, which are comprised between 32,000 and 50,000 vibrations in the second, about eleven octaves; to those for the eye which are comprised between 450 to 880 trillions of vibrations the second. But as those media are traversed in all directions by vibrations of every length, which coexist and are superposed without being confounded, this restriction does not imply any difficulty or real gap in the exercise of the senses.

"The organs of taste and smell are affected by excitants whose physical nature, modality, and medium of propagation are absolutely unknown to us, but which it is possible to conceive of as being also vibratory changes of a special nature. . . .

". . . Each organ of the senses is provided with a special resonator. The shock of the external medium, when it transgresses certain limits, is nonexistent for the resonator; but when it possesses the right totality, it finds a gate of entrance in this sense, and penetrates the nervous system, where it finds itself in conflict with a crowd of others, and remaining there a longer or shorter period, leaves it in the condition of a motor phenomenon.

"But, to a fact which we call psychical, or one of sensibility, in one work, to sensation, in opposition to the physical fact of impression.

"Specific nature of the sensation.—We have said that impressions are specific, and we may add that sensations are also specific, for to each particular modality of impression a particular modality of sensation corresponds. Before ending in the deepest part of our being, in the most abstract notion of general ideas, which has the conflict of sensations for its origin, these latter put to port somewhere in the nervous system; there is, therefore, a functional partition of sensations, as there is one of impressions.

"Sensation is a fact of purely internal observation; can only be defined by its contrast with the psychical fact of impression. It is not in the very least a geometrical representation of the physical changes which gave birth to it. The ignorant person who can distinguish between a sound and a color has not the least conception of a sonorous or luminous vibration; the educated man also is acquainted with this detail, or believes that he can explain it. Sensation results from an association or stimuli. It is a synthesis of these stimuli effected in the nervous system.

"Uniformity of function of the nervous elements.—Further, we may add that a shock of a particular sort which has arisen in a sensitive or sensory resonator is never transmitted to the brain by the sensitive or sensory nerves, retaining its original character. All these shocks, specific in their origin, are brought back to single or at any rate to almost a uniform state, the nerve wave, as soon as they enter the nerve system, properly so called. The nerve wave (with some trifling differences) appears to be of the same general form, or, in a word, of the same nature, in all nerves (sensory, sensorial, or motor). Each neuron, taken by itself, is functionally equivalent to any other neuron; there are not any specific neurons, properly so called.

"Specificity of the neurons.—The data furnished by morphology and experimentation have so far pointed to the predominance of fundamental resemblances between nerve elements, rather than to real differences between them, except as regards those which are contingent and without known relation with the function of these elements. There must, however, exist between one and the other certain quantitative or qualitative modifications, in order that these elements, by being associated, should be able to form functionally differentiated systems. These modifications may bear only on characters which are but little obvious and be themselves individually very unimportant. The multiplicity and the complexity of the associations are sufficient to enlarge them and to elicit from them very dissimilar effects. On the other hand, these modifications may be confined to certain parts of the neurons—for example, to their extremities in the areas, by means of which they become associated the one with the other. In fact, more notable and more significant differences are discoverable in their polar fields than in the axons of their cell bodies.

"Further, we are ill equipped for the struggle required in order to seek for and understand these differences. The nerve wave, of which so much is heard, is almost unknown to us as regards its real form. Some facts about its rate of progress are all that we possess. . . .

"It is obvious that the optic nerve is not a chemical for light, nor the acoustic nerve for sound. But the component elements of each of these two nerves have not, as regards structure or properties, anything which distinguishes the one from the other, or from all the other nerve elements. They possess the common excitability of the latter, but nothing else. The luminous ray appropriate for the stimulation of the retina has no effect if immediately thrown on the optic nerve; and this because the adaptative apparatus is lacking in both cases. But, on the other hand, ordinary, commonplace excitations of the nerve system, such as pressure, pinching, electrization, excite these just as all other nerves, and so give rise to specific sensations corresponding to the specific excitant of the organ to which they belong. . . .

"There are within us sensorial systems which react specifically to every stimulus which reaches them. These systems, at their surface of contact with the exterior, are furnished with special apparatus (organs of the senses) which select, from the excitatory shocks of every form and origin by which we are surrounded, those which can in an isolated manner penetrate into each of these systems, to the exclusion of the others. Thus is created for us a determinant relation between each order of sensation and the external excitant from which it originally arose. This relation is an empirical one, but is sufficient for the daily requirements of existence; it teaches us all that is necessary for us to know, but not concerning everything external to ourselves.

"Sensation is a phenomenon of evolution; it is at the same time both a process and a progress. . . . We have said that the stimulus invaded the system and advances therein in the fashion of a wave, whose form becomes more and more complicated in proportion as it approaches and reaches the cerebral cortex. In this forward march of the impulse, where is the precise locality of sensation? Has it an exclusive and defined habitation? What parts are sufficient for or necessary to it? What does experiment tell us on this subject? How are the facts which it has displayed to us to be interpreted?

"An effort has always been made to arrange the recognized facts concerning the structure of the nervous system in accordance with the information furnished by observation. Interpretations have necessarily varied according to the state of our knowledge on these points and also with the general theories obtaining in biology.

"Sensation is a phenomenon which impresses us by its unity; the nervous system and the component systems which it includes are, on the contrary, distinguished by their complexity. Hence, no doubt, arose the repugnance which has been felt to attaching and superposing the first of these to the second; and by logical sequence the converse tendency to imprison sensation in the smallest known biological element—namely, the nerve cell." (Quoted from Morat. Physiology of The Nervous System.)

He does not say, "We have proven this by dissection, vivisection, or anatomy." He says that by a "logical sequence" they reached the conclusion that the nerve cell receives the first impression which goes to make sensation—by logic, not by demonstration. He further says: "For ourselves, our nervous system is one and indivisible; this is because we comprehend it with internal senses, which precisely realize its analyses, or syntheses. On the contrary, the nervous system of one of our fellow-creatures appears to us in all its complexity; because we grasp it with our external sense which is incapable of analyzing it. In the first case, the nervous system is ourselves; that is to say, the subject, on which its quality of sentient being confers its unity. In the second case, the nervous system is outside ourselves; that is to say, an object which we can divide into as many partial beings as the power of our means of analysis permits. The two operations employ different and in no way superposable modes of procedure. The internal sense, like the external senses, proceeds by analysis and by synthesis; but their situation in relation to each other is such that the one often builds up that which the other analyzes, and reciprocally, an absolute harmony between the two would cause all the practical benefit which we draw from the arrangement to be lost." After working upon sensation at great length, Dr. Morat reaches all his definite conclusions as a result of logic, often reaching a conclusion in logic which is not proven by experiment—which, in fact, is disproven; but we cannot understand the experiment, and fall back upon logic.

A patient comes to the Chiropractor; he has lost the sense of smell. You who believe in the twelve cranial nervous physiological system, as taught by medical standards, and you who believe in the premise of Chiropractic as regards to pressure upon nerves, must turn to this patient and say, "I am sorry; there is nothing in our science for you." Being honest to yourself, you take that standpoint because the first cranial nerve has to do with smell. It does not have a common exit in any intervertebral foramina, and is not subject to pressure following a subluxation. Consequently, your premise of adjusting the subluxation to restore smell is wrong, and cannot be involved. You shake the hand of your patient, shed a tear, and let him go. But you don't do that. You would do as we have done. Finding smell involved, you search the nose for a tender nerve, trace that to its inlet into the spinal column between the third and fourth, or the fourth and fifth, cervical vertebrae. If the right nose is affected, the tracing will be on the right, down to the right intervertebral foramina; if on both sides, you will trace both sides; your tracing leads to certain vertebrae; you palpate and find them subluxated; adjust the subluxation, and smell returns. The question is, is this a nerve that has to do with smell? Seemingly it does. Seemingly we have done something that anatomical research, physiological-vivisectional experimentation has not done. Is anatomy right? It is. Is physiology right? It is not. As a general conclusion, logic says the man who gets results is right. The man who fails must be wrong in his premise.

Take the second cranial, or optic nerve. An individual has atrophy, which is but a neurasthenia; but you, being the true, honest disciple of Kirke's Physiology and Butler's Pathology, and being the good, conscientious, sincere Chiropractor, believing in its premise, must say to the blind patient, "I am sorry; there is nothing we can do." But there is a question or doubt in your mind, because, after saying these things, your patient has bared his neck and you are already tracing from the eye to the fourth cervical, and you will find that on adjusting a subluxation a stimulation runs like a flash to the eye, and the patient says he saw the color of your coat. He says it is blue, and he is right. There is no fooling this man; he did see, because you stimulated temporarily the impulses running to that eye. You adjust the cervical subluxation and sight was restored. Did you trace an optic nerve, or not? Does it have to do with sight? Is it the main nerve, or an accessory? Is it important or unimportant? Have we found an optic nerve not known by the anatomists? Can it be that we have found a nerve that has never been under dissection? You are joking with logic, by demonstrating its existence in giving to man the thing he wants—sight.

This third one moves the eyeball. Your case has strabismus to one side or the other, or both. There is nothing you can do, anatomically and Chiropractically speaking, because this nerve is beyond reach; it is beyond being trifled or fooled with by a movable foramen which might produce pressure upon it; but it is a fact you can trace these nerves to the fifth or sixth dorsal, and, under adjustment of a subluxated vertebra, the eyeballs straighten. Maybe it is an accident which might have done so without adjustments; but it is peculiar how it occurs in 99 per cent accidents in a 100; the medical man doesn't get such accidents.

We have analyzed the twelve cranial nerves; we have showed new tracings for each. B.J. believes man has a broader nervous system than is given to us by present books; we believe man has the nerve systems the book says he has; but he has more—a system independent of that. When you properly understand Chiropractic work, you will appreciate this distinct brain-cell-to-tissue-cell nervous system.

11

HOW ARE THE CRANIAL NERVES
REACHED BY THE CHIROPRACTOR?

WE HAVE ASKED, "How are the cranial nerves reached by the Chiropractor?" Proven by clinical results, the Chiropractor reaches no nerve; he reaches the surface of skin over the backbone. Surface has no thickness. Therefore, he reaches something which has area. But the force that is impelled from his hands to the surface of the skin is transferred to the vertebra subluxated, which force, by shearing itself with vertebrae above and below, moves the subluxated vertebrae into place, releases pressure upon nerves, and permits normal amount of current to flow through nerves which anatomy has seen fit to misfit physiologically the "Twelve Cranial Nerves."

Man forces himself to reach a conclusion: (1) there are twelve cranial nerves, as taught by anatomy: or (2) they are not there, or (3) if they are, they do not do the things he says; because the Chiropractor, playing upon other conditions, utilizing his force at other places, upon nerves, restores function of the thing that he says goes through another set of nerves.

Sight is said to go through the optic nerve, which is in the rear of the ball and passes through the optic foramen, which is beyond the reach of the Chiropractor. It is in the skull, from origin to insertion; that is, none of its fibres go to or through intervertebral foramina. Any subluxation that might occur anywhere in the spine could not in any way

246

affect any branch of the anatomist's optic nerve. Consequently, if a subluxation did occur, it could not phase sight. But sight is phased; people are blind. The Chiropractor by his adjustment does restore sight. The Chiropractor does trace fibres from the eye to an intervertebral foramen. These nerves are tender. Under stimulation they return sight for a second, seemingly to prove a fact unknown heretofore. Is this nerve an optic nerve, or is it not? Patient says yes, Chiropractor says yes; Chiropractic adjustment proves yes; anatomist says no, "because I haven't found it, and the nerve that I have found is the one I dissected."

We have the pneumogastric nerve, the one said by the anatomist to go to the stomach, lungs, etc. Then, presuming that the pneumogastric did come through an intervertebral foramen, a subluxation causing pressure on that nerve would necessarily affect lungs and stomach. But we find lung trouble without stomach trouble, and stomach trouble without lung trouble, and we find the two together, sometimes. We find the Chiropractor can adjust a vertebrae subluxation and restore function in the lungs, or adjust a vertebrae subluxation and restore function in the stomach. He can adjust one without the other, or both, voluntarily; and then we wonder what the "pneumogastric nerve" really has to do with the voluntary or "involuntary" functions in these organs.

The anatomist undoubtedly has found them—he has dissected them; the Chiropractor undoubtedly has traced, adjusted, and they got well. Who is right, and who wrong? It would be as inconsistent to believe the functions of the twelve cranial nerves as taught anatomically, and adjust the spine medically, as for a mouse to play "America" on a pipe organ. It is one of the inconsistent impossibilities.

You cannot be a consistent Chiropractor and adjust the subluxation and restore sight in the eye, and believe that the optic nerve has its point of origin at the rear of the eyeball and goes to the optic thalami.

All of the common diseases of the eyeball, in which sight may be involved, are characteristic vertebrae subluxations wherein we get these diseases where the eyeball and its position is involved; where we have subluxations found in connection with granulated eyelids, etc.

There are no known nerves—anatomically—from the fourth cervical to the eye; there are no nerves from the sixth dorsal to the eyeball which control the movement of the sets of muscles around the eyeball; there are no nerves, anatomically, that radiate from the twelfth dorsal to the eyelids or the glands around the eye; but specific adjustment where they exist will change the incoordination as outlined. Anatomically, then, where are you in your knowledge of neurology?

Function is specific and direct—not indirect. You have sick headache; you go to the physician, who says, "You are sick at the stomach, are you not?" "Yes." "Then it is the sick stomach that causes the sick headache." But you go to another physician, reverse the order, and say, "I have a sick stomach." "Then it is the sick headache that causes the sick stomach." Go to a Chiropractor; he finds a vertebra subluxated; finds pressure upon nerves leading to the stomach, upon the right leading to the head. If he adjusts the subluxation to the right, releases the pressure upon the left, the sick stomach is no more; if he adjusts the subluxation to the left, releases the pressure upon the right, the sick headache is no more; adjust the subluxation superior or inferior, as necessity demands, your sick headache and sick stomach are both gone, showing the directness of the nerve flow of mental impulses through two different places. There is no such knowledge of neurology in anatomies.

There are only two sciences that live by precedent. One is "law," in which we do not want radical theories. The state supreme court judge says, "What has the United States court to say?" The judge on the district court bench says, "What did the state supreme court say?" The justice says, "What does the judge rule?" Precedent. If the justice were radical, the judge would rule it out; if the judge in the district court should be radical the appellate court would overrule him; but the United States supreme court can set at naught the entire case.

Congress makes a statute and says that any corporation that shall work in restraint of trade is criminal and illegal; and the United States supreme court, the body that it is, says that if a corporation should be operating within "a reasonable restraint of trade" is all right, places a radical interpretation upon—but there is no body to set at naught the United States supreme court.

The other science that is domineered by precedent is medicine. To sidestep precedent is to bring forth ostracism.

The point is, we haven't enough independence in people of high position, because they play to the people underneath them for support. The people who can think new thoughts don't do so because they are afraid of what others higher up may say. The people who want to think radically don't do so because they are afraid; and the people who delight to do so write it, smother it away, and wait until people catch up, and then have it published. This is as true of anatomists as philosophers.

12

---◆---

CIRCULATION, SEROUS AND BLOOD

SEROUS CIRCULATION WAS DISCOVERED by B. J. Palmer. This chapter is to present these thoughts in as thorough and interesting a manner as possible. Undoubtedly your dog is petted more, for he represents your personal labors. This dogma is B. J. Palmer's. As its discoverer and developer, B.J. has greater interest in its propagation. Fundamentally, there is no one function so absolutely necessary to the maintenance of life as the serous circulation. The more it is studied the greater is the interest. That it has never been conceived before is no fault of B. J. Palmer's and is one great evidence of its truth, for predecessors have been working effects, not foundation principles.

Go into medicine, if you will; study therapeutics in any form, and wherein have they raised one foundation principle. There isn't a single physiological effect in a man's body that is studied by them in a truthful manner. With this fact before us and the further fact that they do nothing but treat effects, can you blame B.J. for making this statement, broad as it is?

Contrary to many ideas, which eventually became great, this discovery was not accidental, but the outcome of years of study to answer "why" for abnormal symptoms yet unsolved.

By way of explanation: Certain patients enter B. J. Palmer's clinic, presenting peculiar conditions, and his first thought was, "Why so and so?" Then he would consult Butler, Osler or a dozen other authorities in his library, and he could find no reason, look where he may; so finding that they did not answer it, presumably because they could not, he turned in and answered it himself, so that what you have here is the product of hundreds of questions B. J. Palmer asked himself.

Undoubtedly about the same arguments were used against Harvey as against the serous circulation. The cause of all disease is not in the air, in vegetables, etc., but IN MAN. (When you find that all the medical profession are endorsing a certain thing, you take the opposite and you will have the truth.)

If you want to get some idea of where Chiropractic stands today just imagine you are at the entrance to a cave which has no limit as to the height or depth and whose walls are covered with glittering gems. Reach out your hand and take a jewel from its place, turn it over and pass it to the man behind you, who has been too timid to do the same. That is where we are today, barely on the threshold and with only two or three gems in our hands, but as we go on we will gradually get bolder and lay hold of more and more.

The arguments to be used against this principle will be, "If it has existed, why (a question they have not answered on many other subjects, let alone this) did not the M.D.'s know it? It cannot be so, or they would be teaching it." Experience has proven, not alone to B.J., but all liberal schools, that medical knowledge (?) is contrary to natural reasoning. The strong opposition, from that quarter, is the most potent evidence of its exactness.

Upset medical knowledge and you have the truth. When they say "you have caught a cold," reverse it with, "the heat has caught you"; or "I will give you something to move the bowels" with "the bowels have increased their action to get rid of the intruder." When an M.D. maintains, "The knife cut the finger," invert it to "The finger came in contact with the knife."

A mere handful of mentalities, who dare to think, have opened a large cave in which are many uncut, priceless jewels. It costs money to work any mine and as capital permits, shafts and "runs" will be made deeper and show larger and more brilliant gems for study.

B. J. Palmer's conclusion was reached when the embryo was a multiplicity of germs matured to cells. The germinal structure of a cell, in minute depleted form, becomes enlarged.

"The typical organic cell consists from without inward of cell membrane, protoplasmic contents, nucleus, and nucleolus. Whether the cell membrane is anything more than the wall, or outer surface of the protoplasm, is open to further investigation. The composition of the protoplasm (the fluidic contents of the cell) varies with the age of the cell. At first it consists of a homogenous albuminoid (resembling albumen, like the white of an egg); but later there appear granulations, coloring, or fatty matter, and the whole may become hardened into horn, or bone. The nucleus (kernel) examined with the microscope presents the appearance of a sphere, the contents of which are more or less liquid and transparent." (Dutton's Anatomy.)

Serous circulation is that dissemination of liquids passing thru connective and supportive tissues and other intercellular membranes of the body. Passing between all elemental cells it remains for such a distinctive kind of cell to absorb to itself some of this circulatory material for its metabolic needs—This becomes, then, the intracellular circulation. One dozen, hundred or thousand cells may be involved in a circumscribed area, in excess or lack of this secretion; or its functions of excretion may be implicated in one or more of the many combinations, the cause of each still being the lack of characteristic mental impulses. Whether it gets it in proper quantities and makes of it the consistent quality needed or not, depends entirely upon the amount of mental impulses that go to each cell thru nerves. Each cell acts as an absorber of its own. This idea makes the individual areas a specific study and gives to each cell its individual cellular activity as regards the serous circulation. While the circulation is general, yet its utilization becomes specific to each cell.

Look to that which expands everything, and water, in one form or another, will be the result. No vegetable substance can be taken, but what, if placed in water, will expand. For instance the sponge, bean, wood or corn. The hyacinth as a bulb represents little until placed in water and then the transformation into a beautiful odiferous flower takes place. Place a grain of corn in the ground; as long as the earth remains dry it cannot expand or mature. The early coming of a shower after a dry siege or drought is welcomed by the tiller of the soil. Why? Because he, knowingly, recognizes one of the greatest fundamental principles which the most expert physicians have ignored. Can you blame the M.D. for trying to defeat B.J.'s attempt to show them their long unknown mistakes?

"Heat—The force, agent, or principle in nature upon which depends the state of bodies as solid, fluid or aeriform, and which is recognized by its effects in the phenomena of expansion, fusion, evaporation, etc.; and which, as developed from its natural resources, fire, the sun's rays, mechanical action, chemical combination, etc., becomes directly known to us thru the sense of feeling"—Webster. Heat has long been regarded, by many, as sufficient in itself to increase the size of tissue, but this is not the case. The size of an inflamed area for instance, may be smaller than when normal or it may be larger. The size depends upon whether more serum, in modified forms, has been drawn into or placed within the cell with counteracting intentions, or if the amount has been decreased for the same object. If more serum exists than is normal within a certain limited district, and excessive heat is added, we have the example of a boil; if, on the reverse, we have the opposite, excessive heat with a lack of serum, we have the condition of a fever where the body wastes away. These are but two combinations that are found by systematically studying the serous circulation in combination with other functions in relative degrees.

Applied Chiropractic knowledge proves that water, in various consistencies, is indispensable to expand germinal cells. In B. J. Palmer's clinic, the symptoms of a case were traced, one by one, and combined with the history, which proved that the physiological difficulty was an absence, in large per cent, of certain general liquids. A Sherlock Holmes analysis was applied, the details brought forth, deductions were decisive for a circulation of liquid substances other than blood. The latter theories did, could nor would not fit the given symptoms of this case, which is but a sample of what is daily brought before your attention. Heretofore medicine has claimed that blood was the necessary conveyor. They haven't made one step forward in principle since Harvey's time, outside of creating theories and retracting them when proven fallible.

Considering that blood has been that supposed foundation of life. They naturally gave to this continuous blood circulation the spreading out or propagating of (1) serum, (2) nutrition, (3) heat, (4) repairing, (5) conveyor of "life." Everything, good, bad, or indifferent, has been heaped at the doors of his "Ship of State."

As yet, we have not made any attempts to define the paths and say that just such and such tissue has such and such serous channels. When you step into the areas of connective and serous tissues, you will find that anatomy and physiology are silent.

All liquids under normal conditions enter the mouth. The epidermis absorbs a very small percentage even if remaining some time in a bath. If immersed in an ice-cold bath, the pores would close like so many gates. If a Turkish or other hot bath is taken, the perspiration is from the inside, outward. Either condition is sufficient to make the intake extremely limited. There is, from practical deduction, nothing taken in by the epidermis.

"Kidney Diseases—The relation of the secretion of the skin to that of the kidneys is a very close one. Thus copious secretions of urine, or watery evacuations from the alimentary canal, coincide with dryness of the skin; abundant perspiration and scanty urine generally together. In the condition known as uremia, when the kidneys secrete little or no urine, the percentage of urea rises in the sweat; the sputum and the saliva also contain urea under those circumstances. In some of these cases the skin secretes so abundantly that when the sweat dries on the skin the patient is covered with a coating of urea crystals. The sweat, like the urine, must be regarded as an excretion, the secreting cells eliminating substances formed elsewhere."—"Kirk's Physiology," P. 579.

We can readily prove to ourselves that the assertion is true regarding those cases which secrete little urine but throw off large percentages of waste material through the skin, by the odor, as well as dry, scaly skin.

All foods, meat or vegetable, contain a very large per cent of water. The banana could not have expanded if it had not been for the liquids. The only substance that permits the orange to enlarge from the seed, is water. Orange juice is water with sufficient of this or that solid to transform its color and taste. You know what coffee is: 99 per cent water and 1 per cent of the bean that flavors it. What caused the coffee bean to expand? Water. Do you realize that tea, wine, beer, or any beverage, is water? Everything that waters the mouth is or represents what water has accomplished.

Water, then, is the basis of your or our existence in two ways; 1st, keeping the body expanded; 2nd, caring for the bodies of growing things in a normal condition to maintain their entity. It is the essential for living.

The argument may be brought forth that air is more essential than water, as man can live hours, days, weeks, without the latter, and but a very few minutes without the former. On this question Webster says: "Air—The fluid which we breathe, and which surrounds the earth. Modern science has shown that it consists essentially of two gases, oxygen and nitrogen, in the proportion of 20.81 parts of the former to 70.19 of the latter" (both equal to the whole of 100 per cent). A question could be raised on "what is 'fluid?' " In reply, Webster further declares: "Liquid or Gaseous—A 'liquid' is, 'Liquid and fluid are terms often used synonymously, but fluid has the broader signification. All liquids are fluids, but many fluids, as air and the gases, are not liquids.' "

If an individual dismisses the water problem from his existence, eats food absolutely dry, his duration on this plane would be short and bitter, for no death is so horrible as that of the parched traveler on a desert, unable to locate a drop of moisture.

Saliva is 993 out of 1,000 parts water. In speaking of faeces, Kirk's Physiology, p. 517, 17th Ed., says: "In health from 68 to 82 per cent; in diarrhoea it is more abundant still"; in costiveness it would be less. Semen is 82 per cent liquid and 18 per cent solid, according to Gray. Gray further says: "The fluid portion of semen carries and probably nourishes the living cells known as spermatozoids."

The water we drink and the food we eat pass through at least five channels. As they enter the mouth, they are mixed with saliva; in the stomach they are churned with splenic fluid and become chyme. From thence it proceeds through the first third of the small intestine, the duodenum, and becomes mingled with pancreatic juices and bile, and is called chyle. This is in turn constantly blended with mucin and is the transitional change of the original fluid. Saliva is the product of three sets of glands; splenic fluid is the fruit of the spleen; the pancreatic juice is the tissue following activity of the gland, which it is named after, and the bile is the excretion of the liver. Proceeding into the ileum (the end of the period of digestion) the chyle is absorbed, taken up by and passed along through distinct tissues and channels of its own, which is known today under many heads, e.g., connective and supportive tissues, epithelium, mucous membranes or serous tissues. Call it what you may, it is but a transitional serous structure. This fluid (now serum) is advanced to be distributed to any and all organs, in quantities demanded. It goes to the brain, feet or anywhere in between, and is utilized. A large portion, in its circulation, goes to the glands collectively, each receiving its needed amount.

B.J. mentions in one place that the food is mixed with the mucous and gastric juice and splenic fluid. We wish to further comment that he believes the gastric juice to be only the combination of the juices produced by the glands of the stomach and the splenic fluid, which is to maintain that there is a direct connection between the spleen and the stomach. This is contrary to all anatomies; they refer to the spleen as a "ductless gland," and ascribe to it no known function. It is in the body and it must have a purpose, even if anatomists do not know what it is.

Some years ago B. J. Palmer had in his clinic a patient with an enlarged spleen. It took in the entire abdominal region and must have weighed, when in the patient, much more than when removed from the body—92 ounces. A normal spleen weighs between 6 and 8 ounces. Under dissection a direct tube was found to lead from the spleen into the fundus of the stomach. This was not an artery or vein but a direct tube from which splenic fluid could pass into the stomach.

Under adjustment the spleen rapidly decreased in size, and whereas, before, the bowels hardly ever moved, after adjustment they began to move very profusely; patient sometimes going to stool 20 to 60 times an hour and passing from an ounce to six or eight ounces of a liquid which burned the intestines and bowels—he could feel it the moment it left the stomach.

In proportion as B.J. adjusted the subluxation he could check or increase this flow; if he gave 3 or 4 a day the flow would increase. This liquid passed was of an oily, greenish-yellow consistency and color, and was analyzed as a splenic fluid by a chemist who did not know where it came from or anything about it except what he gained from his own work. This spleen is now in B. J. Palmer's clinic, and although it is not so distinct as it was formerly, yet the opening can still be seen. This tube was named in honor of its discoverer, Ductus Palmerii.

Under normal conditions B.J. would ascribe to the spleen the function of secreting one of the essential liquids (or largest portion of it) which goes to make the combined chemical known as gastric juice. If physiologists and anatomists do not know the function they will tell you that just before digestion the spleen is at its fullest and during digestion at its lowest—and still they call it a ductless gland.

Glands are most important organs. It is these which transform or convert serum to the chemical—a necessity to reduce external substances to internal condition for absorption—the smaller proportion going to muscles, bones, ligaments, etc. After osmosing into and through the cortical substance of glands, it and the other juices, which are the product of other glands, combined, are excreted and technically known by the name which physiologists have seen fit to suggest.

It passes to the muscles as serum, is seeped through them and becomes a liquid. The waste, on the other side, is urea. That waste portion which passes through the epidermis is perspiration, although technically it is urea.

In, around, and between all deeper muscular fibres is a very fine connective tissue, serous in function, which B.J. will give briefly, as follows:

The serum approaches the muscles; now by a process of osmosis, gradually working and worming its way through, into, and between the muscle cells, so that by the time it has worked its way through it has left behind certain nutritive materials that the cells, themselves, extract from it; consequently the product emerging is a waste product, and B.J. calls it urea.

We should like to be able to show you a unit of serum approaching a unit cell, then that unit cell in action (subtracting the nutritive materials from the serum), then the unit of expulsion (that which is left of the serum), leaving the muscle cell as a unit of urea—afterward, the accumulation of many units of urea from many cells which are collected in the kidneys (some in the skin, expelled as perspiration) and by them expelled through the proper channel. In the absence of an Innate mind and brain and body with which to illustrate these things, B.J. must explain it as best he can upon the basis given.

Such cannot reach the surface, but must pass onward and continue into the circulation, eventually reaching the external world by way of kidneys.

You will notice, pre-eminently, that B.J. differentiates between liquid and solid foods, although this one circulation carries and distributes both. The value of foods is just so much as its consistency is carried in soluble form, with corresponding chemicals. Do not think B. J. Palmer a water hobbyist, far from it, but this body is the product of indispensable principles which must be deduced regardless of where and what they reach. This machine represents the aggregation of liquids and chemicals, therefore must be maintained, likewise properly prepared. "Properly prepared" means that man, externally cannot mix or compute the relative values and proper quantities, such as may be and are needed in the human, when abnormal. The mixing or conversions are within the jurisdiction of Innate alone, who was the first and is the only master chemist.

When we study the glandular system of a man's body, it is surprising to find that glands which have ducts (that are observable) have a known function and are written about, but it is more surprising still to find that several of the largest and many of the smallest glands in the body are regarded as ductless; consequently, not being able to trace an inlet and outlet for secretion and excretion we are left in the dark as regards their functions, and this is why B.J. says glands, with or without ducts, are most important organs, and make no exceptions.

Water, as a liquid food, is digested and assimilated; passes thru each change, as does a vegetable or meat. Thence it passes to small intestine, where true preparation and absorption take place. Water in its raw state must undergo conversion, as well as solid foods, and passes every assimilating condition. Solid and liquid foods are acted upon in the same cavity, but each by its chemical necessity (constituent) to bring about its liquidization. The mechanical analogy necessary to digest liquid food would not be equal to mixing solids. The chemicals, acting upon lemon, apple or orange juices would not act upon their pulps. It may contain a part of one or the other, but the proportions will be differently adapted to the various acidities and solidities of the ingredients. Chyle (representing the nutritive qualities) is acted upon by the absorbent system, and by the same transporting medium is taken likewise to every tissue cell for utilization.

Liquid food is absorbed by the intestinal papillae and carried forth by this distinct and complete serous circulation. This is as thorough, well marked, and as well defined, as to starting and ending channels as the arterial venous circulations. It is more eminently capable of entering more intricate places than blood.

Closely investing every organ, gland, and tissue in the body, and thoroughly entering into every muscular or osseous fibre is its serous membrane and this is named to denote location—pericardium, around heart; endocardium, within heart; pleura, sack of lungs; periosteum, around bones, etc. If between various viscera, it is a supportive membrane; and that recticulum between muscular, cartilaginous, or osseous fibres is connective membrane. So minute does this subdivision become that there is not the smallest fibre or cell thereof but what has its serous tissues, so that in studying Chiropractic physiology we refer to them, in general as "serous in function." Students of B. J. Palmer coming thoroughly imbued with the knowledge of this study, see that, next to the discovery of the subluxation of vertebrae being the cause of disease, this exception has more consequence than any other developed in the last few years.

Such displacements of vertebrae produce pressure upon nerves leading directly to the kidneys, the most important excretory organs in this system. Interference with the mental impulses, on their way to those glands, interferes with the control of these local functions.

Many authorities could be quoted to show where medical apprehensions come very near to accepting the idea of what B. J. Palmer teaches as a serous circulation. Osteopaths today are handling such ideas as if they were hot irons. They slyly give it their deepest thought, but do not dare let anyone know they are studying it. Osteopathy is trying to handle this as well as many Chiropractic ideas with rubber gloves and is afraid of getting a shock. Chiropractic is the first science that dared to fearlessly pronounce subluxation to be the physical representative of the causes of all disease. B. J. Palmer now takes another measure ahead and proves there is a serous circulation.

13

———◆———

SYMPTOMATOLOGY OF THE

URINARY SYSTEM

ACCORDING TO B. J. PALMER in Chiropractic Philosophy the Urinary System goes one step further than has been conceded. There are two kidneys, one on either side, from which runs its ureter; these join inferiorly and anteriorly at the bladder. From the latter organ is the urethra and—external world.

The kidneys are, according to medical parlance, organs that secrete urine and expel it from the body. What the urine is, where it comes from or starts, we are left to guess. A Chiropractor will maintain that the kidneys are that ending point of serous circulation which starts as water. After mixing with the saliva and other glandular juices in the intestine it makes of that, serum. The kidneys secrete urea, that which has been used as a lubricator and food throughout the body, and converts it to urine and then carries it through the ureters to the reservoir, and, when this is full, through the urethra to the external world. This is speaking of how it is done, minus what does it. To reply that action performs, leads us to "What is action, and how is it made?" That deficiency is Innate.

Let us study the various transitions thru which these changes occur. In subdividing the urinary system it is found composed of elementary tissues. First, the muscular; second, is serous (subdivided to connective and mucous); third, lymphatic; fourth, adipose; fifth, arteries; sixth, veins (each of the two latter having their ample anastomoses); seventh, nerves.

Consider the functions performed in these seven fundamental structures. First, motor—action; second, nutritive—that type of motor which is trophic in character; third, calorific—producing heat; fourth, secretory; fifth, excretory, which is, especially in the kidneys, highly developed and in point of relative values stands highest in these organs; sixth, reparatory—should there be hernia, prolapsus of the kidney, or a diseased condition—there must be reparatory impulses to repair that to normal; seventh, circulatory.

The circulation of each gland in the body varies somewhat according to its position and parts of the metabolic transformations that it has to perform. For instance, the kidneys will have four circulations; 1st, the serous—the receiving of serum and conversion of that to urea. 2nd, the ureaic circulation, that of receiving urea and converting it to urine. The by-product of the first eventually becomes a part of the second. 3rd, the arterial and venous circulation. Further comment is not necessary. 4th, the mental impulse circulation.

Each gland has its varying changes only in the second circulation. Instead of being ureaic it will be splenic juice in the spleen, bile as a waste product of the liver, the thyroidean juice as a secretion of the thyroid, etc.

We have seven basic substances and an equal number of functions performed in them. In addition to these let us meditate upon the senses which are necessary in completing the circuit. Do the kidneys taste, smell, hear, see or feel? They do sense, but by a process of Innate Voluntary afferent nervous system. Therefore, we shall put down one sense—tactile impressions.

We have considered tissues, functions and senses. Our next regard is for the conveyors; that which transmits functions and senses. To help the elucidation, B.J. gives to functions the letter "A" and to senses "B" investigating both accordingly. "A," the outward manifestation of life, passes through efferent nerves—out, going from the inside outward; for "B" we shall place its opposite, afferent nerves, that which proceeds from the external inward.

We have, so far, observed tissues, the basis of known physical life; functions; senses; then the conveyors of these. The next step will be one of origins. "A" is at brain and "B," tissues. Its ending points are: "A" at tissues, and "B" brain—reversing the former. Showing that we have definite starting and ending points for each.

So far the unit is incomplete, as we have no intermediates—that through which these are expressed. "A" in tissues, one to seven. "B," intermediate, would be in the brain. We have summed, briefly, a definite, specific starting and ending point of the entire urinary tract.

We have so far linked the external tissues of this system with those of the brain and vice versa, giving to the urinary tract a philosophical aspect not studied nor taught by any other science.

We have tissues; functions performed in them; the senses thru which Innate is aware what functions are doing and how they are accomplishing it; the ways and means of conveyors of functions and impressions; the starting and ending points of these and their intermediates, which act as expressors of and as interpreters thereto.

The next step in this progressive analysis must be the complete path of each. The origin of each "A" would be from a characteristic brain lobe, thru foramen magnum, spinal cord, passing outward thru intervertebral foramina to kidneys on either side, inserted into and expressed at ending plates in kidneys, ureters, bladder and urethra. And at that point they express that characteristic impulse which is given to it at brain. For "B"—tactile impressions—would start at the urethra, bladder, ureters or kidneys, proceed into and thru nerves passing inward between that movable space known as intervertebral foramina, the impression carrying fibres passing either one above or below its motor mate, entering and passing inward thru its spinal cord fibres, proceeding upward thru foramin magnum and ending at specific brain lobe cells.

You now have a conception of the urinary system. Let us consider briefly the diseases, excess or lack of normal function, of the urinary system. The function of the kidneys is to suck into them the urea from serous circulation, converting it chemically to urine. Its drops gather in the infundibuliform which, when filled, contracts, expelling the liquid contents into the ureter and then to the reservoir in the bladder. If the kidneys work in excess, the general body becomes dry, epidermis harsh, scaly eruptions of many kinds appear on the skin. If the kidneys are working below normal, we have excess of urea in the body and the result may be dropsy or seradoema. The chemical action of the kidneys is to transform urea to urine. If this be working in excess—an excess of chemical solids—too much of sugar in the urine. If there is lack of it, here or there, thruout this tract, then certain chemical properties are minus. To test out these abnormalities by any one of a dozen methods of urinalysis is but to analyze an abnormal product—treat effects—without knowing or trying to ascertain where and what the cause of such is.

If a certain kidney chemical acts in excess, it settles in the infundibuliform, and under the fusion of heat forms renal stones, which may experience considerable trouble in passing thru the ureters.

Excessive heat might (due to expansion of tissues) close the ureteral orifice—structure—thus creating trouble with the passage of urine.

The bladder is a reservoir to hold the urine as fast as gathered. If the muscular fibres act normally, they will maintain a 100 per cent of tonicity and hold the urine until full—then it is voided. If this action be in excess, as soon as a little urine gathers it is expelled—the result—micturition. The reverse can be possible also. The bladder may retain the urine, lying in the pelvis like a small balloon, and great pain will be sensed, severe pain and other symptoms be met with.

The function of the urethra may pass thru the abnormal stages as enumerated for the ureter. There could be an excess or lack of any one of the seven in these organs. There might be too much motor; again, not enough; too much nutrition deposited at a certain point without being utilized, the result—tumor, which might be internal or outward, or in the canal. The most notable difference in the two tubes would be that in the former it passes renal stones; the latter, bladder stones.

The third function—calorific—may be in excess; too much heat, or not enough. Each function, in turn, could be followed in the same manner. This is noticeable in floating kidney, where surgery is oftentimes needlessly resorted to. Its supporting tissues relax, dropping it into the pelvis; the physician removes a portion of this relaxed tissue, draws the remaining edges together and sews them. It is but a short time before what is left of this tissue again drops and a second operation becomes a necessity.

This chapter by B.J. has given you a more comprehensive idea of how each tissue, organ or system and its points of receiving that power which moves all its expression commonly termed function, can be enlarged upon. The study of the human body, when thus subdivided, and its superior force, Innate, studied side by side, is most interesting.

14

SYMPTOMATOLOGY OF THE

ALIMENTARY CANAL

THE SPECIFIC, PURE, unadulterated, philosophical Chiropractor analyzes all that he comes in contact with. In this chapter B.J. will discuss the alimentary or digestive apparatus, or what other name you may see fit to call it, through this partition process, which is the reduction of organs, tissues, functions, etc., to their component, functional relations.

The alimentary tube is that hollow concavity from the inside of the lips of the mouth to the external lips of the anus. Anything in between is a portion of it. Start with the mouth or buccal cavity; the next is the oesophagus, third, pharynx, fourth, stomach: next the small intestines; and, following that, the large bowels. There are, at basis, six "primary" viscera. In addition, there are "accessory" viscera (why so termed with this misnomer we do not know). "Accessory" conveys the thought that it is something which is occasionally used, but is not essential; is similar to an ornament; can be dispensed with. The "accessory" viscera are as necessary in the performance of the functions of these glands as are the original organs. The essential glands are: viz., parotid, submaxillary, sublingual, liver, pancreas, and spleen. The alimentary tract alone is not sufficient to bear or express all functions necessary. The one cannot maintain itself without the other, nor the other without the one.

One more, which is not enumerated by any anatomist, must be added —Serous Circulation. Without the latter the buccal cavity would be dry, the oesophagus parched, or would cease to be pliable; the stomach would be as so much dust; the small intestine and large bowel could not act nor perform functions; none of the glands enumerated would be a gland in function, although such in structure, were it not for the Serous Circulation which keeps them united. Serous connective tissue gives to all glands its juices which are soon converted to the liquid for which that gland is noted. It is the liquefier; that which holds dry substances together in wet form.

Chiropractic is a science of the cause of things natural; not a science of symptoms; not a science of how to treat them; not a science of how to chemically analyze the constituents of the human body (normal or abnormal). But it is the science of how to analyze certain conditions quickly back to the cause, and we only utilize conditions in so far as they exist as a guidepost or mile-post on the road, telling us purely which way we must go.

This is why we say to one who is a Chiropractor (there are different types of Chiropractors—some who believe in having a stretching machine beside them; others a hammer and mallet, etc.), a pure unadulterated Chiropractor. "Remember the coordination between Innate and physical and analyze everything you come in contact with." Everything that a Chiropractor meets in his daily life he analyzes.

In what sense do we use the word "analyze"? We will read Webster's definition and see if it does not carry the meaning as given.

"Analyze: To resolve into its elements; to separate into its component parts or proportions, for the purpose of an examination of each separately, etc.

"Analysis: A resolution of anything, whether an object of the senses or of the intellect, into its constituent or original elements; an examination of the component parts of a subject, each separately, as the words which compose a sentence, etc. The tracing of things to their source, etc., etc."

We cannot see why they should name some viscera "primary" and others accessory. Suppose we step into a factory and a man shows us machinery, telling us that these machines are making the product for which the factory is famed, yet he adds, "I want to call your attention to an accessory machine here on the side which is making the oil to lubricate the machine, without which it would not turn." In that event this other machine, instead of being purely accessory, becomes essential.

The word "accessory" as defined by Webster, conveys the idea of something that can be dispensed with; that is not necessary. The function of the entire Alimentary tract is to receive food in the raw and take from it nutritive elements. In the accomplishment of this duty it utilizes chemicals which are brought to it from these glands on the side. If it did not receive these chemicals, there would be nothing doing in that entire alimentary tract, but it is because of the union of these internal chemicals with the external that we get good; and instead of being accessory, the system cannot do without them.

We have enumerated some six primary organs and six necessary glands and now connect these by the only means possible, an oversight for hundreds of years—serous circulation.

Specification of the elementary tissues of which any one of these is composed is our next step. They are seven in number (for future reference they will be spoken of as "A"): First, muscular; second, serous; third, lymphatic; fourth, adipose; fifth, arteries; sixth, veins, and seventh, nerves.

Take the stomach as an example. It has more or less of each of the seven tissues. You may carry the same comparison forth with any organ or gland of this tract.

So far, analysis has brought forth the viscera and tissues of each. Investigation proves that these tissues have the following functions (to be known as "B"): First, contractility; second, trophic; third, calorific; fourth, secretory; fifth, excretory; sixth, reparatory and seventh, reproduction. Eighth, expansion; ninth, reproduction.

You will notice that this list is headed with "motor." Every function expressed is motor in some character. You cannot enumerate any expression of a function but what its fundamental is some mechanical action. Movement is motion and this is motor mental impulses expressed. Motor is subdivided into many classes and each is named according to what character it maintains.

Were we to study the world we would find it divided into two things—energy and matter. Matter can take a multitude of forms; energy depends entirely upon what matter it is traveling through.

Examine the first issue of "A"—muscular. It is composed of fibres. Muscular fibres must have motion, nutritive impulses, heat, secretion to and excretion from, circulatory impulses; and should that muscle, in part or whole, be strained or fractured, as sometimes occurs (which is nicely illustrated in B. J. Palmer's Osteological Studio), it needs reparatory (REPARATORY IN THE SENSE THAT EXPANDED CELLS, PERSONIFYING THE EIGHTH FUNCTION HAVE COME FORTH FOR THAT PURPOSE), as each fibre is a section and each cell of a fibre is a living unit.

The only way that man can prove that he is a unit is by proving every cell a unit and every protoplasmic particle of a cell is a unit, because it is only a collection of small units that makes a large unit.

Nerves must have the capability of being moved; they have nutritive substance to be maintained; must have heat, secretion and excretion; and you question "Has it a reparatory?" A patient in clinic recently gave an interesting account of tic-douloureux, in which two inches of the middle branch of the tri-facial nerve was removed by an operation. For a time the patient suffered no pain, but after a few days was tormented by all the agonies that he formerly had; but he noticed, between times, characteristic knitting pains that are found when fractured bones are healing. Having experienced fractures, he knew. Instances are rare, but the annals of surgery portray that nerves do repair and heal when cut.

Function has been outlined—that which comes from inside outward. Reverse it—what comes from outside inward? The senses (to be known as "C") of the alimentary tract are two: one is taste, noticeable only in the buccal chamber; second is tactile impressions. Through these the Innate brain is in contact all the time with what is taking place in any of the organs or their structures.

THROUGH THESE TWO NERVOUS SYSTEMS, INNATE AND EDUCATED, EACH OF WHICH HAS AN AFFERENT AND EF- FERENT SYSTEM, ARE RECEIVED IMPRESSIONS, ETC. Thus Innate has a means of knowing just what is taking place.

Now reverse the analysis. What comes from outside inward?—all the educated mind's impressions. Take this function of tactile impression arising from the alimentary tract which may be subdivided again to include motor impression; the trophi impression, calorific impression, secretory impression, excretory, reparatory, circulatory and expansive; because every particular function has its equivalent afferent half of the cycle, making an afferent impression; so that when we say "tactile impression" we use it in a broad sense as a few moments ago we used the word motor.

Through what conveyors are impulses and impressions transmitted? For "B" efferent nerves; "C" afferent. Step by step analyze and see if this is correct. Prove and see if it is reasonable and conclusive. "B"— function externally expressed—is carried through efferent (going from a center) nerves. The impressions (which become sensations) "C" are transported by afferent (going to a center) nerves. Starting points, in this separation, are for "B," the brain. "C" starts impressions at tissues. For "B," tissues.

So far the segregation has shown organs; structures of each; functions senses and conveyors of both, the starting and ending points of each.

What are the mediums between? What is betwixt the origin of impulse generation and its point of expression? Function is that which the substance does, and must be performed through something. The intermediates of "B" would be any of tissues "A." For "C" would be right the reverse, the tissues being the brain substance proper.

A brief allusion to the paths, that are necessary, from starting to ending point, or vice versa, would be interesting. In "B"—function—its point of origination is from each characteristic brain lobe (each type having its special division) from the skull, emitting a foramen magnum, passing downward through the spinal cord, various intervertebral foramina, efferent nerves, branching at various places and degrees, according to the locality involved.

Starting at the organ, a Chiropractor must follow "C" into the brain and see clearly the exact path that impression would follow before reaching the interpretation of sensation. Its point of beginning is at tactile corpuscles in tissues of any organ, "accessory" or otherwise, through afferent nerves passing inward through various intervertebral foramina, ending at a specific brain lobe which has that Innate ability to incorporate, impress or receive it. Concentrated investigation will elucidate the "paths"; if studied, they are simple. Not only does his teachings analyze man; but also everything that he makes; and leads both back to first principle. The comparison would be as follows:

Functions ....Purpose of machinery
Nerves ....Pipes or wires
Brain ....Dynamo or boiler
God ....Man
Mechanical Actions ....Action of machinery
Mental impulses ....Steam or electricity
Immaterial units of energy ....Wood, coal, or water
Innate ....Innate—God

Starting from the bottom, going upward, God is to Innate what Innate is to the man. Innate is to the brain what man is to the dynamo or boiler; its builder. Brain is to the immaterial units of energy what the dynamo or boiler is to the building, its receptive station; the immaterial units of energy, after passing through the brain form mental impulses. The same is true with the wood, coal or water; it becomes and makes steam after passing through the dynamo or boiler. The mental impulses are conveyed by nerves the same as pipes convey steam or the wires the electricity; when the mental impulses have reached the tissues it makes mechanical actions. The same is true with the steam or electricity when it passes to a machine, it makes mechanical action. The mechanical actions produce functions in man and the action of machinery designates its purpose.

The last named personage has emanations—Innates—similar to the sun's rays—emanations of that solar body. These are capable of utilizing forces to make brains; the latter converts external forces to mental impulses—internal power—and are transmitted through nerves. Expression in muscles equals mechanical action; this is function; and thus we live as a complete unit, deducted, step by step, from the original starting point.

B.J. explains that Innate is in each being, next to which is the brain;

this makes the impulse, which passes through nerves and makes mechanical action; this movement is function. This stage is where man, with function, substance, or electricity that is conveyed through pipes or wires, makes action of machinery; it expresses the purpose of the machine. You have reached, by fundamental, the basis of everything. From that can be elaborated all that Man's function has or may create. It is giving to man a unity that never existed before the advent of Chiropractic.

No man ever linked the two mentalities with two brains, through two intellectual nervous systems, and gave to the brain the power of transforming or converting, of giving God the opportunity to express His quantities through man in that form or manner. It is not our purpose to express any opinion as regards religion, but we must take Life step by step, and show its basis as it is. No matter what opinions each may have, it must have one basic truth. The alimentary canal alone, is but a set of dead organs, but when analyzed through each successive step, and given an Innate, we have the physical canal philosophically complete.

As far as the medical man, in his studies or practice, is concerned, he goes no further than the physical organs. If indigestion or any disease of the stomach appears he figures, "What material chemical can I give this person which will counteract that chemical poison which he has in excess in the stomach, the effects of which are named dyspepsia? I will try this, and if it fails, will strive with something else, and I will continue these attempts until the patient dies or leaves me disgusted." But meanwhile the patient has "chronic stomach trouble." In a disease of the liver the M.D.'s first and only aim is to chemically diagnose what condition the liver is in. "If it lacks a certain chemical of this and has an excess of that, if I give so and so I can neutralize it." He tries to fathom its chemical affinity and it does not nor will not permanently give the desired result, or may merely do it for a while; or if it is going too high, he will endeavor to hold it down but never is able to restore it to normal function. The product, chronic stomach trouble.

It does not matter what is the degree, character, percentage or combination; for instance, a case of pharyngitis is no more nor less than excessive heat in the pharynx.

We have previously taken man as an entity; taken him to pieces and built him up again.

The physician, the chemical man, gives a chemical poison to a chemical body and thinks of the pharynx as nothing but a physical organ to be dealt with by like methods. Does the physician ever get away from that view of the subject? He is a chemical and physical fanatic.

B.J. is reminded of a Negro who was so poor that he and his family were hungry all the time. He went to his pastor and told him that he was hungry and that he would like to have a chicken to eat and the minister told him to pray for it. The darky went home and did as he was told; but he had no chicken. He went back and told the minister that he was still hungry and was told that he didn't pray right, but I done prayed, " 'O good Lord, dis darky is hungry, send him to a chicken.' " Well, you go home and pray again. On the way home the darky did some thinking and when he prayed it was like this: "O, good Lord, this darky got to have a chicken before morning; O, good Lord, take this darky to a chicken." He had chicken pie next day.

The solution of the problem is all in how you pray; the thing of telling you how to direct your mind does not always bring chicken, but when you see to it that your body is in a shape so that the mind can work through it, then you will have a stomach that can digest chickens when it gets them. To B.J. if a philosophy does not appear reasonable or consistent, he is inclined to think there is something wrong with it—it is incomplete.

For instance, throat trouble, character pharyngitis. The M.D. is able to give the patient something which will cool the throat. If it is not acting fast enough, he will give something which stimulates its movements, but the patient has and will have chronic throat trouble. It may start as pharyngitis and finish as catarrh of that region after his treatment; the latter being the chronic condition, the former the acute. The patient is no better than at first. He feels better at times, we admit, but what we must determine by is permanent results. He thinks of nothing further than the pharynx as a physical organ, the stomach has physical purposes, the liver has a chemical action, to be dealt with by like methods; never gets any further. He is a physical and chemical fanatic. The Christian Scientist is the opposite type. He or she maintains that "Mind is all in all; it runs the body. Mental rules all, everything must exist in this form, therefore if that (the mental) is perfect the rest must be," is the line of justifiable argument used. "When you have stomach trouble you should concentrate your mind and you must study to know how to tell your mind how to run the stomach. If you are insane, cannot think sanely; concentrate your (insane) mind upon how to think as you ought to." "The fact that you are insane and cannot think properly is no hindrance," for if you cannot think we will have friends to do it for you; and so the mental theorist pursues his path. You must think that you have no stomach, and it is "the mental that is in error, it is making mistakes, is insane and sinning. What you must do is to eradicate the mental sin by concentration, then you will eradicate all disease." The Drs. are sincere in their belief; the patient tries it, but the stomach and liver trouble becomes chronic just the same.

Chiropractic is the first science that harmonizes the two. We maintain just as steadily as the Christian Scientist that all is mental first, but it must be physically interpreted, it must show its expression in the body, and have a definite path and a precise something to send through that which performs mental thoughts. Chiropractors, step by step, analyze the existence from God to physical function. We are not fanatic upon the mental aspect, nor are we clinging alone to the physical, ignoring everything else. Remember that, in and all around us, all the time, is this intelligent power or force; that this is the individuality, that places power in contact with physical; and our mind, through brain, receives and places it through a transformation—mental impulse. The latter is God personified in you and I. Mental impulse is unseen and unfelt in itself, cannot be sensed in any form, yet it is the exemplification of all that is pure, holy and righteous. B.J. explains that these mental impulses are so infinite in quality, quantity, character and every other attribute that is above the finite mind that the educated mind cannot see them; has not invented a microscope yet to observe them; has not invented a machine so delicate that it can perceive them by sight or feeling. It must have expression through a physical medium, which is our body. It has reached the form of impulse and while still power, internally manifested; it passes through nerves and from them causes action in muscles; which is mechanical action. This function, the outward expression, should be, if normal, a counterpart of the original principle. Man cannot assist nor give advice to Innate, therefore Christian Science is wrong; at base the M.D. is one-sided because either or both hold fast to only one-half of the unit. That is why Chiropractic is the only philosophical study; it unites the two, makes of it a completeness.

B.J. was amused in reading over a book the other day which went at quite length to explain that all function was innervation, and what "innervation" was he didn't state. Innervation is "nervous force," but further than that; where it was generated, came from, or what it was, were questions left unanswered.

Mechanically speaking, "the alimentary regularity of organs is the various machines which receive the rough materials and put them through the manifold processes; thus preparing them for the finished function. It has a refuse system of solid substances. The liquid and solid sewerage orders must work hand in hand. The raw material enters at one end of this long tube, makes many successive progressive steps, each having its particular action to perform until it comes to, first, that which is utilizable as nutritive materials; and 2nd, that which is waste materials, the shavings and scraps, as it were.

15

"REFLEX ACTION"

IN "REFLEX ACTION," we must revert to when we studied how little is known regarding the "sympathetic nervous system." Obliterating the "sympathetic nervous system" knocks the props of "reflex action," which is supposed to be the movement that takes place within this starting from somewhere—and going to nowhere system. If one is removed, where is the other?

The following definition of "Reflex Action" is from Dunglison's Dictionary, 22nd edition, page 953: "Term applied to an action which consists in the reflection by an efferent nerve of an impression conveyed to a nervous center by an afferent nerve. A reflex action is generally regarded to be one executed without consciousness."

To make the above clearer we refer to this author's definition of "Reflection," page 953: "Bending or turning back; duplicature. Bending or turning backward of a ray of light." He does not speak of any transformation that must take place before it is "duplicated." Bear these in mind for future reference.

The solar plexus is an "abdominal brain" and from this go forth "reflected actions" which control the body. If you could invent a man of machinery, who would work, walk and perform actions "without consciousness," then we have an ideal "automatic" or "reflex" individual. Any mechanical device which has its spring or power giving mechanism which must be wound by man, daily, weekly or yearly, within itself, is an automaton. A watch is a good illustration. It has behind it no intelligence; and upon that argument is founded the basis upon which M.D.'s account for your existence.

Discrimination means the additional factor of intellectuality, therefore it is not a reflection.

"Automatic." We do not like this. For instance we are angry. Analyze the thought and expression—is the thought and action following it automatic—just happened? We bring out the thought that we are angry, but we had nothing to be angry about.

Whenever you find discrimination, just so surely do you get away from reflex action.

We take food into our mouth—it is digested in the stomach. Good. It is acted upon favorably. We take some other kind of food into our mouth, it enters the stomach but it doesn't stay long—it is out again. The point we raise, is what is IT that says one food is good and another is bad? Something discriminated between these things! Everything in life is in a constant state of discrimination. When you form your cycle then reflex action forms no place in that logic. The physician who originated the thought of reflex action was not an analyst.

Why do we "like" things? Is it reflex or intellectual? We maintain that when there is discrimination there is intellectuality.

Is there not a difference between automatic and reflex action? Do you not get reflex action by bringing two "automatic" things together?

When you are hungry and sense the necessity for food, your mouth waters. Say we smell a beefsteak frying; the nose is receptive and wants more of the same kind of smells and they send impressions up to the brain. If it was pepper, the nostrils would try to repel the odor.

The cycles are all working towards the appropriation of something for the good of the body. The cycles of smell and taste are complete within themselves and yet they work together, resulting in a good ideation. There is no question but what the tissue cells in the mouth are working along normally according to circumstances. We do not know whether all cells are working up to 100 per cent or not, but when food is taken in they increase their action and it may be that behind the interpretations of food they are working for and with something else.

For instance, are we using more power when we are running than when we are standing still? Our muscles keep up to a certain tonicity while we are standing still, and we would hardly say there was less than 100 per cent of impulses or power—when we run there is still 100 per cent of power and yet we are performing more action.

Doesn't something change the vibration of impulses, else we would not get impressions other than we have all the time? One hundred per cent in speaking of quantity is confining it according to the circumstance with which it is dealing. There is 100 per cent in the mouth in the active state. Now it is not active and still there is 100 per cent, making a difference necessary activity and the passive condition. We are not unhealthy when we are standing still, nor when we are running—we are healthy in both instances, yet we are using 100 per cent of current according to the circumstances which we are meeting.

If normal we can appreciate 100 per cent of taste or smell, whereas if capable of only 50 per cent we would not appreciate either.

Here is a vibration from tissue cell to brain cell—the quantity of current that passes is 100 percent per minute in the non-active state. In the active state the same amount of current is going through, only a great deal faster—the question of time enters into this, if you are considering 100 per cent of a given quantity.

A person gets up in the morning feeling well, does his normal work, and then is called upon to do extra work which he does, and remains normal. If abnormal, considering the amount of movement, per a given time, you will find that the extra work put upon him makes him feel bad because he has only been able to have a certain amount of current in a certain period of time, getting no more current in the same space of time.

A question of intellectual adaptation enters into this. The question arises as to whether we have 100 per cent of current when muscles are inactive, and if so, is there only the same per cent of current when they are in their most active state? Let us make comparisons with a 2-candle power globe and a 32-candle power globe, and we will suppose that one minute is our standard of time and 100 per cent is our standard of quantity of current. We will find that the 2-candle power globe will use up 100 per cent of current in 32 minutes—change to the 32-candle power globe and it will use up 100 per cent of current, just sixteen times faster than the first. This can be applied to the body. Have a brain cell fibre and a muscle cell, completing a physical cycle. The brain cell manufactures 100 per cent of current per one minute; the nerve fibre transmits 100 per cent of current per one minute to tissue cell which acts out that 100 per cent of current per one minute.

We want to emphasize that the quantities of current are different under the same length of time only as regards circumstances.

As to the abnormal, to a muscle in repose 100 per cent of current is being expressed at a brain cell, 50 per cent is being transmitted beyond the point of pressure, and only 50 per cent is being expressed at tissue cell—pressure upon the nerve cuts off 50 per cent of current transmission—you call upon that muscle to do some quick work and it will be unable because it is supposed to receive a greater quantity of current than when in repose, but owing to the pressure upon it, it does not get through.

When the muscle is in repose it is equivalent to the 2-candle power globe and when in the active state, to the 32-candle power globe. Call upon the same muscle fibre in the active state to perform the duties of the 32-candle power globe; it is equivalent to the 2, owing to the 50 per cent pressure shutting off the current.

In the illustrations just given you must not overlook the prime moving factor, or the idea of pressure beyond the current. The current in this instance is the intellectual adaptation taking place in the mind. It is possible in some conditions that are abnormal that you can inject some preparation or give to the body something which increases the necessity for action, and in this way calls for a greater force of intellectual adaptation, and in that way make it appear that you have stimulated conditions, but eventually you get back to the standard as before. This may be summed up in more current for the same space of time—you must have a basis.

Matter may get to such a fine quality standpoint that it becomes immaterial—blending from solids into vapors. Therein exists the physical basis for spiritualism. While spirit is immaterial, yet it is possible for it to be condensed or verging on the material, under certain conditions, and exist on a plane midway between the immaterial and the material, and then go off into the immaterial again—they can take semblance or not.

While it is possible for a question to arise as to material things always remaining material, and immaterial always existing as such, yet we believe it can be maintained from logical standpoints that material things are capable of taking higher grades or qualitative steps and thus get into the immaterial and that the material returns to earth—in other words, that nothing is lost. It may exist for a time in one form and gradually take on another and may some day come back again. Electricity is one form of a material or immaterial thing, just as you please to call it, and we believe that mental impulses are the same material or immaterial consistency, just as you wish to term them, but of a finer quality than that of electricity.

The fact that this high power comes through the mind of man is what puts it through a refining process, because the brain of man is a much finer quality of material than a dynamo through which the electricity passes.

When you are hungry and sense the necessity for food, your mouth waters; that is "automatic," "without consciousness." The actions and power expressed but represent "reflex actions," "reflexed" external conditions. You are "reflecting," unconsciously, what we have stated. No matter if you disagree, the power necessary to perform the function is but a "reflection." Why have you an appetite and eat certain foods which taste good to appease it? "Automatic," "without consciousness." The femur is fractured; it is built to normal, healed by the deposition of osseous matter. Why? "Automatic," "without consciousness." Your food digested, converted to chemicals, transported to all tissues of the body

and utilized to your physical needs. Why? "Automatic," "without consciousness." Your bowels act, the kidneys empty themselves into the
bladder, they are voided, and all because it is "automatic" and "without
consciousness." How do you do anything? Does "automatic" or its syno-
nym, "reflex action," explain the how and why, behind each and every
action? One has not improved the other, nor the second its mate. Do you
grasp, now, what "reflex action" is and what it is supposed to do? It is
but an "automatic" action taking place in the "sympathetic nervous system," constant "reflections" of external conditions through the reflection
medium (as a mirror to the sun)—spinal segment, ganglion or nerve
centers.

B.J. was at one time known as a peculiar sort of a crank. As odd as
he was and he was considered to be, he had succeeded in keeping people
guessing as to what he would do next. His actions and thoughts were
sharp, alert and ahead of the times. He held at one time an enviable
honored position because others were being taught to reach his intellectual level. His every thought was WHY? Originality combined with strict
discipline and stick-to-itiveness, joined with principle and honor, had
made him many enemies, the majority of which were knowing him
better, turning from enmity to respect.

B.J. would study two bones and by comparison would find one normal
and in its opposite very much abnormal. Why? would be the first question. "Here was evidently a fracture united by a pier of exostosis," "automatic," "by means unknown," did not answer the why and how. When, by
accident, a calvarium was held between himself and the light, he observed
two beautiful forest fires, as fine as any artist could paint on canvas. To
say that such was "automatic" did not reach his ideal nor answer the
question.

When, in B.J.'s earliest collections of osteological specimens, a pig's
femur overlapped three inches as the result of an unset over-riding fracture and upon which was much porous surrounding spiculae and this was
gradually being torn down in proportion as the fractured surfaces became
better knit. To maintain that such was done by "reflex action" or "duplicature" of the original conditions, which was a fracture reflected, "ending or turned back," did and would not answer.

The destination was to place behind these actions an intelligence to
disprove the "without consciousness" fallacy. To go to your daily
business, return and rehearse that innervating function, performed
thereby, are "automatic," does not state the intelligence of your objects
for so doing. Can you conceive that digestion is "automatic," "without
consciousness"? Imagination cannot carry B.J. far enough to believe
that the great intelligences are manifest under abnormal, diseased
conditions, as we daily see in his specimens from the largest and finest
collection in the world, and the many accommodating changes studied,
where and how, is answered by Innate, who shows the greatest knowledge

in curcumventing obstacles; a pattern from which a man must first trace back all his mechanical ideas; that all of these are "automatic"?

Reflex Action—A thing which starts out and comes back without any modification whatsoever—a thing which is sent in without anything having been accomplished. Then what's the use of it?

Reflex Action.
0—Nervous center.
2 3—Efferent nerve.
2—Afferent nerve.

0—Tissue Cell.

If the cycle be correct, and we think you concede there is good sense in them, then we must recognize that everything is guided by an intelligence. A Chiropractor would tell you that a current is carried by a nerve and we have an afferent nerve only for carrying such to the mind which would decide whether it was good or bad and the impulse which goes back is adaptative in character. Vibration precedes everything. Here is a fractured bone. Keep this definition in mind. "They take it for granted that an intellectual interpretation takes place."

Dunglison says: "Every function not done voluntarily is supposed to be guided without sense or knowledge." We want to account for man as an intellectual proposition. You speak of a sub-conscious mind—it is a super-conscious mind—to B.J. it is the most important mind.

The cycles show intellectual function. The foundation of their existence taking place within you is supposed to be guided by reflex action, according to medical and osteopathic authorities. It is their foundation as much as the cycles are ours.

Reflex act teaches that with a certain stimulus, at a specific spot in a direct manner, and every time that the same is employed the results must always be directly the same. Equal "stimulus" must demonstrate a like result, inasmuch as the entire circuit is purely a physical process and acted upon by nothing but what is material. The reflex act must, as a consequence, return with the same as it sent. This is not a fact with the human body, as the most careless examination would portray. You have but to notice any act that was not previously considered, something that you do on the spur of the moment, to contradict the reflex act, which is not definite nor direct in any manner that we have been enabled to study.

According to adaptation there are no two responses alike in form, character or action, direction of movement or with the same degree of force; therefore there is an adaptation, and this could not occur without more than a corporeal material transformation to receive, interpret and respond. It involves the brain of man, his intelligence and mind as intermediates to accomplish that. Therefore reflex act cannot be computed upon or recognized as the basis of all that adapts itself to the innumerable circumstances that we are called upon to deal with every day. In every responsive action there is adaptation, whether it be Educated or Innate.

Medicine is based upon this "reflex action" by and thru the "sympathetic nervous system."

"The heart of a healthy adult man contracts about 72 times a minute; but many circumstances cause this rate to vary even in health. The chief (circumstances) are age, temperament, food and drink, exercise, time of day, posture, atmospheric pressure, temperature." From the above we conclude, according to medicine, that external "circumstances" can and do "cause" changes to take place by "reflex action." The following questions are a consequence of disbelief:

1. Can "circumstance" cause adaptation?

2. Can Adaptation be the result of an intelligence plus the circumstance?

3. Can circumstance be the result of adaptation?

The first is answered in the negative; the latter two in the affirmative. The M.D. would consider it as a long settled fact that the above enumerated "circumstances cause" the adaptation of the bodily functions. In what way and thru what physical definite channels are age, temperament, sex, food and drink, etc., anything to do? Where and what is that substance, thing, goal or place where such "circumstances" are discriminated between? A spinal segment, nerve center, or ganglion has not thinking abilities, and surely our brain is not in our belly; therefore age, sex, food and drink are all as one. There is nothing in that which knows or realizes any difference between them. Where is the thinking propensity or direct connection: Innate power is no respecter of persons, plants or animals, and will always adapt herself to the conditions presented for her to act thru. Adaptations are the results of an intelligent, thinking individual who has ability to thoroly control bodily functions; who can harmoniously adapt one or more or any combination of functions; to any kind of "circumstances," internal or external (where it comes in contact with the object which she is controlling), at one time. Place your finger upon a hot stove. Instantly it is removed. Did your spinal segment think and know the difference between a hot or cold stove, or did it even know the difference between that and a cold potato? It is plainly evident you did not do it, for the hand was far from being in contact when you were aware of the burned portions' existence. Did you or your ganglion "without consciousness" place this new tissue? Where did these new cells expand and how manufactured? A power is necessary, but is this but "reflection"? Can nothing be the genuine force? It is always the same answer, "reflex actions."

Regarding the place where circumstances are discriminated between:

When you bring in a question of discrimination you are bringing in an intelligence. If the solar plexus was furnishing the power for a man's body it would not affect the working of the body to cut off his head: or take a man with his head on, whose Innate is away, you can put him in an ice-box—he doesn't care—there is no intelligence there, even though both the solar plexus and brain are present.

The law of adaptation has never been considered much anywhere; it is a union of intellectual forces adapting itself to a condition in material things; yet where is the philosophy, science or art, today?

The "circumstance" alone cannot "cause" adaptation. Something greater than an intermediate effect must exist, and that something is our Innate performing through Innate brain, which, situated within the skull, receives all impressions from the external, interprets them as normal or abnormal and adapts herself in expressions accordingly. This intelligence is not known or recognized by the M.D. other than as "Nature," and they might as well have nothing as to know what little they do about that. No wonder their failures, thoughts and actions are constantly being "reflected" ("bending or turning backward").

If the first "circumstance" be a fracture, the impressions must travel inward, be interpreted as such, and impulses of the right quality, quantity and character are directed to the distressed point to proceed with reparation. They, through the deposition of new cells, heal this break to as normal as is possible. By so doing Innate makes of the abnormal circumstance, to all practical purposes, a normal one. Thus abnormal "circumstance" may be the result of Innate adapting her forces to the abnormal external or peripheral conditions. It is but the common law, that is daily observable in and all around us, the law of adaptation. Knowing what to look for and how to find them will show many occurrences.

To replace "automatic," "without consciousness" or "circumstances" with something that is intelligent, we must show that which is more rational. Behind every responsive impulse is the intelligence which gives character. Common sense reasoning and playing the Sherlock Holmes on Innate has given us a direct system, in which every fibre leads from tissue to brain cell, or vice versa, which receives its impressions or transmits impulses and that is interpreted or expressed in tissue cells; a multitude of these, acting in a harmonious whole, is but the normal living body.

A ball is struck against the wall and it glances somewhere or anywhere, just as liable one place as another into the audience, altho it has been proven that the law of angles proves where it will go.

Do such actions give an idea of directness? Yes, to an intelligence or a man who understands this law.

The law of angles is a specific and definite law. B.J. maintains that there is a specific lobe in the brain with specific cells where interpretation takes place and the responsive action is intellectual, therefore there is a direct responsive adaptation, and the cell that needs it is the one that gets the responsive action. We put one foot on a hot stove and that's the foot taken off—that's a direct law, not reflex action.

Man has along his spine a whole series or chain of "ganglia" which are the crossing and recrossing of the nerve fibres, forming about 129 brain centers.

Impression, traveling inward, happens to "reflect" to a segment, or nerve venter, and, like a spark of the electric wire, jumps to any surrounding fibre that is handy, expressing itself at its periphery, altho that may be far from the point of necessity. Can you imagine a human unit, complete in mechanical work and functions that could exist upon such a hypothesis? It does not meet the comprehension of the grandness involved. You will admit, this type of principles, if applied to machinery, would not deliver the work in any shape or form that you or I care to buy. This body is the grandest business in existence. It has lived thru eternities and man with his comparative feeble intellect has never added or improved upon her work. How much greater must be the application of such principles in preference to commercial work? If success is system detailed, then how majestic must be the "system" upon which the "involuntary" body is managed? Could such accidental means run you or me?

At the central end of every brain fibre is its Innate brain cell and there receives external impressions, put them thru an intellectual cross-examination—interpretation—so that the extension (nerve) can transmit to the periphery an intelligent impulse denoting character, that directs where it should go and what it must do; then we have an intelligent response (not a "reflection, duplicature," of what went inward) to the external appeal for help.

Why not eat poisons as well as nourishing foods? Why does the stomach portray rebellious actions against medicines? Why shrink when the surgeon's knife enters the quivering flesh? Why object when instruments of torture (traction tables, for instance) are injected or applied against that which damages this temple or with open arms becomes receptive, submissive and loyal to that which is needful and beneficial? If "nature" be your reply, we would ask, "Where does she live in this system? by what means and thru what physical channels does she exert or demonstrate her intelligent force? When these questions have been definitely answered, the mystery blown away, the mist evaporated, we will have reached some conclusion; head and tail to our entity. A need which suffering humanity has long needed and supplied by B. J. Palmer's philosophical teachings, thus reaching, proving and allowing physical vent to that which M.D.'s still cling as "reflex action" or that "connection existing between the action of two or more organs, more or less distant from each other, so that the affection of the first is transmitted according to the others, by means unknown." (Dunglison.) The M.D. is not "conscious" of an Innate brain or its "consciousness," but his Innate is. It is well that Innate "consciousness" is so placed that he, fool man, cannot trifle with it.

In the study of spinal branches of nerves all fibres do not spray immediately as they leave the spinal column. A cable may remain as such, for some distance and then begin the process of segregation. The abdomen is a large cavity and contains most of the necessary viscera, thus it need have many mental impulses and nerves to transmit them. Many nerve cables proceed to a given point (solar plexus) and there separate to twig ramifications. The belly ganglion is but a branching point for the various functional nerves, pairing off to ultimately let each tissue have its complete set of functional convening fibres. A blow, at this allotting point, would produce great responsiveness upon the part of Innate, who would, normally or abnormally, adapt her powers to the "circumstances," be it great or small.

A patient entered B.J.'s clinic one day. Left side of nose was bleeding. Nose bleed is a disease, and if Innate could adapt itself to such conditions, would try to heal it. Some people never have nose bleed, others have it occur upon the slightest external "circumstances." One adjustment, in the proper manner, stopped this hemorrhage within two minutes. The quick action, two minutes, following this adjustment is but evidence which shows how accurately and exacting is the adaptation of Innate if but given free range with her power, which healed or brought those muscular fibres together, thus closing the breach.

Reference to the condition of the nose previous to and after adjustment and what change took place will be interesting to illustrate what kind of responsiveness followed the Chiropractic adjustment. Every tissue has its small capillaries of arteries or veins. These, as minute as they may seem, have three muscular walls. The first set's fibres run lengthwise; the second, spirally; the third, transversely. Each has its rhythm of mental impulses, contracting as it goes along, and thus the added motion keeps the blood running forward.

There are membranes covering the external, internal and permeating between is serous, which gives to the blood, by osmosis, its serum. If this liquid was not in the blood vessels, the blood would cease to flow; become solid. Take from blood its serum and histologists will agree that man could not live, yet the larger proportion of serum, in transitional stages, has no blood.

These walls, minus mental impulses, partly or completely, become proportionately relaxed and, sooner or later, a rupture is present. If the hernia, lack of muscular tonicity-incoordination—be complete thru the three walls, then arterial blood will permeate thru the interstices between muscular fibres, osmose thru serous tissues and, hemorrhage, large or small, according to the area thus involved, follows.

Withdrawal of mental impulses or current causes the tissues to weaken or relax, and a hemorrhage is the result, the blood oozing out between the openings in the wall. By adjustment you restore the normal transmission of currents, going right down to these relaxed muscular fibres, and immediately they draw up to the normal rigidity, close up the opening and the hemorrhage ceases.

That is what B.J. calls an intellectual adaptation of inaction—"by means unknown"—showing more than an ignorant activity of muscles.

In this case, nasal hemorrhage took place because we had a definite, specific, local subluxation which impinged upon direct nerves, which conveyed the mental impulses to a direct locality. Adjusting this subluxation, within two minutes, returned coordinated functions (the Innate law of adaptation), and normal condition was the result.

B.J. had a case of uterine hemorrhage some years ago, which was nigh unto death, and in two days there ceased to be any flow. Adjusting the subluxated vertebra immediately began to return normal adaptation to the abnormal circumstance—responsiveness—in which that mentality, discriminating in character, sent impulses to these muscles and gave them the tonicity to contract to their normal state. The fibres drew together, the chinks closed—the interspaces grew together, and then and not until, would there have ceased to be an opening. Can you explain, in all sincerity, that those actions of healing are the result of "automatic" work? that such is performed "without consciousness," "by means unknown"? If it is "reflex action," "turning back" upon itself, would it not be worse? "Itself" is the disease, and to reflect "back upon" disease is but to make more disease. This is the M.D's basis—lesion makes lesion—because lesions "reflect" lesions, by means of "reflex action" thru "sympathetic nervous system" "by means unknown." Isn't that beautiful philosophy?

Your living body, if normal, is but the work of and shows what intelligent responsiveness, when given full sway, will do. Your sick or diseased condition but illustrates the inability of responses to reach their destination and adapt themselves to abnormal conditions.

If there has been a long pressure upon nerves, the system be depleted or the organ unable to maintain its equilibrium, then this responsiveness, even under the best adjustment, will appear tedious, but even adjustment is farther from effects and nearer to normal. The Chiropractor is an assistant to Innate, opening channels to responsive actions.

If you have belief (belief—partial assurance without positive knowledge or absolute confidence), to think that "reflex Action," as outlined and taught in Medical books or schools, does exist, please give us further proofs than have been advanced. If you suppose that the body is acted upon and being guided by a haphazard, catch-as-catch-can, Graeco-Roman actions, we will give you opportunity for debate.

B. J. Palmer's library is most thorough with authors which can be quoted in numbers. The most flowery speech, couched in the finest of words, galore with medical scientific terms and tests, taking hours to deliver, can be floored by one philosophic Chiropractic student asking the lecturer a few common sense questions which he cannot answer. Why? They have unstable promises; none dared to think, to get from ruts, for fear of the code of ethics.

The "reflex action" is on a common with the "sympathetic nervous system." We do not know what it is and do not know anybody who does. Like the man who could not bear limburger, he did not like it and did not like anybody who did like it.

It is hard to talk about something which is not provable. We have tried to speak about "reflex action." B.J.'s knowledge of cause and law of Innate adaptation to the normal or abnormal proves to thorough students the supplantation of that which is practicable and demonstrable on the every day feeling and living subject, and, after all that is what counts, is to adjust the causes of ailments and deformities in the living person, in preference to destroying sex, removing useful organs and otherwise mutilating our bodies, while living and making us well, that is what is left of our tissues after they are burned out by stimulatives or extirpated by the surgeon by hypothetical "sympathy" explanations, and paper, after we are "stiffs," dead and buried.

B.J. does not believe such a system of "reflex action" (as worshipped, stimulated or inhibited by M.D.'s) exist.

The thought of belief comes in here with the condition of religion. Does the ordinary theologian know there is a cycle behind all? He thinks there is; he has faith there is. Does the Chiropractor know! Yes, we can say it with absolute emphasis. B.J.'s religion is not a belief; it is a fact.

Physical strength is limited to the medium through which it acts.

What little results they have had was obtained through the stimulated impressions trying to and, in a measure, were accommodated under great pressure, accomplishing the extra or limiting the responsive impulses, thereby when the normal supply had been exhausted a relapse follows eventually, leaving the patients worse, just the same, dying, perhaps, a trifle sooner than if they had been left alone.

The person who does things without intelligence is nonsensical and Chiropractors cannot recognize such as prudent or judicious to follow. Their testimony is only too often riddled by authority of courts, therefore, with the following summary of facts we will dismiss the case for want of sufficient evidence upon the part of our opponents to defend themselves in this trial of results before the world:

Elbert Hubbard wrote this to B.J. "But youth and age are not always a matter of years. Some minds are born with the crow's-feet and the wrinkles of a sapless conservatism chiseled on their every move and opinion. They are spiritually dead before they are born. They are creatures of reflex action."

Chiropractic vs. "sympathy."

Origin of Power and Point of Expression vs. "sympathetic nervous system."

Direct Functions vs. "duplicature" of "reflections."

Intelligent Responses vs. "Superstitions."

Intelligence vs. "by means unknown."

Knowledge vs. "reflections."

Acute results vs. "chronic diseases."

Knowledge of cause, its adjustment and law of adaptation vs. "Circumstances cause."

As "reflex is the foundation upon which scientific medicine is based as the unit of action," it is worthy of serious consideration from a standpoint of elucidation of their ideas as compared with ours.

By general consent you admit that cycles are correct. B.J. has yet to meet an objection to any statement contained in cycles. None of those details have been assailed to the extent of proving any step out of place or that cycles as a total were wrong. Therefore, cycles stand because not proven wrong. When a statement cannot be contradicted or proven wrong, then it is as truth. If those cycles are correct, everything is guided by an intelligence as a premise to start our hypothesis with.

You admit that an afferent nerve conveys a given quantity of vibrations from one place to another through or over an afferent nerve, you know that the destination of that given quantity of vibrations is to keep its identity until it reaches the brain where the mind gives interpretation. Interpretation is the action that intelligence places upon a given quantity of vibrations. Having seen that an impression started at the tissue cell, did go in, reached the mind, the mind interprets it to the extent of seeing a necessity at the end of this afferent nerve for something to change the given quantity of vibrations to a more harmonious quantity consequently adapt to that given quantity of vibrations known as Mind, Thought, Innate Intelligence sends down a given quantity of impulsive vibrations. The given quantity returned adaptatively is not the given quantity going inwardly, consequently there is a change in the conditions at the tissue cell. Then the second quantity of vibrations going afferently towards the mind is of a different quantity than the first. There is a different interpretation and a different quantity sent down adaptatively.

We are presuming that there is a constant changing and a revolution of an immaterial current through these four mediums, and we suppose that under normal conditions every atom, tissue cell of that complete cycle is continuous, that there exist no broken links between one and the other. Everything actually touches just as much as every atom of chalk on that board touches every other atom so much so that we have a continuity of chalk substance. We presume hypothetically, that 100 per cent of current is passing through 100 per cent of matter per one second of time. Supposing there were 100 tissue cells necessary to make this complete circuit. There would need to be 100 per cent of current in one given second, providing that we consider one quantity in each tissue cell at the same time. That is, there would be 100 per cent of current in each tissue cell in any one given second of time. This is providing everything is normal, Intelligence is interpreting accurately, tissue cell performing function accurately, impressions are formed exact, transmission is being formed in accordance with the impression or interpretation and, responsive function is the same. Normal in every respect; in every attribute, every consideration; brain normal; lives and dies normal; every function normal in every viscera and muscle; then we could argue that the afferent half of a cycle is exactly as per the efferent half. There is never any fluctuation between one side and the other. One-half would then be but a counterpart of the other. The interpretation would be as function and vice versa.

We are fluctuating. Today a person says, "I don't feel good." Yesterday, "I feel fine." Tomorrow, "I feel miserable." Two weeks ago he was flat on his back. Next day, feeling fair; the next stomach ache, etc. The man is not normal any two days. He is fluctuating at all times. Running up and down the scale from our set standard to any variation your imagination can conceive.

Cutting off ten per cent of current represents a lack in the tissue cell, consequently only 90 per cent reaches there, 90 per cent has transmission and only 90 per cent interpretation takes place. We can't say we have ten dollars when we have nine. We can't interpret that we are worth a million when we don't know where to get a dime. We can't presume to argue on things that do not in fact exist. We can't presume there is wealth of normality when there is not, but we do presume there is wealth of intelligence behind. It has no limit to its wealth, and so unlimited is it that we say, this is infinity, meaning everything.

Going back to source, you have interpreted only 90 per cent, Innate finds 10 per cent absent. We try to adapt conditions to normal. If we do find, by process of function, that there is a change between the efferent and afferent halves of the function, if in your observations you have seen man does meet an obstacle and circumvent it, then one-half does not accord with the other, and, so far as we show a process of adaptation, whether small or great, just so far are you getting away from the theory that man is an automaton.

Take, for instance, the unexpected occurrences. Walking down the street, feet slip, you fall; down go your hands; you light not only on your hands but—on the hips. At such times you receive a concussion of forces. Adaptability put out the hands. You fell braced with little damage. Walking along the street, the sun is shining and, as you walk, you squint the eyes. There is adaptation. Do you purposely do this? A deafening noise approaches, muscles are all contracted, especially in the ears. Somebody hands you a lemon, get a taste, spit before you thought. Even though you did, there was a spontaneous influx of water that diluted it. You drink laudanum with suicidal intent, immediately the stomach is flooded with splenic fluid, gastric juice, etc.

All shows the process of adaptation. B.J. could enumerate thousands. Take, for instance, the best process of flying today is birds, imitated by flying fishes. The best aviators are those who copy after birds. It is but a process of adaptation. Thus man is getting away from the automatic. We use the term automatic on things that are automatons, but not in relation to intellectual beings. As far as they become intellectual we cease to use the word automatic and automaton and use terms that express the given quantities as they are.

Dunglison says, every function that you don't do voluntarily is supposed to be guided without sense or knowledge. For instance, you do not regulate your foods, neither does the mother regulate the building of the child, and this is done "without sense or knowledge." Can you, in your experience, conceive that such is a fact that these are recurring haphazardly? B.J. wants to account for man in every unit action as an intellectual function. The very foundation of existence, taking place within you, is supposed to be guided by reflex action, according to medical authorities. It is their foundation as cycles in ours, and you know what consideration we give to man if we didn't have cycles. We could not answer any problem or physiological action. Our adjustments would be, so far as practical explanation is concerned, useless; and, without the actual transmission of cycles, nothing in man would be accomplished. To us, cycles; to them, reflex action.

Consider the question of whether circumstances cause adaptation. Can adaptation be the result of intelligence plus circumstance? Can circumstance be the result of adaptation? Take the illustration of a man falling. Falling is the circumstance; can the fall bring forth the adaptation of putting the hands behind, checking itself? Remembering that you cannot answer the question of law of cause and effect without considering intellectual adaptation, can adaptation be the result of an intelligence plus circumstance? Yes. Can circumstance be the result of adaptation? Yes.

The M.D. has passed through many years watching the old hypothesis and theory that circumstances cause adaptation. When you omit the problem in any way, through what physical channels have age, temperament, sex, food and drink, anything to do with man, you fall back upon the logic of cycles. You can't sustain this any other way.

Suppose B.J. grants the point they argue upon, what and where is that substance, thing or place where circumstances are discriminated between? Argue ganglion, then you have 129 and your complexity increases. You argue plexus and you have many variously distributed, in what way are they united? You argue spinal cord segments, and your complexity increases because you understand no intelligence. Go back to even one brain, do it by one route, and B.J. will show Chiropractic. B.J. has never known a physician, philosopher, scientist or medical man but what in logic, in writings on the philosophy of medicine dealing with it from a hypothetical standpoint, talks Chiropractic philosophy. When he comes to doing, he forgets what he wrote. Question a physician severely upon one given point and he will run back to the brain in the skull, impression going to brain, there interpreted and we have the action as a result. "Now, doctor, you have made a bona fide statement. Let us analyze this according to physiology, or anatomy," and watch him squirm. His two arguments won't hold.

Five hundred years ago common carp lived by the millions in China and Japan. They invaded those streams worse than ours. Breeding and selection brought a change though. Some of them were redder than others, another year of hatching and some were redder than the last; and so progress was in vogue year after year. When China and Japan were opened to the United States, lo and behold! the streams were filled with red fish. Later, some were bred yellow. They kept working until eventually they had white, brown, green, and black gold fish. And they were not satisfied. Gradually they had the fan-tail gold fish, and, as he grew, generation after generation, had three tails one split down the center and they called him the fringe-tailed gold fish. Some fish had more tail than body. Today you can pay from fifty to one hundred dollars for a gold fish. He wasn't satisfied, he changed the characteristic shape of carp until it became short, chubby, fat and thick and they called that the barrel-shaped gold fish. Not being satisfied yet, they bred until the eyes changed from the side of the head to the top. Later, those eyes grew on stems outside of the head, called telescope gold fish. Now they have the fringe or fan tail, barrel-shaped, telescope gold fish, and order any color you want. Thus does the process of evolution go on. This is a constant change of adaptation from the brown and greenish carp to the magnificent gold fish of today.

All this change is purely a process of adaptation in the unit cycle by unit quantities per unit matter per unit time. Thus, more than reflex action.

Suppose B.J. grants the hypothesis of the M.D.'s. Along comes a man, slips, falls, produces a fracture. The circumstance is a fracture. Suppose B.J. grants the hypothesis that circumstance caused adaptation and circumstance will cause adaptation purely and only through the route of reflex action. Admitting we have a spinal ganglion, here is our efferent nerve, there our afferent nerve, immediately an impression went to a ganglion. There no intelligence acted upon it. There is none in that ganglion. It makes crude impressions which reflexes them into crude impulses, because everything involuntary is done without sense, knowledge or consciousness. We have reflex coming from that ganglion, the same that went in. The thing that went in was the impression of a fracture. Back went an impulse of a fracture. B.J. has introduced something into this which was not in it before. Now that a fracture is introduced, you must introduce something which will heal, develop osseous cells; tell them where and how many to go; at certain rates of speed; where to be deposited; how many are there. All this demands intelligence. You must introduce that in addition to what was there before.

Even though we present this, we know if you were called into a house where a fracture had occurred, without warning, "Explain what is going on in this arm," you would say, "The Innate Intelligence in your brain is aware of the conditions." The first impression then interpreted. The cells are coming forth rapidly, and in a few minutes there will be many there. That is the logic you would use, because it is logically logic; but do you mean what you say?

There are many who have not become reconciled to the complete revolution these questions make, and yet they would use these ideas B.J. has been presenting. You could not offer other argument that would call to mind just what others want to know. Are you to be a living contradiction of self or conscience? You can get away from your patient, but there is one fellow you take with you all the time. Are you to argue one thing and do another?

To replace automatic with consciousness, ignorance with intelligence, we must show that which is rational behind every responsive impulse. If you admit there is a single one without, then there can be others; and they can all be without. If you admit that a tree grown without intelligence, then all can do likewise. If you admit that an animal is a brute, then all animals, birds and fishes are alike. If you admit one man is unconscious, then all are. Admit that one function is ignorant means that all can be, and to admit that a single unit function can be by automatism means they all can be. Before you build you must get a unit system. If this reflex unital action is right, then all must be. That is why we spend time on the unit.

If this one unit reflex action is wrong, then ten nor a thousand of them would be right. They are all occurring in different places in different quantities of matter and different quantities of force, but the fundamental is wrong.

There is a specific lobe in the brain with specific cells where every interpretation takes place and responsive action is intellectual. There is a direct specific responsive adaptation and the cell that needs it is the one that gets it, not some other.

While more could be said, we are not going to take time. When you sum up the fundamental physiology of the "sympathetic" nervous system and reflex action and find that it is founded on superstiticn, dogmatism, studied and taught to cover something not known, using it as a cloak to shield themselves against the knowledge they know they must have but haven't. It is a question of having direct functions; a direct place to start means with a direct finish as opposing the idea of duplication of functions.

16

BIOLOGY

B.J. IN THIS CHAPTER will not dwell upon any one subject, but regard life in a general sense, showing where advancement has been made in the last fifty years. B.J. likes to feel, when every day's work is done, that he has made progress. If no point has been carried, in advance of yesterday's, the day is lost. We need all of Chiropractic that can be deciphered. Every time a lame person is helped over the stile the world has been given what it is clamoring for. In Chiropractic you and I have the only knowledge that gives to humanity a specific science of cause of disease in an exact manner and delivers results. We do not mean that we have it all, nor can any one science in 63 years know so much.

In B.J.'s lecture on the embryo we conceded to the spermatozoon and ovum a future unit. That gave to this conception that took place at the union of these elements a new light, placing it in the aspect of the future child, a phase that no other school but Chiropractic has given to it.

B.J. has also brought out the idea that fusation of the two elements, male and female, when expanded, was the future adult. Taking it upon the same basis, this concentrated form is the unit. It is just as much the person now, when it lies in the uterus; is equal to the son or daughter; as it would be thirty years after birth.

The expansion is only its maturity of form, which is its shape, quality and quantity. This extensive process is the shaping, and as soon as the embryo has received all that is possible internally, it is expelled from the mother body, and begins the process of maturity to size on the outside.

B.J. next took us into the brain system. If there is any one point that Chiropractic is extremely radical upon, it is this question. We have one brain system. This alone cannot be considered, but must be divided, to make the study complete, into an educated and innate mental nervous brain system; although each is finished in detail. Educated is that which moves at command of the will, moves limbs when walking and uses hands in doing Chiropractic work.

On the opposite we have an innate nervous system, that two-thirds of the entire system over which we have no control. It is the impulse conveyed by this system which is performing work on our dinner, acts upon the fecal matter in getting it ready for expulsion, and causes the secretions to be made in all parts of our body. It is that force which is causing nutrition to be carried to all parts. We cannot command these powers to act here nor there as we might will. If normal functions, with all channels free and open, cannot be controlled by Educated man, is it not the height of folly for the same fellow to try and dictate to Innate how to correct abnormal functions, when foramina are occluded, nerves impinged? The division exists into that which can be commanded by the will and that which cannot.

We transferred the name of this system. When a portion of it is a nervous system, to our comprehension the term does not convey its entirety. B.J. wishes to give one universal name, to show its generalities. Consideration must be given to the place from which these nerves come— brain. To convey B.J.'s idea, or give it a term that explains all, B.J. will use Brain System in preference. The common term but represents the outgrowth or expansion of the former. Immediately we get the conception of brain system we have the added interest of the brain, its functions and ramifications; spinal cord and all its segregations.

B.J. has added another new study to Chiropractic Philosophy. The brain takes precedence over nerves in point of superiority as the force or power generator; the thinker and impulse starter; as a forerunner because it preceded them. It is the seat of all intelligence. Previous to this direct body to brain connection by means of nerves, it has been "sympathetic," "reflex action," which are but indications of retracing steps; dancing back track; to do over again; to harp on the same string; by one who cuts one's coat according to one's cloth.

Does any school consider the brain system and its nerves in connection? No. Although a few in the field have attempted monographic imitations about Chiropractic, this foundation upon which Chiropractic rests is ignored. B.J. has yet to find any publications, journals or books, that technically or scientifically have advanced, by discoveries, its study, outside of his own. Several journals have reiterated what they have copied from the literature and ideas as advanced by B.J., but the above remark is above question. It is an original physiological discovery, and although it has always existed, gives the proper man (B.J.) the credit for finding it out. B. J. Palmer has given certain highly developed innate faculties and years of practical experience; with the use of the largest osteological collection in the world; which is a necessity to give substantiation to the original thinker; and these, connected with superior intelligence, have and will continue to make him capable of deducting facts that no one else has or can see. It is that peculiar individuality that makes B. J. Palmer a pace setter and win the race at every turn.

With this brain system we are placing behind the nerves something which controls their output. Previous to this the M.D. has looked upon brain as brain matter, composed of so many convolutions, fissures and lobes. He can tell you what kind of tissue it is, that there is a spinal cord and nerves. He does not say, though that one is a counterpart of the other nor maintain that one could not exist without the other.

Conan Doyle says, "Observe things." You strangers have passed those steps for the first time. What proportion of you can tell how many there are? None. We question whether half could tell whether they are pine, oak, walnut or birch. Train your senses to observe. A man walking in front of us, today, stepped over a pocket-book. We observed the lady who dropped it and he didn't. Why? His observation was limited. Many people go through the world seeing things, sometimes seeing snakes, but never observing them. Many men make fine personal appearances to show external beauty, but the observing man, penetratingly, sees only shallowness. The keen observer is the man who perceives when you think he is in the abstract. He itemizes all ideas, salts them away, places them in respective pigeonholes, and some day it is he who gathers the innumerable observations of a specific character together and springs upon the world a Brain system or a Serous Circulation because, he has observed while you were looking. Your seeing abilities will poo-hoo his observations because your penetration is not as sharp as his.

The next immediate step in connection with the brain system is to consider the senses and those organs which have the ability of interpreting the incoming impressions or observations. Man, outwardly, is known to have at least five, but the little pig is just hog enough to express one more. Place him at two or three weeks old in a bag and drive ten or twenty miles away, and, when let alone, he runs home. A sense of direction.

Some women have this perception highly developed. Twist them as much as you will and ask them to locate certain spots in a foreign city and they will do it. Man has more outward senses than he is given credit for. We observe five of the educated mind, but how many more of the

Innate that are unsensed is a question that yet needs determining and future Chiropractic investigation.

Senses are for Innate Intelligence to determine two things: (1) What is going on externally to her castle to protect the inner man, and (2) to know exactly at all times, day and night, what the inner man is doing. Quicker than you and I realize it, after a violent jar, the muscles are suddenly contracted. Your educated did not do. The muscles were drawn taut before you or I knew it. This is but one illustration of how innate, through impressions going inward, preserves the body from force or contusion.

Suppose we should get poisoned; medicine is taken in the form or morphine or laudanum with the intention of committing suicide or thinking it will cure some disease. Innate would immediately adapt her forces by sending impulses which will contract the oesophagus and stomach, purging its contents. You cannot contract your stomach to heave its contents.

A sense is that interpretation that Innate places upon impressions when received at the brain from the external. For instance, we put our finger into hot water. How do we know it is the opposite of cold? The finger alone has no intellectual pursuits. Certain impressions are received at that moment at tactile corpuscles and, interpreted by the brain, which "senses" them.

For instance, we maintain a pointer is square. With our eyes closed we cannot see it. It cannot be smelled or tasted. Then how do we know? By turning it around between the fingers certain impressions follow to the brain. Sense again, is but that interpretation of external things that the Innate places upon impressions. Pain is the interpretation of abnormal external conditions.

Let us dare to observe another link in this chain; an idea that no one else has seen: that directness of the path that carries impressions. Where do these nerves go? Consider the foregoing illustration—through the arm; spinal cord to the brain. There are no switch stations. The impressions proceed in a direct manner; then if that substance is found to be hot it would be dropped. Why? Because your mind interprets it and knows it is damaging to tissue. The muscles contract and draw from it.

If any other school has ever questioned whether there was or was not a sympathetic nervous system, B.J. has not seen it. Schools, medical, have always taken this system as a matter of fact, as being the order of the day, a custom we have long fallen used to. They followed the fashion as a matter of course, and coupled it with the lack of knowledge of a brain, with its mind or mental intelligence. For this mental intelligence they had little less than contempt; turning a cold shoulder upon it; trying to take the starch out of it, to tread or trample it under foot; not caring a continental; considering it all poppycock. It was "small potatoes" and few in a hill; an empty noodle. All this, which has been shown, has made a wall so high and thick that the layman with superstition over his eyes could see so little that attempts to scale this wall were futile. It required a type of man like B. J. Palmer whose observation was deep, concentrated and penetrated to go through and reach the top of this with a home-hewn ladder, this hocus-pocus make-believe, hanging out false colors; throwing tubs to whales propositions. B.J. has scaled this wall, stone by stone, until he stands on top and is capable of observing how small the man below is. The above pulling of wool over one's eyes has been handed down as an heirloom and, with his present faculty, are the first who ever dared to question it. There are indisputable facts, that it is not true. B.J. would say: Briefly—"Sympathy," according to Dunglison, Gould's Dictionary, the encyclopedic medical dictionary, is some trans-formation which takes place in nerves, "by means unknown." This change is supposed to take place in this something kind of a system "by means unknown." You, with a prophetic vision, a flight of fancy, a stretch of imagination, castle building peculiar to yourself; figuring with fanciful numerals, giving rein to your chin music, trying to crack, or cudgel your brain; you are supposed to visit the land of dreams (Health) and deduct the possible factors of ignorance; you, not knowing a hawk from a handsaw, having films over your eyes, and being unable to see or having anything with which to make something. You are supposed to gild the pill with make-believes and gouge it down with a feint and then set the question at rest by being in a perpetual stew. When we have dared to go behind the superstitious fellow who has always shared these mysteries, it clears everything which has been before. Instead of B.J. saying "by means unknown," he definitely states what power it is that expresses these actions and he has proof of what channels this force goes thru. Specific, pure and unadulterated, philosophical Chiropractic has a direct path, from brain to tissue or vice versa, for every nerve ending in tissue, and beginning at the brain. No matter where the fibre is, it must have a starting point at some brain cell. If you can conceive of the grandness or unlimited facilities of that thought, you will see that we have something different from a "sympathetic nervous system." Man is too grand an object to run without a mind that personifies thots or interprets impressions. Therefore, we must discountenance a sympathetic nervous system and drop reflex action because the latter is that change which is supposed to take place in the former. If we disprove one, the other cannot be.

If you comprehend the obstinacy of "reflex action," how it sticks to nothing, is wedded to an opinion, you can then bring into resurrection that which for thousands and thousands of years have been trying to clean out of their heads; which, gathering from the value that has been and is being delivered to humanity, is still consigned to the tomb of the Capulets. You will have a knowledge as basis, equivalent to that oscillation, to and fro; up and down; backwards and forward; wibble-wabble movement that they have in vain tried to subdue but cannot.

For instance, here is a disease and there is a spinal segment. This disease has two nerves. A stimulus takes place at the peripheral of that fibre; goes to spinal cord and somehow (as we are informed) these fibres intercross. They reflect to some fibre somewhere; may go to the spleen; but is just as apt to go to the stomach or heart as the point from which it started. If it "reflects," kisses the rod, licks the dust; humbles itself; is willing to play any one of a thousand fiddle strings (nerve fibres), all is well, but, according to superstition, it must grab, jabber, cackle, rattle, gibble-gabble on the return what it has received. If it wakes a wrong passenger external man howls louder; if luck should allow him to get a few impulses, then he pats himself on the back. It is rebounding disease upon disease, which but makes the disease worse and that is the principle of medicine and osteopathy in accounting for your disease.

When a man starts to reach a certain point he is not ashamed to say so and tell the path thru which he came. When he attends a medical college it is to study medicine. He does not go to study causes, but what little he has is based upon bacteriology—the present fashion. If he is puzzled as to what to name symptoms, when in practice, what must be his position as regards cause, of which he is not posted? B.J. has, during the fifty years, dared to question the sympathetic nervous system and is brave enough in the backbone to place in preference that which you can place your finger upon and say, there is the cause of this disease. Only one, who has discovered and developed the fundamental ideas surrounding these branches, has sufficient grit to maintain the present state of efficiency and continue to unsolve them for future perfection.

Many of the so-called sympathetic diseases are direct responsive actions, what B.J. terms "adapted conditions." It is not a disease and represents no subluxation, but an accommodating change to maintain the first law of Nature—preservation. Your hand was placed against something which burned the flesh and a blister was formed. A blister is not a disease. It can be in some cases of general excessive heat, but not in this instance. Did you ever reason that behind this was an intelligence that thinks? "If we allow that hand to remain it would be burned"? The first layer of the epidermis is raised and a sac of urea is formed. It was created to protect or act as a non-conductor to the excessive heat outside. How often have you noticed when a person was scalded by heat that there were blisters? B.J.'s advice is "leave the blisters alone. Do not prick them." When Innate put them there she had a specific purpose and knew what she was doing. Her superior knowledge is more capable of regulating them. "What God has joined, let no man break asunder," is the Bible's commandment. Don't argue with superiors. When this sac has served its purpose Innate will dispose of it.

We have taken up briefly the analysis of the urinary and alimentary tracts. Chiropractic, differing as it does upon fundamental basis, its superstructure must correspond. It is our aim to have essential principles there and all other studies correspond. We do not mean by that we claim to be cranks or supremely radical, but, looking as we do upon past educations as wrongly based, we must originate new ideas to replace those which are dismissed. When B.J. says an M.D. diagnoses diseases, he means just that. Let us analyze the thought "diagnosing diseases." The M.D. enters a sick room or has a patient at his office. His questions are confined to "What is your disease? Pain so and so, fever, don't urinate, bowels do not move, gas upon the stomach, head dizzy at times." He gathers symptoms—juggles them around, meanwhile churning them through his mental superstitions, seasons with a pinch of a thrice-told tale, doles out a little of a long yarn of hypothetical terms, considering the title with the bullion possessed by the sufferer, and finally delivers the bolus entitled "Misnomer"; adds, subtracts, divides and then multiplies; sums up and down "by means unknown" with symbols of dead languages until he decides that certain sympathetical medicines are worth trying to reflect the disease anywhere else but where it now is. He has "diagnosed" the disease, jumbled the symptoms into one name. When asked "What is the cause"? Causa ealet, vis est notissima. "The cause is hidden; the effects are notorious."

What does the Chiropractor do? "What are your symptoms?" Sixteen, perhaps are named. All of those have one or more subluxations. He knows, just the moment that person says excessive heat of the stomach, that there is (and where it is) a pressure upon a calorific nerve. He has analyzed that symptom back to cause. The patient will tell, "I have a great deal of gas from the stomach." The Chiropractor will say, "That is the result of excessive heat."

Let us go a step farther. The bowels are constipated. The M.D. says, "That is from indigestion." The Chiropractor, "Nerves going there are paralyzed by subluxations." There is pressure upon the nerves which conveys motor mental impulse. He has analyzed symptoms back to cause. Every symptom is followed thru the same analysis, back to primary sources.

Of the following two systems B.J. prefers the urinary, as it is the best to study systematically. We took these vague organs and resolved them back to original tissues. Each was resolved to function. The definite path or avenue of each nerve to each tissue was located. The structures, which combined to make an organ, were found; two or more organs put together, making a system of irrigation, and in the urinary system we found, or grouped together, organs which worked harmoniously. Innate was shown to be capable of coming in contact with every tissue cell both day and night, from life to death. When you can get that specific, you are reaching something which is scientific and cannot be answered in any other form.

We shall next encroach upon what is to B.J. one of the most interesting and necessary physiological truths, long ignored—Serous Circulation. Many have remarked, "It is a surprise that B.J. should have discovered it." His reply was, "That I should have discovered it is not astonishing, but the wonderful feature is, why it was not discovered before?" M.D.'s have been cutting, mutilating, butchering thousands of bodies, both dead and alive, and they have not deduced today anything relative to serous circulation, which we claim is the very material foundation that holds physical man together. You might have a bushel of tissue and unless you add water it flies to the four quarters of the globe. If the cementing material is absent then "dust to dust and earth to earth." The reverting to original conditions is the result. We cannot overlook the fact that serum, urea or water composed two-thirds of our body. While called serous circulation, it is, in a measure, a misnomer, because part of it is urea, and part serum. B.J. has named it serous because that is its central condition. This has been so well carried that a review would be tiresome.

All life is expressed as action, which is motion. Life is the expression of motion, and vice versa. Function is that characteristic expression of energy utilized in motion, which is given a name. Action reverts to the brain, from which its impetus, in the character of mental impulse, starts. Mental impulse enters all tissues and assumes various characters in expression.

"One impulse will be calorific." B.J. is designating character and quality with the term "impulse" rather than to say calorific nerve, secretory nerve, etc. On the reverse, all nerves are nerves and alike, but the impulse varies just as much as vibrations vary. For instance, we could talk into twelve telephones at once, providing all had a connecting trumpet to one large trumpet which centered at our mouth. These twelve telephones would have twenty-four wires. Wires are wires—all alike—yet in a five minutes' conversation we presume there would be possibly 4,000 different characters of vibrations passing over these wires.

It is the character of the vibration, passing over the wire which makes the sound different at the other end. It would be foolish to say hot wire, cold wire, simply because that word indicates the current passing over the wire, or the character. Vibration is what makes the difference at the other end of the wire—not that the wires differ. It is the impulse that is calorific, excretive, reparative, etc., because impulses differ in the number of foruns that come together to make that particular mentiforun.

0								0
B.C.								T.C.
I	am	go-ing		down	town	to	see	Wales.
1	1	1	1	1	1	1	1	1
0	0	0	0	0	0	0	0	0
4	3	1	1	6	7	9	0	9
2	2	9	8	9	4	7	8	2
4	2	2	4	3	8	3	6	2

We want this sentence to pass from the brain cell to the tissue cell because we want the intelligence behind that cell to receive the successive series of vibrations and interpret them. We will say that the steady, permanent voltage, passing afferently along this wire is equivalent to 10,000 vibrations per second for a given distance, between the tissue cell and the brain cell (which we will say by way of illustration is four feet). The consideration of quantity, time and distance is entered. When we enter quantity, time and distance, we are beginning to consider speed as a requisite.

We have said that this steady voltage of 10,000 vibrations is the normal flow of currents. The 10,000 vibrations are going to pick up 424 vibrations when the word "I" is spoken. That passes on out to the tissue cell; then in the next second the person uses the word "am," which is equivalent to 322 vibrations; immediately the 10,000 vibrations pick up the word and that travels on, immediately following the one above, and then the word "go" comes on and the syllable "ing," and it travels onward after the rest; then we take the last word, "Wales." The permanent vibration of 10,000 picks up 922 additional vibrations.

Now, we notice that each quantity of vibration is different, consequently each character of vibration, when it reaches the brain cell, is immediately interpreted so you have a succession of very rapid interpretations taking place at the brain cell; as fast as they keep coming in they are interpreted until the sentence is finished and the sum total of eight quantities is idealized, until you have the ideation: "I am going down town to see Wales."

We have said that 424 vibrations go to make up the word "I," then I is made up of 424 given units of force and we call these force units FORUNS. When they reach the brain cell they reach an ENCEFORUN; the brain cell forun acts upon one of these force units, technically known as an AFFNEUROFORUN, and interprets it; the process of interpretation is called INTERPREFORUN and is interpreted by the MENTIFORUN; then comes the return half of the cycle.

Whatever force the educated brain gets comes from Innate. The educated brain (mind) says "It," but we took "we" to say it. We get all our intelligence and thought from one source, altho we have two brains divided into two lobes or portions. The educated brain in itself can do nothing without the power which comes from the Innate mind; so you say, where did I get the power to say "it"? I did not say it—we did.

You have received from the periphery an impression, or a successive series of impressions which are equivalent to successive grades or quantities of vibrations. You have interpreted them and this brings forth the necessary intellectual adaptation—the adaptation is in your brain cell in order to have a thought—"I am going down town to see Wales." Suppose we had been telling you something about Wales which causes you to think you, too, will go to see him.

The brain cell is like a factory; it begins to manufacture, thru the process of transformation, thoughts which are products just as much as the juices of the body, etc. Thoughts are the expression of the function of brain cells in the thinker brain. For you to have the thought in mind that I am going down town to see Wales you had to form vibrations equivalent to those which I received. As your thoughts were manufactured they traveled to the point of interpretation.

The educated brain is active thinking about the topic of conversation passing between itself and another educated brain, the subject being, for example, beefsteak and potatoes. Presently the other party leaves—you are alone—practically no impressions are being received, externally, which would have any possible relation or bearing upon the Matterhorn in Switzerland, and yet we find without any apparent incentive the mind blends from the things before us to things thousands of miles away, and we wonder why, or how.

This is but drawing upon the impressions which have already been interpreted and recorded in the educated mind (memory), perhaps hours, weeks or years before, when we have read an article or seen an illustration of the Matterhorn, then gradually blending with the Matterhorn a distinctly original idea comes forth which has never been thought before by human mind; i.e., so far as we can find trace of it. There has been no impression made upon the educated mind regarding this subject, because it has not existed in the realm of analytical thought, printed or spoken, so far as we know. Where did that thought come from?

Innate intelligence in Infinite—it knows everything. All things, all places, altho its individualized labor is confined to one body. But for a perfect body to be made, the mind behind had to have an education upon many other correlative facts which seemingly obliterate this connection or communication with the human body, which facts are really necessary to be able to make material education in our material body.

The thoughts coming from apparently original sources are but the very close communion between the Innate Mind, through its definite function, of creation of Innate thoughts in the Innate brain; then the transmission of these thoughts thru the Innate brain over efferent fibres to the educated brains where they are received as impressions. The impressions are in turn presented in the educated brain as apparently a new thought—they are interpreted to the best ability of the educated mind in the educated brain and are consequently educationally expressed. While they are original thoughts to the educated mind, they are "old as the hills" to the Innate Mind—the educated world now has an "original" thought coming from the "Innate mind."

Going back to our first illustration, we wish to impress upon you the fact that Innate Intelligence is so powerful that she can be forming the words and express others simultaneously. She can be forming 100 words, transmit 100 words and express 100 words, and do it all in a continuous and endless stream, so much so that these thoughts are poured forth much as rains from the heavens, a continuous flow of thoughts, a continuous volume of words being expressed at the afferent ending of nerves.

This brings to our minds again the idea of how nicely Innate Intelligence modifies the quality of vibrations to suit the adaptation necessary under our observations. We wish to know definitely just how quickly one cycle takes place, from the moment the vibration is received until it has passed thru all the processes back to the intellectual adaptation.

As long as no pressure exists 10,000 voltage is normal, and when you say "I" 10,242 is still normal—equivalent to natural stages; each one of those is the limit under the circumstances; each is the capacity at that time, considering the circumstances that it is dealing with; each word is its capacity at that moment, but we must have some basis to stand on. We do not know how much power is passing thru this telephone, but as soon as the receiver is taken off, we have made connection and the word travels on.

We next assumed the subject of functions. Function is characteristic action. All life is expressed as action, which is motion. Life is the expression of motion, and vice versa.

Function is that characteristic expression of energy, utilized in motion, which is given a name. Action reverts to the brain from which its impetus, in the character of mental impulse, starts. Mental impulse enters all tissues and assumes characters in expression. That is, one impulse will be calorific; others, excretory, secretory; reparatory, etc. The motor function causes churning food in the stomach, or issues juice to lubricate the mouth. The function is but naming a peculiar type of action.

In the foundation of function we led every motor impulse to the brain, giving it a starting point, which the M.D. does not do. He does not know where it comes from or what it is. His study is incomplete. He looks upon man from a physical standpoint and fixes up a chemical compound and gives it to the physical disease. If he ever gets beyond the feathering of his nest, taking care of number one, furthering some professional end, he says it is "Nature," which is significant but not making both ends meet; out at the elbows; dead broke; is being put to flight by a person who is on the scent in hunting for facts.

Chiropractic has assumed a new position, thrown aside the worn clothes; has bought no pigs in the poke, tempting superstitions; assumed no false pretenses without ballast, happen what may basis; but on the contrary has mounted guard; reached sure ground; made the coast clear; come forth from the dusky woods; caused storms to be blown over and has analyzed what Innate is, where Innate works, what Innate does, how she does it, and putting it thru that analysis gives us the philosophical knowledge that today stands unequaled.

We also want to bring out briefly what Chiropractic is. In the Science of Chiropractic, Vol. 1, (by B. J. Palmer), we find it is the science of cause of disease, and art of adjusting that by hand. Bear in mind the emphasis that we place upon those words. It is not a science of disease, but its cause. Chiropractic students, when graduating, have spent but a small portion of their time studying symptoms of diseases; the largest part is devoted to causes, what they are and how to correct them, by hand adjustment. That is Chiropractic work.

Let us analyze cause. Man is composed of two structures, soft and hard. It is a positive fact that the brain (soft tissue) transforms impulses. These pass thru soft substances, nerves, until they are deposited at a tissue cell, which is still a soft material. All that which makes power and expresses it is a soft matter.

We know of no other portion of the body, aside from the spinal column, where the nerves (soft substances) are surrounded, entirely by hard substances. We know that frequently they lie up against a hard substance and may be surrounded by same on three sides, but there is always remaining an avenue of escape on the other side, and it is only when they are entirely surrounded that they can be constricted; not otherwise.

Do nerves—soft substances—pass through, around, or are they encompassed entirely by a hard substance? The brain is enclosed within the skull, which is its dome. Thru the vertebral column is a long canal containing the spinal cord. From this issue bundles of nerves thru little openings, formed upon the sides of the spinal column, technically called intervertebral foramina. These apertures can be enlarged or made smaller by normal or abnormal movements of vertebrae upon their articulations.

Suppose, while performing the thousand and one occupations, you receive a sudden wrench, twist or strain; cause a subluxation; make that or those openings smaller than normal and cause a constriction. Can you not see that occlusion would shut off the transmission of mental impulses, that which is power to a body thru nerves? Shut off force and what is the result? Inability to perform action. Partial lack of action means disease; if complete, it is death. No action—death; partial action —abnormal conditions; partial death—disease.

The disease producer, in man and woman, the cause of all diseases is in subluxations of vertebrae, impinging nerves as they pass thru the spinal column, at various regions, because that is the only place in the human body where it is possible to have a nerve so constricted as to shut off mental impulses. There is no other place where nerves are surrounded by bone. Therefore, Chiropractic is fundamentally based around an exact and precise knowledge of the spinal column, because that is man's backbone. You have heard the quotation, "Brace up; show the world you have backbone."

In B. J. Palmer's chapter, "Disease; What It Is and Its Cause," the first elaboration was upon the inability or excess of action—disease. Only two are a possibility; that tissue in which there is not enough action or its opposite, too much; as shown in Diabetes or Bright's Disease of the kidneys. The bowels may represent the two contrasts, as in diarrhoea and constipation. The same is true of heat or any other function. Just what name symptoms ought to have depends upon who is to entitle them; in what way he proceeds and what process is used. The M.D. diagnoses symptoms and re-echoes thousands of diseases. What difference does it make whether you have a temperature of 98.1 or 98.6, and the different grades constitute a disease? The cause is the same—it is a graded degree of pressure, from 1 to 100 per cent—it is a different grade of pressure, and why dwell upon it at length?

The Chiropractor analyzes effects of two diseases, excess or lack of, any one or a number of combinations between nine primary functions. The naming of the cause is our profession.

According to medical principles the latitude between opinions is only restricted to the number of physicians who see the case. One man, for example, called upon and paid for sixteen different examinations by the best physicians in New York City. For an answer to "What was the disease," he received sixteen different diagnoses to the same symptoms given.

B.J. elaborates very carefully the allegorical illustration of man as compared with a factory. He likened him to a complete factory with its many machines, and as they were brought to light we could see how much greater man was than the factory and how man displays greater discerning judgment considering the factory than when considering self or family. In mechanical work there are only 310 movements, and they are in the human body.

Man cannot make a ball and socket joint so nice, a ball-bearing proposition so perfect but what he will find its superior in the human body.

17

—•◆•—

NINE PRIMARY FUNCTIONS

IN THIS CHAPTER B.J. will take up the nine primary functions of the body. Before that he will briefly review the important parts of the nervous system that we should bear in mind while reading the nine primary functions.

First, we have the nervous system, composed of nervous tissue, the most delicate and highly developed of the four elementary tissues, the larger portion being found in the cranium and called the brain. These brain centers have elongated portions called nervous or nerve fibres. They are formed in the brain and converge toward the base of the skull where they form the spinal cord, pass down through the spinal canal and give off thirty-one pairs of nerves to the various parts of the body. That makes thirty-one nerves on each side of the body. These nerves leave the neural canal in pairs through the foramen and pass to all parts of the body. They are all the same in structure but different in function. The one carrying or conveying the mental impulses or the vital force from the brain to the tissue is called the efferent nerve, and the one conveying the mental impulse from the tissue back to the brain is called the afferent nerve.

These functions are called: Motor, Sensory, Secretory, Excretory, Calorific, Nutrition, Expansion, Reparation and Reproduction. Each of these has an abbreviation which stands for the word.

302

M—Motor.
S—Sensory.
T—Secretion.
E—Excretion.
R—Reparatory.
C—Calorific.
N—Nutrition.
X—Expansion.
Y—Reproduction.

Can these nine primary functions exist merely by the transmission of mental impulse to the cells themselves? Or, can mental impulse alone be expressed in the tissue cell? In other words, you might ask for an explanation of anabolism to outline the action of the impulse. In the process of anabolism three things are necessary. Food is required; it is taken into the mouth where it is masticated and comes in contact with salivary glands; it passes down the alimentary canal and is taken into the stomach where gastric juices act upon it. There are various chemical and other changes here and then it goes into the intestines, or at least what remains goes there, for the mucous membrane of the stomach has absorbed some of it. In the intestines it undergoes intestinal digestion; and that which has not been absorbed is excreted. After the intestinal digestion, the process of digestion is complete. All parts of the food which were soluble have been absorbed and will be used by the various parts of the body.

With food alone the cells cannot expand and grow, something else is essential and that is oxygen. We obtain oxygen through the air by purification in the lungs. The blood is made up of two kinds of corpuscles, the white and the red—the red being given their color by the hemoglobin—during respiration, oxygen passed from the air sac cells of the lungs, through the blood vessels and the oxygen is carried to every part of the body, to every tissue and cell.

The third thing which is necessary is mental impulse. These are carried to every part of the body, even the most minute parts of the nervous system.

The result of the harmonious union of the food, oxygen and mental impulse is anabolism or function. In other words, if some food is carried to the cell after it has been digested, if we breathe in air and oxygen is carried to the cell, if the mental impulses are carried to the cell, then we have as a result of this the function of anabolism.

The mental impulse acts as a spark which unites the oxygen with the food and the food with the oxygen. It is transformed so that it can become a part of the tissue cell of the body, which, without any nutrition, could not exist. For example, the nutrition is carried to the right arm and the three functions are working together. The result is life in that arm. Without any one of the three essentials, food, oxygen and mental impulse, that arm will not grow as it should; there will be a condition known as atrophy.

In outlining each of these, B.J. found that the first function is motor. This has to do with the tonicity of muscle fibres; whether they are in the proper tone or not.

Next, the sensory function has to do with the sensations to be felt.

Then we have calorific, which has to do with heat.

The function of excretion is that which has to do with the elimination of any material or fluid which is found in the body, which is of no value or that is poisonous or injurious to the body.

Nutrition is that function which has to do with anabolism, as B.J. just described.

Expansion is that function which has to do with the growth of new tissue.

Reparation is that function which has to do with the replacing of old worn out cells or exhausted cells in the body, with new ones.

Reproduction is that function which has to do with the production of the species.

B.J. said before that it was necessary for three things to make normal function. We know that there are only nine different kinds of function. For instance, if we have the combination of food, oxygen and mental impulse the result is nutrition. With food, oxygen, mental impulse and calorific, the result is heat. Does the mental impulse act upon the food or oxygen alone? No, there must be the harmonious union for normal function.

We know that all muscles of the body are made of many bundles of fibres. Each is supplied by each one of the nine primary functions through nerves. Muscle fibres are also endowed with the power of contractility, as long as the muscle fibre is receiving 100 parts of normal motor function there is normal tonicity.

Take the sensory function. There are in various parts of the body in the skin small organs, called tactile end organs and sometimes end bulbs. Each end organ is supplied by sensory nerves or nerves having the sense of feeling. When any impression is applied (and by that B.J. means any external agent, a chair, table, heat or cold, or any change), when it comes in contact with the end bulb or touch corpuscles, the impression is taken up and sent over the afferent nerve to the brain where it is interpreted. You may think the pain is in the finger, but it occurs back in the mind. There are various kinds of impressions, but that can be taken up at at another time.

Take Secretion; this is a function which has to do with the glands, both internal and superficial, such as the stomach is lined with mucous membrane which contains glands which secrete. The liver, the largest gland, is supplied by nerves which give it the power of secreting bile. There are many glands in the body, and they all have the power of secreting.

Excretion is that function which throws off from the body anything which is harmful or poisonous to it. There are certain poisons being constantly formed in the body and, if conditions are not abnormal, this substance is excreted. If the excretory apparatus is not acting normally, it causes an accumulation of poisonous material in the body. It is dammed back and there is disease. Those organs which have to do with excreting waste are the bowels, kidneys, skin, and lungs. In the lungs the carbon dioxide is purified and the bad air is given off, and the pure air is carried away by means of the blood to all parts of the body. In the kidneys, we have the excretion of poisonous materials in the form of a fluid. The bowels excrete all solid material which is of no value to the body or injurious to it. The sweat glands of the skin work in conjunction with the kidneys in excreting fluid; they excrete sweat, and help in cooling the temperature of the body. All these excreted substances are of no value to the body.

Reparation is that function which has to do with the replacing of old worn out cells with new ones. They can become duplicated to a certain extent and can be repaired by nutrition to some degree, but when cells become old and worn out, they have to be replaced by new ones which come from cell centers throughout the body. The process by which these are replaced is called reparation. B.J. wants to say here that expansion, nutrition and reparation work in harmony one with the other.

Then the last of the functions is reproduction. This is a function which is located in the generative organs and is practically the same in both sexes. In the female, the ovary secretes the ova, and the ova is the female element of the fetus of the future child. The testes of the male secretes the spermatozoon which is the male element of the fetus. These two become united in the fundus of the uterus of the female, where the blastoderm is formed. It is first composed of two layers but later a third layer forms. There is the hypoblast, the epiblast and mesoblast. Hypoblast is developed into the epithelium and the lining of the alimentary canal; the epiblast forms the skin and nervous system and the mesoblast forms the muscular and intervening tissue. This function may be absent in either of the sexes.

18

———◦•◦———

EXCESS OF FUNCTION—HOW?

B.J. WANTS TO PRESENT what is known in electrical problems as Ohm's Law. Possibly, many are familiar with that law, but undoubtedly many are not. A good knowledge of Ohm's Law will assist you in understanding what we mean with 100 per cent of power or force through 100 per cent of matter per 100 per cent of time, etc. B.J. wants to explain what relation one bears to the other, so that knowing any two of the three you can always get the third.

In all electrical problems this rule applies, we deal with the electromotive force, the current and the resistance through which the current flows. A change in one of the three will make a change in the other two, or possibly, in one of the other two. That is, a change in the electromotive force may make a change in the current but not in the resistance, the resistance remaining constant. B.J. will explain, if he can, how you can determine what the current would be with a given electro-motive force and a given resistance. You can apply this explanation to your Chiropractic problems; B.J. will give it electrically.

Ohm's law is based upon the fact that one ampere of current will flow one ohm of resistance as a result of the application of one volt of pressure. The three divisions of electricity—the voltage, current and resistance—are named after investigators and scientists who have made the discoveries of the unit of force, or current and of resistance. Ampere, a Frenchman, was the discoverer of a unit of force, and Ohm, a Dane, was the discoverer of the unit of resistance; voltage named after Volta.

So, in all electrical problems we have electro-motive force and resistance or ohms. We call the electro-motive force "voltage," the currents, "amperes." When we say "current" we mean the total amount of currents passing through a given circuit. When we want to state the exact amount of currents passing through that circuit we name it in amperes, and the amount of resistance in ohms. Ohm's law states that the current in any electrical circuit is equal to the electro-motive force divided by the resistance, from which we get the following formulas:

Current equals Electro-Motive Force divided by R.;
E.-M. F. equals Current multiplied by Resistance;
Resistance equals E.-M. F. divided by Current.

If we make a change in the electro-motive force, the current will vary directly with it; that is, if we increase the E.-M. F. we increase the current, if we decrease the E.-M. F. we decrease the current. But if we make a change in the resistance, the current will vary inversely with the change; that is, if we increase the resistance we decrease the current, if we decrease the resistance we increase the current.

We will take, for instance, a dynamo capable of manufacturing 100 volts of current, a lamp connected to the dynamo with a resistance of 100 ohms. We wish to get that amount of current we will have, as a result, 100 volts acting through 100 ohms of resistance. Dividing the voltage by the resistance, we get one, so one ampere would be the result. B.J. doesn't expect you will grasp this at once, but it is as simple as "A, B, C," being a mere matter of multiplication or division. When it comes to working and figuring out cycles, pressure upon nerves, which is the interference with the flow of mental impulses which is a sort of resistance in the circuit, for the nerves are part of the circuit, you will find that Ohm's Law will help you greatly in getting a good clear working idea.

Q.—How would you burn out that globe?

A.—By increasing the E.-M.F.

Q.—Increasing the speed of the motor or the size of the motor—something to that effect?

A.—That would be increasing your E.-M. F. There is a capacity to every electrical machine. If that machine is, in any way, worked to a higher speed than the machine's capacity, so as to manufacture more than its maximum capacity, something will have to give away, it may be the machine or the lamp may burn out. For instance, the lamp requires one ampere to bring it up to 16 candle power of light. If we introduce one and one-half amperes, we shorten the life of that lamp. If we were to double the current and force going to the lamp, it would burn out instantly.

Q.—Could you do that by a rheostat?

A.—No, for the rheostat is a resistance. The lamp in a circuit is a necessary resistance, while the rheostat in an artificial resistance, inserted there for the purpose of using the excess of current.

The current is lowered by the introduction of the additional resistance offered by the rheostat. As I said, any change in the resistance will work an opposite change on the current; that is, increasing the resistance will decrease the current, etc. When you introduce the rheostat, you are increasing the resistance, not the current.

Q.—Is there a method by which the current can be made greater?

A.—Yes; there are step-up and step-down transformers. On the alternating current we have both, either one way or the other.

Q.—Would that resistance bring an excess on the transmitter?

A.—Yes.

Q.—By that excess of resistance?

A.—Would the insertion of resistance in an electrical circuit bring an excess on the transmitter. Is that your meaning?

Q.—Yes.

A.—Do you mean: Would it bring an excess of current flowing through?

Q.—Yes.

A.—Yes, by either increasing the E.-M. F. or decreasing the resistance. For instance, if we have a 200-ohm lamp in the circuit, we have a resistance of 200 ohms; if we take that lamp out and insert a lamp with 150 ohms or 100 ohms resistance, we increase the current in proportion to the amount we decrease the resistance.

If you wish to insert resistance in your circuit and still maintain the same amount of current, you will have to increase your E.-M. F.

Q.—Does this problem explain to you readers how you can have an excess of mental impulses by a subluxation?

A.—We think that we can show that, where the pressure upon certain nerves having certain functions will decrease the amount of mental impulses, resulting in a disarrangement of the function in the tissue cells to which the nerves lead, which would leave too excessive a function on the other functions concerned.

Q.—That would not be Chiropractic, would it?

A.—Nerve functions are of an electrical character, and where you interfere with the proportions of ingredients in any chemical composition, you change the nature of the whole. For instance, the comparison of manufacturing vinegar. Say, for instance, we had citric acid and wished to make vinegar. We would have 100 per cent of acid and 100 per cent of water combined, and we would have a dilution which we would call "vinegar;" but if we should put in but 50 per cent of water, then we would have a different solution altogether, stronger and more active. It takes 100 per cent of one function added to 100 per cent of another to produce a certain effect in any tissue cell. The cutting off and abridging of one function will alter the other so that it will act in excess. In the cutting off of 50 per cent function in one nerve, the functions of the other nerves to a tissue cell need not necessarily be curtailed in their expression, making it below normal. They would be performing their function up to 100 per cent but they would be lacking 50 per cent of the function disturbed, so that we would have a disarrangement of the chemical process. That is all disease is—a combination of chemicals, normal or abnormal. When all nerves are free to act, we have a normal performance of the chemicals of the body; when there is any interference with any nerve or any set of nerves, we have a disarrangement of the chemicals of the body, and disease is the result of the action of the poisons which are the result of the chemical disarrangement.

In our general premises there are three things we consider, viz., force, matter and time. It takes force to move matter, it takes matter to be moved by force; without force and matter there would be nothing in motion, without motion there would be no vibration, without vibration there would be no life. Whenever force acts through matter or force passes between the atoms of matter, it takes a certain percentage of time. We say that it takes one hour for the large hand of the clock to get from the figure "12" around the circle. The hand, as it is being moved upon by force, represents matter changing position, and it took an hour for a certain amount of force to move a certain amount of matter around the cycle once.

You can take any consideration of anything material that is being moved by immaterialities, and it takes time to do it. For instance, we have 100 per cent of Innate force which acts upon 50 per cent of spermatozoon and 50 per cent of ovum, which two being combined make 100 per cent of matter, called the "embryo." The 100 per cent of force and the 100 per cent of matter acting together represent absolutely nothing until we add the ratio of time or 280 days. Two hundred and eighty days to do what? To accomplish a normal unit. It would be impossible to say, "Given 100 per cent of force and 100 per cent of matter and you would have a child," because that would not be true. You must add to it 100 per cent of force acting through 100 per cent of matter in 280 days and we will have a child.

How long it takes a thought in a brain to travel from there to a tissue cell at the tip of the finger and return to the brain cell is computed to be 100 feet per second. Even time here becomes a factor.

If a man is well today and six months from now sick, you cannot expect to get him well in one minute of time. Time must be taken as the third factor. In the majority of your considerations, you think of force and matter, but you do not add the third element—time—into your equation as you generally argue and debate upon these things amongst yourselves as students.

B.J. has stated what would be necessary to make the normal child. Supposing we had 100 per cent of force acting upon the same kind of 100 per cent of matter in only 140 days. We would have half a child, the reason being not but that the amount of force or matter was normal for the given space of time in which it was working, but the time was only one-half of what it should be. Supposing, on the reverse, that it were possible to have 100 per cent of force acting upon 100 per cent of matter in 340 days. The product would be a child too large, not but that the force or matter was right in quantity, but that the given amount of time to the space where located was excessive, consequently the product is unequal.

Take the given illustration. Here is 100 per cent of force per 100 per cent of matter per 280 days; the child is born weighing six pounds, which is a trifle below normal; the child lives, and at ten years weighs 16 pounds; at twenty years is only 24 inches in height and weighs 20 pounds; the child lives to forty and is 32 inches in height and weighs 50 pounds. There is evidently something wrong. This individual is commonly known as an anomaly, a pigmy or dwarf, and is exhibited as "a freak of nature." Nature makes no freaks; it is the perversion to the acts of "nature" that makes freaks. What was wrong in this "pigmy"? The amount of matter was deposited originally; the amount of force was ready to be expressed, but the amount of time has shown that at forty years we have only the work accomplished that should have been done with a boy of eight. In other words, he is still living at eight years with a growth of matter over forty years of time. He is growing too slow. The amount of force that actually got inactivity into the matter was reduced. In other words, there is only one-fifth of the force per five-fifths of the time.

Take the opposite result. A child is born at the end of 280 days, and weighs eight pounds; inside of two years weighs 60 pounds; in ten years the child weighs 460; so we might go along until we get to records of people weighing seven or eight hundred pounds. What occurred? Take the concrete example of where the person at forty weighs five times more than the average human being. The force that acted through the matter was greater, the matter was approximately the same except as the pro-ratio increased, but the time in which this force acted was much reduced. That is, the person was living the weight of ninety years when thirty.

B.J. will explain this differently by saying: If one gains a pound a day, and loses just a little less than a pound a day, he gains in weight and grows; if a person gains more than he loses above this ratio, he increases in weight and decreases less than he ought; consequently fattens.

Take the illustration that we use so often of tumors. If we lose one cell a minute and we have another cell take its place in the same minute, it is a condition of normality; but, if, as we lose one cell three cells come to take its place per minute of time, we would have two more cells than is normal per that amount of time. You keep that growth, for hours, days and weeks, and eventually you have a tumor. If that condition be prevalent all over in adipose tissue, we call him or her the fattest man or the fattest woman in the world, the idea being that we have "two-more" tissue cell than is normal per one minute of time. For every cell that increases above its ratio, there must be a forun of force to increase it; consequently our matter has increased, and the time in which this should have taken place has decreased. He is living three times as fast as he should per the amount of time in which he lives, for that individual's full life should have been ninety years and he would have used up all his cells in reserve in early youth, and at thirty his ossific and other cell centers would have been depleted, then he would have died the "natural death"; but if he uses them three times as fast, and in that ratio, when he is thirty he will die because he will have used up all of the cells in reserve.

The amount was normal, he was simply living ninety years of time in thirty years. Consequently, we may say he lived three speeds of life in one physical period of existence. At thirty years he will die. There is not an excess in the amount of force or in the amount of matter, because there could be more matter than what was in reserve, there could be no more force than the amount of reserve demanded to be used, but the amount of time was reduced, consequently the action was excessive.

We have a tank above which holds one hundred gallons of water, a tank below which is filled with one hundred gallons of air, a pipe between that is able to carry one gallon per minute. How long will it take to transfer this water from one tank to the other? One hundred minutes. One gallon goes from the tank above to the tank below in one minute of time. Supposing this aperture of this pipe was reduced so that only one-half gallon went through per minute. How long would it take to fill the tank below? Two hundred minutes. You see where there is a lack of current. Supposing, on the reverse, the pipe remained the same size but the pressure on the water above became twice as great, and the water rushed through at the rate of two gallons per minute. How long would it take to fill the tank below? Fifty minutes. In any one of the three illustrations you haven't added any more matter in the form of water; you haven't added any more force in the illustrations, but you have transformed it from one to the other in different periods of time by increasing or decreasing the period of time in which the act took place, which increase or decrease was brought about by increased or decreased pressure. In electricity we can place a rheostat upon the path of the positive current, which will introduce a resistance to the transmission of the current, and introduce an element of minus quantity at the other end. We can introduce a transformer or a "booster," and we can lessen the resistance and increase the amount of current at the other end.

The three elements remain the same—force, matter and time. We see where we can offer resistance to the transmission of currents, and we see where there is a lesser amount of resistance offered with the subluxation.

B.J. does not know, however, of an experiment that has been worked by people that beats the water company. They place a meter below the main carrying pipe, which is small. On the inside of the meter is a dial. The water, as it come into the pipe, registers its force upon the dial. If the pipe is a small one, the water goes through quickly and with great force, hits the dial hard, registers a high amount of water used, especially when the outlet pipe from the meter is a large one which takes the water away quickly. If you want to beat the water company, reverse the pipes, put the large one on the incoming side, the small pipe on the outgoing side. The amount of water comes in easily, touches the dial lightly, does not register high, the small pipe going from helps to hold the water into the meter and keeps the dial from registering high. Thus, you get the same amount and in the same time and at less cost than you would if you were to let the water company fix your meter.

Here is the same amount of force used, same amount of water, time is equal; in one place it registered a high dial measurement, in the other less.

Man's normal temperature is 98.6, as it averages. We know that because thermometer tests have proven it to our satisfaction. We know that at other times the thermometer will register 104 and 105; still other times will register between 90 and 98. This thermometer represents a fluctuation above and below; doing nothing more than registering the activity of structure. When tissue works fast, high heat; when it is slow, low heat; when a wire vibrates high we have high sound, when low we have low. We know that the body fluctuates in speed of activity in its normal and abnormal functions; and, as matter functionates quickly or slowly, just so fast or slow must the currents be in their transmission.

Supposing we divide a fever in three periods—incubation period, that is when the man was normal. Then he reaches the maximum of temperature, that is the feverish period; it may drop from time to time and come up again, but the time B.J. means is when it reaches its maximum the first time and reaches its maximum for the last time. The third period is during recuperation, or, in eruptive fevers, the period of desquamation. Putting them in another form, the period of invasion, the fever period and the sweat period.

Take up the normal period. The conditions are 100 percent of caloricity that being the name for this particular kind of force—is acting through 100 per cent of matter in 100 per cent of time; the product is 98.6. To make it more explanatory, we will have 100 per cent of temperature. The second period shows that we have 100 per cent of force acting through 100 per cent of matter, but we have shortened the time in which it is acting. The result is that our temperature is high. In the third period we have 100 per cent of force working through 100 per cent of matter in an elongated amount of time, and the temperature is lowered.

We have 100 per cent of electricity going into a 100 per cent globe in 50 per cent of time. How long would our globe exist? We would have twice as much electricity going into the globe as was necessary to give us a normal standard which was 100 per cent of candle power per 100 per cent of time. We would theoretically have 200 per cent of candle power in 50 per cent of the time. We would burn out the carbon in the globe. In fact, that is what causes carbons to burn out. Reversing that order, we have 100 per cent of electricity going through 100 per cent of matter in 200 per cent of time. How much candle power would we have? Just one-half of what we should have, or the globe would burn twice as long, time computed. Now, you see, we haven't lost the original standard of the amount of matter, which was 100 per cent; but the time in which these two got together has fluctuated which made them appear to be in excess or in minus.

Coming back to B.J.'s original fever illustration, we find that the temperature of this man was—conceding that the fever period is three weeks of time—for the first week 100 per cent; we find that for the second week it was 105 per cent. To again reach our standard of time, force and matter being equal, the third week the temperature must drop to 95 per cent per the given amount of time to again give the possibility of starting out even on our fourth week with 100 per cent of force acting through 100 per cent of matter in 100 per cent of time to establish 98.6 degrees. In all pathological conditions wherever there is an excess there must be a minus. The excess and the minus can not be at the same time, and usually are not, but there always come these two following each other closely and it matters not which comes first.

You have a case of typhoid. The fever is up for a period of time, the percentage is high, and the patient is stron ;, feels able to do things; but once the fever goes down the patient feels temperature is low and he feels weak. He is going through the period of recuperation. Notice the drop is in ratio as before there was the rise. In other words, the time must be equalized in the performance of functions.

There is where the damage follows stimulation. Stimulate and you must go through the inhibition period following. You who have taken Turkish baths, know how good you feel while taking the bath; but, if you watched, you noticed a sensation of drowsiness, like lying down to sleep afterward. You relax to compensate for the good feeling you experienced while taking the bath. That is true of all pathological conditions, which goes to show that Innate understands the equalization of force and matter with two given spaces of pathological time in which she acts.

We see a case of paralysis agitans. Theoretically we say that he has too much force, working 150 per cent of force through 100 per cent of matter in 100 per cent of time. In reality he is not doing that. He is working 100 per cent of force through 100 per cent of matter in a diminished amount of time. If you observe that man during sleep, you would find that he does not shake, no paralysis agitans then, because paralysis agitans is an educated abnormal function. In other words, it is but the educated muscles that are agitated. Could you watch his period of relaxation and measure it, you would find he would drop below the percentage of relaxation that you or I experience who have not paralysis agitans. The degree of agitation that occurs during waking hours is compensated for at night time by an extra relaxation, so as to equalize the two periods of time, the amount of force of all times being 100 per cent working through 100 per cent of matter.

The great trouble in our observations is that it is hard to explain why one speck is as we see it. Go to the bedside of a feverish patient, put in the thermometer, and it registers 105. We say that the condition is "too much fever," therefore there is too much function, too much function means "too much force." The amount of matter is the same—100 per cent. That analysis would theoretically show the hypothesis of 105 per cent of force working through 100 per cent of matter plus that given space of normal time. We should observe both, the periods of fever and chilliness, and contrast those in their relation with the time, force and matter.

We observe a case, today, without taking into consideration the possibility of the state of that case tomorrow when he is in the opposite condition—and in every case there are two opposites. B.J. has said there were in reality, two diseases, (1) where there is an excess and (2) is a minus of function. We should, in reality, say that there is but one disease having two counterparts, excess of function being the viewpoint of one half and minus of function being the other, and those two form the whole of the disease, consequently should be so considered. In both phases (if regarded as one), the amount of force and matter equalize to the standard of 100 per cent but intensify the time to one-half and there is an excess; reduce the time observed and there is minus. If we do not inject the thought of time we are at a loss to know where we are at in our analysis. One half draws upon the other, or the other one-half has been drawn upon. Today, with the fever, draws on tomorrow's normality, tomorrow's relaxation was drawn upon by yesterday's fever.

Right on this point B.J. brings out an idea that is new. We have never heard it mentioned any place else. We have two kinds of temperature, one being the increased normal and the other is the abnormal or excessive temperature. We will say my temperature is 98.6. There is a certain possibility that B.J. possesses, of increasing or decreasing that temperature within a normal range. It would not be abnormal if he should go out in the sun, run a half-mile and perspire freely. Put a thermometer in B.J.'s mouth, you would find that his temperature would be 98.6, although he feels several degrees hotter. That would not be pathological, but a normal increased temperature. Suppose B.J. sat down in a room at, we will say, 20 degrees above zero and he doesn't move; if his functions be normal his temperature will not reduce but work faster and compensate. A thermometer put in his mouth would show his temperature is still 98.6. Supposing it dropped, that would be a normal decreased temperature because it is working within the normal range of his possibility. If, without normally doing something to increase the temperature, it should rise or fall, even within the range of figures given, that would be a pathological change in temperature. Thus, there are two kinds of raising or lowering of temperatures, that which is normal in activity and that which is pathological.

19

---•---

GERMS DO CAUSE DISEASE

ARE GERMS AN ACCESSORY or a necessity? They seem to be an accessory to promote the welfare of unhealthy mankind; they are not a necessity to those who are hale and hearty.

To apply the present question of therapeutics and theology, we would be led to believe that when this world was made there were all kinds of germs put into it and made as closely normal, as near perfect as could be, and somewhere, lurking in their minds, was given the devilish idea to kill everything they could, get rid of products like themselves. That seems to be the medical interpretation of man and the facts of life. Germs are an accessory under the schematic arrangement of this world. They are necessary to sustain animal and vegetable lives. The germs eat dead matter. His mission is to eat it as quickly as he can so as not to leave it to clog the channels of a living body. Think of that, as a fundamental, and you won't find germs trying to kill you and your family.

B.J. fails to see in his interpretation of things, where any of us are anything else but scavengers. We eat the oyster, he eats what we threw off; because he is a product thereof. We eat him. A scavenger is he (or she) who eats that which no longer possesses the initial individual Innate itself. Even a boa constrictor squeezes the life from his victim before he attempts to eat, and neither will he begin swallowing until he

smells thoroughly that its life is extinct. None of the human family eat
living things—the vegetables are picked, meat is bled or killed,
chickens drawn, pork done up in sausages. It was a well-known and
recognized fact that all we ate was dead, had to be before it became
a food. We did not eat the cow, horse, dog or cat or other large animals
alive—we killed them all. Then came the microscopic age, when all
small things were made large, where the flea was 1,000 times larger than
the cow to the naked eye and lo, and behold, all was not dead as heretofore supposed. That which was apparently dead to the naked eye,
was covered with living things to the microscopic eye. The medical men
threshed around on various theories of the cause of disease, until the
last one—the blood impurities—was threadbare. Then when, by accident, somebody stumbled onto two bugs, the fountain of Youth had
been found, but, as is usual, there are hundreds of angels at which
these narrow-minded children have never glanced. They are caught
right and left. They thought we ate dead materials only, they discovered
we ate life with death, now they are trying to separate death from life
to give us life, not knowing that life and death are one. They found
unexpected life—what was it for and, as usual, they walked from the
solution rather than toward it.

What was, is, and what is, will be. Upon this presumption, students
figure hypotheses. What was good for our grandfathers is good for our
grandchildren. It seems the conclusion that man's idea should never
change, we should believe things our grandfathers taught, and expect
our children to agree with us and hold the same.

Students did not formerly argue that germs caused disease. Scientists
did not formerly teach that parasites were the cause of tuberculosis. College professors, microscopically, did not always believe diseases were
caused by microbes. The masses did not know germs, hence could not
have an opinion. That is the "was." Today, though, the "is" says that
"germs do cause disease." Scientists do teach that parasites produce
conditions from which we die. College professors microscopically have
seen on slides diseases caused by germs. Masses now believe that almost all diseases are caused by some germ. Hardly a week passes but
another disease is added to the category. A hundred years from now
will be—? Today, though, seems to be the minute. It is the time we live.
For us, today, to believe what everybody says is right, is right.

In years gone by Columbus said the world was round. He was wrong,
because the masses did not know it. Franklin theorized about electricity,
he was foolish, because humanity of his day said so. Edison said, "I will
record the talk of famous men"—that was impossible, for the public said
it was. Marconi made the statement that he would talk around the world
without a wire. "Impossible!" said hordes—and the hordes were right.
In each the man was wrong. D. D. Palmer said subluxations did occur—

he was wrong. Gray said it was impossible. D. D. Palmer said there were currents of power in man—he was crazy; because "eminent authorities" did not speak of them. B. J. Palmer brought forth cycles, which were impossible because Kirke, "an authority," did not teach it. B. J. Palmer said germs do not cause disease, but he is insane because Professor McBride and Dr. Joch contradict him. Men who have studied the germ question know whereof they speak, especially in the realm of medicine. Men who have seen man through the microscope know what man is; men who have ripped open men, dead and alive, know what man is made of. Men who have seen "sympathetic" actions know they have seen "phenomena."

(For fear you might misunderstand the trend throughout this chapter, that while apparently conceding the logic of medical men, when B.J. reaches a conclusion he has carried their theory to such an extreme that this chapter will be based upon irony and sarcasm. You must take statements with a grain of salt as you read, see the reversal of viewpoint to appreciate progression held by B.J. He does not agree with what is said in cold type. He means the reverse. Sometimes the best way to reach a conclusion is to show the extreme lack of logic by apparently conceding their point.)

It is foolish to question what these eminent men have accomplished. We are interlopers and have no right to question why they fill cemeteries. We have no sense of justice in asking why they bury so many mistakes. We do a great wrong when we think medicines poison people. Don't the masses say it is proper, consistent and ethical that they should fill cemeteries with poisoned bodies and mistaken diagnoses?

What causes the common opinion to sway? Somebody must be a leader, in the vanguard of even that medical mass. Every flock of sheep has its bell sheep; every drove of cattle its leader. Where is B.J.'s position? Is he at the head, in the middle or at the end? Where is his position? If at the end, he is safe. Everything B.J. sees is in front and, of course, the mass in front is correct, or should he look behind and see all that has gone before? All B.J. talks is old ideas, and the old ideas he cast as worthless. Hence, is B.J. at the tail end of this crowd? If in the middle, he is slow and old compared with those ahead, but progressive, compared to those behind. If in the lead, B.J. is heretical and unscientific to the mass behind. If you happen to be a one-man leader, as B. J. Palmer was these many years, the first sheep with the bell, then all ahead is a bottomless pit in the opinions of that mass behind. All ahead is wrong, everything behind right. Hence, to be right and correct, B.J. shall agree with all deductions of the past in admitting that "germs do cause disease," and he builds on that premise.

Physicians, authorities, eminent men in professions of the mass behind and in front, have said diseases are caused by germs. B.J. won't enumerate all, but mention a few: Cancer, tumor, scarlet fever, measles, small-pox, chicken-pox, whooping cough, pneumonia, typhoid fever, typhus fever, malaria, yellow fever, meningitis, infantile paralysis, tonsillitis, syphilis, eczema, acne, gonorrhea, dandruff, tuberculosis, cholera, jaundice, rheumatism, peritonitis, caries, scurvy, catarrh, bronchitis, colds, etc., etc., etc., without end.

The thing for us to do as individuals is, first, not come in contact with any of these diseases. If we do, we "catch it," beyond a question of doubt. Second, we must keep away from these diseases. How far—ten feet, or ten miles? How far can germs fly? Do not know. Has anybody ever guessed? How far can germs swim before they drown? It does not seem as if they drown, therefore we presume they swim any distance. How may you know but what you are in contact with a contagious disease? How do we know? How do we know an individual in the street has a tumor in his stomach? He does not tell, we do not ask. It's none of our business and impertinent if we inquire. He breathes out germs; we surely get them. How are we to know? How do we know when we go on a train but what somewhere in that body, concealed on that lady sitting next, may be leprosy, or typhoid fever? She might have acne in virulent form. You have a sister, sweetheart, relative, coming to visit from a distance; perhaps a cousin you have never seen. You meet at the depot and kiss. How do you know but on the inside of those lips there is a virulent form of scurvy? Your relatives are no exception to the law of infection and contagion. When you kiss you inhale their breath, perhaps breathing millions of scurvy germs. If you don't inhale you lick your lips to suck in the kiss and in goes two or three million germs of this deadly poison. How are we to know? Must we say, "Cousin, stand at a distance until we inspect you. Have you scurvy, tumor, cancer, small-pox, typhoid fever, and go through this string of one hundred diseases? Are you sure you are safe to run at large? Have you been microscopically inspected?" If cousin says "Yes," we can say, "Now we can approach and kiss, but not until an inspector, some eminent authority, said you are safe to run at large without a muzzle."

A typhoid patient is sick. Who nurses? Certainly not a healthy person. If so, look at the danger he lays himself open to. More dangerous, more deadly than a gun with bullets is that contact. A gun you can destroy, a bullet can be extracted, but when those germs get on or in, you cannot get away, they won't leave until buried; therefore, the typhoid patient, with a fever of 104 for six weeks, so weak he cannot rise, can safely only have as a nurse one who is as bad on a bed alongside. One transmits typhoid germs to the other, and he in return transmits the same, so they are even. Who is coming to watch the two? A third party as bad as they. And who waits on a sick person? It is not safe for one well to wait on a sick person. Germs carry an infectious and contagious disease. The sign is on the gatepost. "Beware—watch out for the dog." Germs do cause disease.

How do germs, from the sick, get to us to make us get down with what he has? There are four ways—fly, swim, or walk, or be carried from one body to another on some article of clothing. Presuming we chat with someone with a contagious disease. The only way germs get to us is to walk down the body of that person, over the bed covers, down the bed post, over the floor, up the leg of our chair, onto our clothing, to some opening and there crawl in our nose or mouth. If he doesn't go by that path he must fly, because we do not swap spit with the patient so he could swim in, or he (or she) must go by walking or flying. We do not know of any breed or family of germs that cannot do all. They multiply in milk, they breed in dust, they propagate on dry glass and in the air. We don't know how we can stop those germs flying. To protect our health we must stop them flying to us from that sick person. How? We do not know. We must stop them from walking and swimming. We must not allow anything material to touch that body and then touch our own. If we do, we are a goner. How are we to proceed? We do not know.

We must not breathe air in that room, whether there one minute or an hour; therefore, we should get a coal miner's helmet, place it over our head, a regular sea diver's outfit, carry our tank of oxygen, open our bag when we enter the room. We must not come in contact with the air of that room, for they will get us by flying, so we don't know how we are going to enter and be safe. If we walk on the floor, we lay ourself wide open to exposure. We must go without touching the air, but how to accomplish this we do not know. It is an easy matter, of course, to not drink liquids found in that room, therefore we preclude the possibility of drinking the swimming germs. We have not found how to knock germs off our private air tank before we leave the room, because they have settled while in the room. We have not ascertained how we could talk, except by telephone, while inside of that room, from the inside of the helmet to our patient. In this event, we might have stayed at home and done the same. It is for us to take every precaution. Do you know whether you have or have not some of the germs of some of those diseases on your body?

We know some of these mixed germs are on our bodies now, but how do we know? There is only one way to prove: Take ourselves to Professor McBride, "an eminent authority," or have Professor McBride come and inspect us. In that way we can know definitely and scientifically that we have 40,462,392 germs on each square inch of our inners and 16,739,163 on our outer body. We can have a blue book of their breed for the same price. He will know that if he placed a pin on our clothing, upon that pinhead there would be a dance of five hundred couples, with room for an orchestra at one corner. We will know where we are, and he can tell what he knows (at so much) what kind they are, whether six or sixteen legged, whether four or two months old. It is of scientific value in determining the disease under which he may be classified. It becomes necessary to live, and our health becomes a serious problem, that the State must be our guardian upon—so says the bacteriologist.

We want to live. It is remarkable that we have lived so long and, remarkable is the fact, we want to live beyond the age that we are now, so it behooves us to boil every drop we drink, drink it while boiling, for just so far as it cools germs from surrounding atmosphere go in to get a drink and when you drink the water they drink, the germs with it that go in the drink, you are on the brink. The safe water to drink is boiling water.

If all continues as in the past, surely no respectable germ would have any chance against our advanced civilization. Suppose the Health Boards are permitted freedom to do as they think best for us. You enter a store and here's about what they'll be handing us: "we can show you a nice demijohn of shirts with a jar of stylish collars. Give them a quart can of underwear and a small bottle of suspenders. Mary bring me a can opener, we want to change our socks." The cook appears and says: "I put a glass of garters in the pantry by mistake." Imagine a man going home with 20 different kinds of hermetically sealed jars, saying: "At last I've bought all of my wedding outfit. Manufacturers of wearing apparel will be compelled by law to put up everything in germ-proof packages and antiseptically sealed cans, no one to be used the second time under penalty of law." Ridiculous? Nothing of the kind— but the trend of the times to avoid the pesky germs.

When you get food from the grocery, meat from the market, or kerosene or gasoline, be sure to boil anything of a liquid character because there are kerosene and gasoline germs; those are more poisonous than others. Never eat anything raw; eat after cooked beyond the boiling point, eat as it is boiling—in so far as you let it cool where it is palatable, just so far do germs in the atmosphere settle in it and you eat them, and they cause disease, for remember, "Germs do Cause Disease."

When you go to the orchard, pick a ripe apple off the tree, think well before you bite. On that skin lurk millions of germs.

Another source of infection, serious in itself, is air. Air, any place, every place, is heavily laden with germs of serious diseases. We have, today, diseases of all kinds in our hospitals. We bare our bodies. If able to see microscopically, the germs are going up in clouds, like swarms of locusts, away from the various bodies. The walls of the hospital are covered, layer upon layer, swarming over each other. On one side is a cancer germ; his next-door neighbor, trying to get rest, is a tumor germ; next to him are typhoid germs. A short time ago there was a small-pox case in this room; his germs are breeding upon the wall.

There is "Walking Mary," "Riding Johnny," "Laughing Anna"—none sick, yet all breeders of specific diseases, that give off germs. Although healthy, so far as pathology or symptomatology is concerned, yet they are dangerous to be at large and for the general good we locked them up as though murderers. These are only three of the notables that strike mortal fear to our existences. Others and, perhaps, by the score assemble daily around us, whose lives would probably elicit duplicate examples. We certainly must not permit these healthy people to associate with us socially and kill us off by the dozen. How to detect them, drive them from our midst as "unclean," would require a microscopic examination of every person, inside and outside, secretions and excretions, before they are welcome to our front door. To play safe, we build an outhouse in which all arrivals must first be examined and their characters as reputable citizens passed upon. It is true, of course, that they might contain none today and tomorrow be alive. That necessitates a daily examination in the outhouse of every person, thereby safeguarding not only present health, but future as well. We appreciate the insignificance of "Germs do Cause Disease," hence will do our utmost to live the ideal germless existence.

To obviate this course of infection, we should breathe only sterilized air in which germs have been killed. We must contract for a plant in our homes which sterilizes air we breathe. It may cost $4,000.00, but what is life not worth? It will kill germs in your home, your rooms are places where diseases breed, and these, in all their joy are bred by the trillions.

To boil water you must have something to do it in. That which kills germs in the vessel in which you boil is carbolic acid. It is necessary, then, to boil the vessel before you boil the water, put carbolic acid in the kettle then in the water which you boil. You drink the remains of the carbolic acid which clings to the sides of the vessel when you boil water. That which kills germs won't kill you, and suppose it does, haven't you saved yourself infection? Doesn't the end justify the means? Man, then, becomes a veritable tank of carbolic acid. What is good outside to kill germs must be better on the inside. Carbolic acid is not good; it's a drug, medicine and poison; yet it were better to have our mucous linings hardened with brass consistency than to be a wriggling, wiggling, writhing mass of bugs of unknown virility and heinousness. To disinfect your tea kettle, coffee pots, etc., the same process should be used.

Do you disinfect frying pans, your oven before you bake bread? Germs stand a temperature of 300 degrees Fahrenheit and 100 degrees below zero. It was testified that germs were found, millions, at the North pole.

So cold and heat have no terrifying aspects to the germ. Even at the North pole or in our ovens we are not safe. What must we do?

We cannot kill him by boiling or freezing; he swims, flies, walks and rides; he's in the air, on our clothes. What must we do to have saved?

Are not the ends of science more important than life? To prove that germs exist is worth more than a hundred lives, if that number must be sacrificed; then so be it, for more will come from where they originated, but the ends of science must be established, the theory extended, the germ discovered at what cost.

A Nobel prize can be extended to a noted Parisian discoverer of a bug, a serum resurrected to destroy him. That $50,000 comes in mighty handy to purchase monkeys to find another.

What is a State, peace of mind, sacrifice of liberty, cost of millions, pleasures and comforts of hotel or traveling when compared to the stripes on a microbe and what kind of matter he prefers to live upon? Those are highly scientific questions which must be settled so the world may exist in future days.

What are not the sacrifices that we give up all to that end? Killing sows, torturing calves for their pus, vivisecting dogs, cats and rats; injecting guinea pigs and monkeys to make tests; doing away with the common drinking cup, cigar lighters, mugs for beer, door knobs, roller towels, wash basins, toilet, urinals, the mop that cleans our floors, etc., anything in fact, that one person used once must not be used again until sterilized, boiled or carbolized. All this must be done, otherwise we die horrible deaths, alongside of which hanging, starving, freezing, electro-cuting, drowning are picnic holidays.

All this is true—we don't dare doubt it. Have not the eminent scientists told us these are facts?

We take it for granted, from the very fact you live, that you have taken every one of the precautions. If you had not, the germs would have killed you ere this, because "Germs do Cause Disease."

The mere fact that we did not know that germs did not exist in years gone by is no excuse any more than ignorance in law makes you scot-free from murder. Germs existed even unto Moses' time, but there were no microscopes then. We often wonder what Moses did to disinfect himself. Where ignorance is bliss, 'tis folly to be wise. If all we do today is necessary, how did they circumvent this wonderful obstacle then, or can it be that this is a modern miracle, one which God forgot to perform then and has brought it about just to torment and tease us in this enlightened and civilized age? We wish there was some way of knowing. If the punishment is keeping with the crime, then forbid: let us back to ignorance and God take them away, for which is worse—ignorance without germs or education with them; ignorance and pure water or education with boiled water? An Arabian was once shown a prune under a microscope. His attention was called to germs. He was told they were unhealthy. He politely handed back the microscope and proceeded to munch his prune. When asked why, he said: "With the microscope in your hand I see no germs."

To have a child live, the moment born from the mother's body, we should clap a sterilized muzzle upon it, and until he dies he should breathe only sterilized air. Mother's milk should be sterilized, the nipple carbolized. If he breathes anything else he would take in germs, and "Germs do Cause Disease." The proof of the pudding is that the child lives—so he must not have them.

People certainly realize that they come in contact with clothing of people by direct communication, which is heavily laden with germs, which will be transmitted to your bodies; you go home to the bodies of your children, daughters and sons, with millions of germs of various kinds on your clothing, you spread a source of infection and contagion.

Are you living safely? Every minute you are dying, might as well be dead, if you don't die this minute the germs will kill you the next. As well die now and be done with it, and say in the words of the punster: "What's the use of existing now, tomorrow germs kill us."

Germs are small, fierce, death-dealing, life-annihilating, ferocious man-eating, microscopic insects. They are of various kinds and sizes; some are striped with various colors, others are of the color of the object upon which they ferociously live, others have a dissembling color; but, in all events, all the germs have one common intent—to attack all life in any form they find it, and we find them when we investigate his surroundings.

We are told in a doubting spirit that germs are of two characters—those which take life and those which seem to preserve life. On the former we're positive; on the latter, quite doubtful. Those that preserve life are about one to nine of those who take life. Neither germ was known until recent years.

If we could imagine a million couples together at one point, we might approximate that a million couples of germs could dance a quadrille on the point of a pin—to give you some idea of their infinitesimal size. We estimate these figures, of course, by actual calculation. A great scientist looked through a microscope, at a mass of germs upon a pin point which he caused to be blown upon it. They stood still and, while living, he counted them one by one, thereby he knew that a million could dance upon a pin point. When a physician tells that it is "estimated" that there are 4,763,000 typhoid germs in a drop of water, he knows (?) because he has counted them or believes that somebody else has. There is nothing in this idea that is guesswork. Far be it from such as scientists to do that character of work.

We have seen these germs in the air, in the water, in all kinds of food, we have seen man breathe air with microbes, we have seen man drink water with microbes, we have seen man eat food with microbes, we have further seen those microbes enter the innards of this man and in a very insidious, persistent, consistent tearing the atoms of matter, piece by piece, eating upon it as gluttons and, when you consider what a mass of fellows live upon man—two millions live upon the point of a pin— you appreciate what two millions of these fellows could do to a tissue cell per minute in man. There are hundreds of thousands of millions in a man; it doesn't take them long to eat his lungs. The man with his left lung all gone and two-thirds of the right gone, when they eat up the remaining one-third of the right lung, so he cannot breathe, the man must die. We have seen these germs in his stomach, floating in his blood, insidiously working in his brain, destroying his thoughts, working in his muscles, we have seen them in every part. We know the man was normal before the germs entered and sick afterwards. Of course, the germs caused (?) the disease that the man had afterwards, that he didn't have before he had germs. That is a scientific conclusion, we must so regard it. Experts have found these "facts."

Once these germs get into man, they tear his flesh. Tearing starts a reactive process in the blood, this brings on fever. When the fever occurs, we have pus; the pus brings on further decomposition. Eventually the man has tuberculosis. When he has tuberculosis, we remember that it is the result of germs tearing away flesh. Then we ask the minister to pray and appeal for his soul and alms, plead with the state for a farm to give him fresh air, keep him from friends and separate him from the germs by using the money that we plead for on tag days to playing chase and tag through his inners with medicines this money bought. It gives some physicians nice fat jobs while the consumptives go out and work on the farm under the guise of fresh air and sunshine killing bugs. We treat him with all kinds of dope to kill germs and prevent them from tearing more tissue cells. We reach this conclusion because all other ideas that we tried to treat man with for tuberculosis seemed to be failures, so we conclude at last that it is a germ disease beyond question. It has only been of recent years that we have been sufficiently educated to use a microscope to see these things. If we had had a microscope thousands of years ago, we would have seen him then; would have reached the conclusion we now do.

B.J. might state, without intimidation of your position, the air you now breathe is filled with tuberculosis germs; you are breathing smallpox, scarlet fever, the germ that produces leprosy, the germ of malaria, in fact, could you analyze one cubic foot of air you would find all the elements that go to make the different germs. And, it is safe to presume, that every drop you drink has contained millions of typhoid germs; the food you are going to eat this noon will be a live, wiggling, soiled mass of parasites, death-demanding creatures.

Breathing this foul, infested air, drinking microscopic water, eating food, we are all ordained now to be dead within a reasonably short time, for no man is safe when there is even one male and one female germ at large within us, for within ten minutes they are great-great-great-great-great-grandfathers and grandmothers. Scientifically, we have proven with the aid of the microscope, that under the laws of reproduction one male and female germ can in ten minutes be forty-two generations advanced, and this again a scientific conclusion, we must reason (?) accordingly. So, could we be as pure as the snow or be washed in the blood of the lamb and be free from germs this minute, in ten minutes we would have something like forty-two million within us, and that would be sufficient to eat up twenty-one pin points of tissue cell—in ten minutes. Keep that up for an hour and you will see you have six hundred pin points of tissue cells eaten.

It is impossible to escape breathing and live. We must drink and have food. We have been giving considerable thought to which was more important—to die by not breathing air, not drinking water, not eating food because of being infected with myriads of germs, or whether we had better breathe air, drink water, eat food with the germs and die of germs. We are bound to die either way, and we don't know which will be the longer. We are still debating that problem, but scientists tell that we seem to live about as long one way as the other.

How they reached this remarkable conclusion B.J. cannot imagine, but they do, and B.J. speaks in the capacity of a humble layman; he does not claim to be an expert on this scientific question. You can see then that we are destined to die, either because we refuse to do the things we should do or we do the things we should not do.

When you think of these things, the physicians are justly entitled to the title "M.D." meaning "Microbe Doctors," so they change their title to suit the character of their work.

Have you noticed how scientific physicians are since they got acquainted with this new idea for curing patients? There is the germ of tuberculosis, we have seen fought, and killed him on microscope slides with injections of anti-tuberculosis serum under his skin. We have known that he did not live for he kicked once when we injected him; he laid down and died before our eyes. We inject this matter into man and since we have discovered this serum there has not been a single case of tuberculosis that has ever died—from tuberculosis. We have discovered the germ of insanity, and we inject this anti-sanity serum into the brain and the individual becomes sane in a short space of time, and we are very rapidly cleaning out the insane asylums. Only a question now of a year or two until those buildings will be turned over to the county and made into orphan institutions for the original insane people.

They further found that criminals were victims of circumstances which they could not help. Germs brought about by propagation in hovels of the underworld made them what they were. We have found that germ; we are injecting a serum and the institutions for criminals are gradually being thinned out. Criminals will be a thing of the past in a short space of time. As to typhoid fever, we abate it within two or three hours after it gets a start because we now have an anti-typhoid serum. We inject that, the fever abates because we have killed all germs by injection.

We have accomplished a great deal. It is only now a question of time until we find the right amount of serum to kill every germ. After such serums have been discovered, disease will be unknown; there will be no more chronic diseases. We call this age and era an epoch of remarkable progress in medicine because we are doing now the one thing we started out to do 3,000 years ago.

Tuberculosis is not on the increase. We don't know why physicians of some cities have stirred the ministers to deliver lectures about the increase of tuberculosis. This is unnecessary. It has been rapidly decreasing in the last few years. Anything to the contrary is foolishness. Take the State Board of Health laboratory in New York, they have made a report which is the height of ridiculousness. The State Board of Health of New York has a state laboratory at New York City. Every physician who has a patient whom he thinks has a diagnosis as a tubercular patient may send sputum to the laboratory for an analysis. They look at the sputum under the microscope. If they see the tuberculosis bacilli, that individual is condemned to have tuberculosis; if they did not find him, then he hasn't tuberculosis. At one time, some five hundred samples of sputa were sent to a laboratory, all from tuberculosis patients, and made public report that in 65 per cent of the sputa from the tuberculosis patients they could not find tuberculosis bacilli.

Some years ago B.J. had a former city health inspector call, he talked over this problem. At the same time B.J. had a Mr. A (meat market man) in his office. This brought to mind an observed fact. Mr. A makes a feature of having the cleanest meat market in the state of Iowa. We presume that it is, but B.J. wants to give an example. When meat is packed at the Packing Co. it is disinfected by being sprayed with diluted carbolic acid to prevent germs from getting on it in transit; there is a heavy oiled wrapping paper around it, another paper around that; then, for transference, a heavy burlap. These are hauled on trucks thoroughly cleaned with boiling water to kill germs. Meat goes into a refrigerator car where they propose to freeze meat and germs. Coming to a town, it is put into trucks—a nice clean paper on the bottom, meat laid on it. In former days, when germs were unknown, meat was shipped in the open, with dirt and filth; today we are careful of germs. The driver of this truck has a clean white coat and cap. It is impossible for germs to settle on white goods; they might on green, brown or purple. Why this is, we do not know; probably because of the light hurting their eyes. (Nurses wear white also.) When a man carries meat into a meat market, he takes a clean piece of white paper, lays it on the scale, which is white enameled. He lays that meat on paper, because there might be a germ on the scale. Of course, there is none on the paper. When weighed, it is unwrapped and stored in the refrigerator. When meat is ordered, it is taken to the block, sawed, cut up and delivered. Meanwhile you have purchased a few millions of cancer, tuberculosis and other germs. We know you put it into the pot where you "kill those germs," but remember they have forty-two legs to hang on with. You cook it to the boiling point; unless you do, you are not going to kill them. Don't you suppose they have sense enough to fly up in steam, come down when the meat cools, go into the dining room and light again? Do they deliberately walk unto death like the human race? No! They are sturdy chaps, stronger than you because they kill you and you cannot kill them. They stand what you cannot. If it gets too hot or too unpleasant, you duck into other climes and conditions. So does he. If water gets uncomfortable, he shinnies up the side of the meat to the top, then takes to wings and flies. If germs have sense enough to pick you out because you are good looking, good eats, fat and juicy, rest assured he's got sense enough to leave you when skin and bone, and surely this is an indication of his temperament when being scalded, burned, roasted or boiled. Wonderful little creature that.

There is the matter of quarantining. You know that when the neighbor gets small pox, they try to hide it. You will find it out; notify the health department. The health officer comes, puts a red placard on the house with the sign "Smallpox." Up till that time all was unsafe; now secure. The fact is, some germs entered that house, perhaps on papa, maybe on mamma, maybe Johnny did it playing nibs. Who knows? Who cares? Anyhow, there in the house one of them is sick and has been "on the dumps" for three weeks. It took that long for germs to multiply in sufficient quantities to force him down and out. Meanwhile friends, acquaintances and the hens of the neighborhood called frequently daily, gossiped over the yard line, etc. Germs have been spread over the neighborhood far enough to be diagnosed by the family physician attending. But lo, on one day he calls, takes another squint, pronounces it smallpox, and the zone of safety has passed. From that moment every germ is dangerous and contagious—safe until he pronounced unsafe after titled. The placard tells us the physician has diagnosed and the time of safety is past. To observe the placard seems to have some mysterious effect upon the germs within the house and person, before calm and peaceful, now dangerous and hideous.

Half an hour after tacking the sign, Mrs. Hennessy walks to the fence where Mrs. B. is and says: "Would you mind lending me a few books? We are to be penned for a month and I would like something to read." Mrs. Brown gets the books. The conversation occurs over the fence—one on either side, not a foot's distance between. "Can you come over to see me?" "I would not dare do that, the doctor said I mustn't. We're quarantined." Yet Mrs. B. is talking to an individual who has just come from the bedside of the patient, and she knew it. That mother is penned. Surely she had small pox germs over her body. Germs recognize a bright object when they see her. Therefore, Mrs. Brown becomes infected. From the other side of the fence they say: "Here is new territory. Let us invade this new suffragette," and Mrs. Brown gets down. This is true and you know it. The result is Mrs. Brown spreads this infection to her next-door neighbor, Mrs. Jones, in the same manner. Remember "Germs do Cause Disease."

How long does it take carelessness to permit the disease to spread over the city? Every act of this kind is criminal. Any person that will deliberately carry these infinitesimal innocent germs from house to house, thereby spreading death-defying disease and filling cemeteries, should be indicted by grand juries, tried and convicted for murder in the first degree, for the design and accomplishment are the same as with a murderer who deliberately intends and does commit his rash act; except in the latter he does it to one, in the former, hundreds, perhaps thousands, as he breeds an endless chain. Ignorance of the evil design of these scavengers excused no one any more than an insane murderer is exempted from his punishment and given freedom because insane.

By this time we are aware that it is germs that cause disease. It is sickness we wish to prevent, hence we are determined to keep those germs within that house at all costs and hazards. We care nothing about the house, but we are positive the microbes must not be spread. They are afraid the house will run away, so they "quarantine the house." You say that is going too far. Perhaps the doctor visits his patient. "How are you, Mrs. B.? How are you, Johnny? Stick out your tongue. Put this thermometer in your mouth and see how it feels. You are in bad shape, Johnny. I think you have measles, but we will pull you through all right. Yes, indeed. Do not be frightened, Mrs. B. It is only a question of time. Let me feel your pulse, Johnny; listen to your heart," and he walks out. He goes to the next-door neighbor. Anna is down with typhoid. From there he goes to the third house. Mary has measles. Of course, the physician is a god and he does not carry germs. It is impossible for him to do such a devilish trick. He is working "for the health of the dear people." When he sat by the bedside of that first individual, those germs did not get onto his clothing. He didn't want them to. Just the same they did. He gathers two million smallpox germs and gives one-quarter million to the typhoid patient. There he takes up ten million typhoid germs and the million and a half smallpox germs which he had left, goes to the measles case. There he leaves a sample of small-pox and typhoid germs and adds measles to his stock. Then he goes to his office, meets the regular run of patients. "How do you do, Mr. Jones? Stomach trouble? Oh, yes, I can treat you for that." He gives her millions of each kind of germ, at the same time some medicine, but "he safeguards the health of the city by quarantining the houses" and enforcing it by state law. That is the proper and scientific way to safeguard the people.

Back of this apparent inconsistency is a matter of fact. This physician has been in practice ten years. He went to school four years before that. Fourteen years ago he would have carried germs the same as you and I. He went to a medical college where they taught the value of knowing which germ was which, which they did, etc. When he finished learning truths, he was given a diploma showing his fitness to tell patients that he knew the shape of one from the other. Then he appeared before the State Board of Health, took an examination in which he told them proficiently, of course, that he knew a germ when he saw it through the microscope. They issued him a license. Now (?) he was immune. The license can do more than all the carbolic acid made. Although his diploma and license hang in his office, the germs know a M.D. when they see him, can tell the difference between a M.D. that has a diploma and license and one that hasn't either, and because of the terror this diploma and license create, they proceed to quietly, manfully and scientifically pass him by. We don't know whether it is the serious deceitful look, the austere manner of the medicine case that strikes fear to their hearts, but he can do as he pleases by going from house to house, entering and leaving under any conditions he pleases, and all is safe and well along the Potomac. You or I could not do this. We did not have four years in college, a diploma nor a license, neither have we the legal right to charge for going promiscuously from house to house as has he. We give him the legal power to quarantine your home, to keep you, me and all others from going in and out—"all for the purpose of keeping from spreading germs." He may do so at leisure, with pleasure, satisfaction, and receive our pay therefor—no harm can possibly come. We pay taxes to build him a school, pay taxes to form various boards before which he appears, pay taxes to have a law made and enforced, pay taxes to pay police to enforce its provisions, pay him money direct to take away our liberties and keep us from doing the thing that he can do under identically the same circumstances. The only advantage he has over us is he has a thought, we haven't. We paid the tax on his thought, then gave liberties away and pay to have it taken. Funny world. All because "Germs do Cause Disease." He does not carry germs in his beard; nor get them in his hair; but, if you and I were to go in that house, we would carry germs; therefore, we are not permitted to enter until the quarantine is raised. Of course, you and I are laymen. He has studied in a medical college; that makes him immune. "Germs do Cause Disease," and that physician knows it. That is why he takes every precaution, is extremely cautious, takes no chances of spreading contagion. He is seriously conscientious and conscientiously sincere in advocating that "Germs do Cause Disease." He is honest, we can do no better than to follow his example. The physician has studied four years to be a scientist, to be a famous Professor McBride. The fact that he is "famous" makes his words ring true, regardless of what his actions may be, which seems to put the lie to everything he preaches—but then this can't possibly be.

Did you ever watch the nurses in a hospital? They are so careful. The nurse in one ward talks to a nurse in the infectious ward. She meets her and the two converse for ten minutes. Meanwhile, those germs crawl from one girl to another. The second nurse goes back to her patient who is not in the infectious ward. Don't you dare say nurses don't know that "Germs do Cause Disease." At noon, when it comes time to eat, all nurses go up together to the kitchen, jolly each other and swap stories of what they did to their patients. Each nurse gets her meal on a tray. The smallpox nurse drops a few million germs on the tray which goes to a different ward, and the germs have as happy time mixing as the nurses. One goes to one ward and another to another, all happy, singing, in the realization, "Germs do Cause Disease," meanwhile taking every precaution. That is where they are consistent. These nurses secretly laugh at the idea of taking precautions against the transportation of germs from patient to patient. Great is the science of medicine! Great are the opinions of medical authorities. Think of the damage that could be done if one nurse was to give one male and one female germ to another nurse. They could count their relatives by the thousands in 10 minutes.

B.J. is reminded of a circumstance. In the Panama region the government has spread petroleum over the ponds and pools. This is a condemnation upon the wisdom of God. They should have made the oil well there instead of in Pennsylvania. If He had realized that people were going to live there He should have made it healthy. The only way we can live is to have germs killed. Then why did God give them birth? You chase them out of one place, the same as rats, but take away the cat and the rats come back if there is anything to live on. Chase the mosquitoes out of one pond and where do they go? There is only one healthy salvation —kill off all germs. As long as one male and one female mosquito escape their vigilance, we are in danger of dying, we are not safe, we ought to worry and get gray hair thinking of this problem of how to live in spite of those germs.

Supposing we start a crusade to kill germs, how high up must we go to get to a territory where germs do not live? Ten miles? How far in the earth must we go? Supposing we did kill them all, we might have a volcano tomorrow and spill up a lot more of a new kind and spoil everything. A volcano would go down twelve miles and we would have everything to do over again. We are not safe anywhere under this germ theory. We should all have germ diseases. I do not see that you are sick, but "Germs Cause Disease."

Someone has said the reason we haven't diseases is that we are not susceptible, not prone to them. Previous weakness must exist. They must have fertile culture ground, and we are not vulnerable. That is a wrong, mistaken idea. We tell the whole thing when we say "Germs do Cause Disease"; we mean that they make their own susceptibility, their own culture fields, for a "cause" starts something from nothing. Don't misquote the use of the word "cause." Two germs could multiply and tear the Rock of Gibraltar down.

We are not going to give voluminous quotations from books, but we will cite page 515 from Gould, which tells practically nothing of the theory of germ diseases, but refers the micro-organisms on page 164, and there refers to page 167 and, on those pages, find 57 columns of germs, averaging forty names to the column. That makes a sum total of 2,280 germs, equivalent to producing 2,280 pathological diseases. Must I go through life with 2,280 diseases? Germs do cause disease; more germs, more diseases. The quicker we die the better, be out of danger and done with it all. Getting no satisfaction there, we turn to Dunglison, under germs, page 481; he refers to micro-organisms, page 705, and it might be well to read these quotations if it were not that we are more actively interested in the theory than we are in shapes, names and sizes of germs, where and how may they be found.

The layman is very careless in the use of words; he speaks of a bunch when he means one, etc. But scientists will split hairs to be exact, as proven by the tyrannical methods, endless expense, labor and sacrifice to tabulate and tag every germ that ever drew breath. When they say "The germ theory consists of the fact that germs cause disease," this is a phraseology that permits no equivocation because, as scientists, they have chosen their thoughts well and express them in words equally as positive. "Theory" is something not yet proven; how can it be a "fact"? "Cause" does not permit of quibbling, it means to make, without which the conditions arising could not have arisen. Hence the "germ theory" is a "fact" which isn't the "cause," yet either refuse, can't or don't tell us how. With such momentous questions, we cannot understand why he lets us poor ignorant dupes gasp in darkness, year after year; notwithstanding our dense ignorance to understand what he means without explanations, he demands that we do all he wants and should we politely refuse, he insists (always manfully), of course, of sicking the statute on us until we do.

B.J.'s last analysis brings the conclusion that germs transmit diseases, from individual to individual. Germs are infectious or contagious only to the extent that they transmit disease from one diseased body to another body without the disease. If they didn't do that, no disease would be infectious or contagious. The germ himself is but an animalculum, it's what he does that we try to prevent. What does he do? He transmits disease. That fellow with a red stripe carries one disease, the other fellow with a black band carries a different form of pathology. Dis-ease means "not at ease." The germ does transmit dis-ease, that state of not being at ease, from one body to another. He does not get into the body and stir up conditions, thereby making a state of dis-ease. He transmits the not-at-ease condition, thereby making a state of disease. Just what he holds in his claws, mouth or body that he carries, that is, a state of dis-ease (not at ease), from one body to that, we do not know, but evidently he carries a state. How this is done, of course, scientists and authorities are not quite ready to state, but it does do it anyhow, because authorities know, and even though we are not able to answer the questions thoroughly as none of our authorities have done, yet it is sufficient for the world to believe what they say, and they don't appreciate your quizzing about their integrity. They have said, that should be sufficient. Notwithstanding, there are always some who take nothing for granted, they're snooping into places they have no business, they want to know too much. Usually this class composed of those who don't know anything about the subject they ask about, hence disdainfully and scornfully the scientists refuse to recognize their ignorant questions. The scientists have settled the subject, the balance should be led blindly on. They want us to pin our faith, believe and swallow all they tell. Don't open your eyes or use your brain, you will get into trouble. Authorities say that the fact that germs eat tissue upon a slide is proof that he eats it in living man.

An English lady who recently became a mother has framed the following set of rules for the purpose of protecting her child from infection:

"Do not kiss the baby.

"Do not handle the baby unless your hands are very, very clean.

"Do not allow the baby to touch your face or hair.

"Do not talk, breathe, whistle, blow, cough or sneeze into baby's face—we want him to live."

Inspired by this comes the following bit of poetry:

"Do not kiss the baby darling, do not hold him on your knees,

There may be a microbe on you, you may give him some disease.

Do not fondly bend over above him, view him from a distance, dear;
Germs may linger in your whiskers, death is always lurking near.
"Do not touch the baby, dearest, microbes in your nails may lurk,
They may wait with cruel purpose to get in their deadly work.
Do not take the little darling, when he gladly turns to coo,
Forty kinds of germs may madly light upon him, if you do.
"View the baby from a distance, 'tis the only proper plan.
Do not breathe while you are near him; let us raise him if we can
You may hunger to caress him, never dare to do it though;
You are a living, moving mass of deadly germs, you know."

"Germs do Cause Disease." A little carelessness may mean the infecting of an entire country with the scourge, therefore be careful, show no carelessness.

20

—◆—

ARE GERMS THE SECONDARY CAUSE?

CONCEDED THAT GERMS were a secondary cause, B.J. logically finds it necessary to admit they were only primary. To admit they were primary would be to grant that there was no other cause for disease than germs, for germs are found with most every disease. To concede a germ was the cause of disease would admit that man was not complete; viewpoint of the medical practitioner would be logically proven, and the supposition of the Chiropractor that he is complete would be fallacious, groundless and not worthy of further thought. This would put us in a peculiar position, and rather than be compromised, we will see if we cannot get something better.

"Are germs the secondary cause of disease?" compels B.J. to define terms.

"Cause: That which occasions or effects a result; the necessary antecedent of an effect; that which determines the condition of existence of a thing, especially that which determines its change from one form to another."—Webster.

Webster speaks of different causes, principally "to be the cause or occasion of; to effect, as an agent; to bring about; to bring into existence; to make; often followed by an infinitive; something by 'that' with a finite verb." He further explains that anything which originates without which the organization could not have occurred, then that becomes a

335

cause. After going carefully through Webster's column of causes, he has not inferred that it is possible to phrase in English language such as "secondary cause." He only knows "cause," he does not understand "third cause," "fourth cause."

In logic, arts and sciences there are two connective phrases without which one could not be nor without the other one could not exist—cause and effect. What does Webster say of "effect"?

"Effect: That which is produced by an agent or cause; the event which follows immediately from an antecedent; result; consequence; outcome; fruit; as, the effect of luxury."—Webster.

And even though he gives a column on "effect," he does not concede that he knows about "secondary effect"; he understands thoroughly "effect."

Butler's Diagnostics gives the causes of pneumonia as multiple, such as sex, age, color, racial tendencies, climatic conditions, temperature, with about forty other possible causes—among the forty is one called "germ."

Webster says: "Germ: A small mass of living substance capable of developing into an animal or plant or into an organ or part; as embryo in its early stages; a sprout or bud; a seed."—Webster.

"Micro-organism, especially any of the pathogenic bacteria; a microbe; a disease germ."

Man is an animal; the germ is possibly animal. The germ is to be the secondary cause in something in the first—man. We have not, as yet defined "disease." We have said logically and reasonably that if 100 per cent of Innate Intelligence worked through 100 per cent of matter, then man was alive; if 100 per cent of matter was not worked by Innate Intelligence, it would be dead; if we had 50 per cent of current cut off from 100 per cent of matter because of mechanical disarrangements of parts, whether there be or not be a germ involved. If current was present, current was "the cause" of life; if current was not present, the absence of current was the cause of disease. What does the term disease mean? "Not at ease," "not ease." What is "not at ease"? Matter is the same in quantity as in the being where at ease. What is not at ease? The amount of function going through matter.

In other words, the current presents the viewpoint of disease, the current is at ease, what there is of it; but there may not be enough or there may be too much.

The current that runs the electric fan at 100,000 revolutions per minute is current at ease. Increase that to four times that amount and it will run not-at-ease because it has over reached its standard. What current you added was still at ease, but it was not at ease when viewed from the normal amount needed for the object to which applied.

Take an example of a fruit tree in the ground. The soil is very dry, the clouds very full of water. The soil is good soil, the water in the sky good water, but what is needed for the tree and its fruit is a more equitable distribution of some of the water from the clouds into the ground so that the tree may gather moisture and its foods in elements so that the fruit may produce itself. We judge the value of earth, clouds, trees by their fruit. Should the right quantity of water leave the sky, enter the right amount of ground, be absorbed by the tree in a consistent amount of time, then perfect fruit is the product. Suppose not enough water left the clouds, went to the ground and wasn't absorbed into the tree; the fruit would be shriveled, dry and runty. Take its opposite; suppose a cloudburst occurred, the ground was thoroughly saturated, the tree would absorb too much and the fruit would be soggy.

The water in the clouds, every drop was good, pure and healthy water. The earth and its every atom was good, pure and healthy soil: That which makes for ease or disease rests entirely upon the relative quantities of each, for each, in each, in the proper time necessary to draw forth what is good fruit. It's purely a study of quantities in ratio that makes for health or ill health, ease or disease.

What is ease? The normal amount of current going through the normal amount of matter. Review B.J.'s terms. There is only one cause, one effect. In philosophy, logic, science, art, there is one cause and effect. A germ is an animal and lives outside of man until he gets in; then he is still an outside part of the inside, he is not a natural portion of man. Disease is a viewpoint of a relative quantity of current as it works through matter.

We have been taught to reason that current flows from brain to spinal cord, through its length to exits through spinal nerves, through nerves to organs, etc. We have learned that a subluxation of the vertebra decreases the size of the intervertebral foramina, it produces a pressure upon nerve, pressure decreased the circumference or diameter of the nerve; when the nerve's circumference or diameter was decreased it prohibited the normal transmission of current going through the nerve; the abnormal quantity of current going to make the organ not at ease. The cause of the not-at-ease condition was the excess or lack of current in ration, nothing more nor less. The subluxation was the result of a concussion of forces which was not at ease. The concussion of forces was the result of a fall in which forces were not equivalent to each other. Let us see if all this is true.

There is a cause for subluxation—concussion of forces. There is a cause for disease—lack of current. There is a cause for the lack of current—pressure on the nerves. Work it whatever way you will, it resolves itself into a mechanical displacement of some portion of our anatomy.

To maintain that the germ—little microscopic animal that he is, so small that 400,000 could dance a quadrille on the head of a pin—is to be a secondary cause of disease would infer that a multitude must be damming the circumference or size of the nerve as it emits through the invertebral foramina. If he could do this without subluxation, he could as well be primary cause as secondary.

If the premise of Chiropractic be correct, you cannot infer any other cause than what its premise includes. It is electricity that makes light when it reaches the globe and meets resistance. We cannot concede anything else. When electricity is not there, the globe is "dead"; when there, the light is on. Supposing we were to turn a button: Is the turning of the button a secondary cause to the existence of light? We may turn the button; if there is no electricity there is no light. So the turning of the button is not a secondary cause for light. Suppose we turn a faucet and water runs. Is the turning of the faucet a secondary cause to the existence of water? If so, then cause and effect must always be alike. We turn on another faucet, and incidentally that cause does not produce the same effect, the water does not come. Is the turning of the faucet a secondary cause for the same effect which is absent at this particular instant? If a secondary cause exists and is manipulated, then we must get like effect because cause and effect has never fluctuated, never will; it is fixed, immutable, absolute, never varies. Suppose we turn on a valve going to a radiator. We certainly should get heat because we associate the idea that the valve is a secondary cause and we should establish a secondary effect to correspond, known as heat. But somehow the heat didn't come. B.J.'s secondary cause has ceased to be because it doesn't. Its effect was absent. When cause doesn't establish effect, or whenever effect is established without a cause, something is wrong.

21

―――◆◆―――

ARE DISEASES CONTAGIOUS

OR INFECTIOUS?

B.J. IN THIS CHAPTER will not stress upon any epidemic phase of the so-called contagious or infectious diseases, but confine his remarks to the specific fundamental underlying it, as to whether diseases are transmissible from one person or thing to another. If this is proven a fallacy, then the epidemic is impossible.

Let us proceed with what is supposed to be known and follow that with contradictions, whether or not you continue to cling to these follies depends upon my capabilities in showing wherein they are not tenable and practical, for this age wants facts, not superstition. The world is progressive and to allow its science to stand or cease to advance from one theory or another would be stagnation.

When we look upon the medical profession and the little use that they have for medicines in their families and yet to give them to others for the dollar concerned, it does seem that all parasites are not of microscopic size.

More animation and life expression is what is needed and a general awakening among scientists. They are in continuous stupor over the study of physics. Physicists teach that all power, life and energy is inherent within matter, therefore do not get the intellectual personality that exists behind all things real. They "have faith" in one thing and deny its existence in the corporeal.

Necessity is the mother of all inventions. Napoleon made circumstances; others waited for them. Therapeutics are blank repeaters; Chiropractors, path blazers.

Let the following words sink deeply into your minds. Allow the importance of every word to be understood. Webster says: "Contagious: (Med) Communicable by contact, by a virus or by a bodily exhalation; catching; as a contagious disease." Let B.J. emphasize one idea: "Contagious as disease." It is the "disease" that is caught.

"Contagious—conveying or generating disease." B.J. wishes to also strengthen that same point here. It is the "disease" that is conveyed and generated in the second party from the first. As "disease" is not ease, then every abnormal function has been caught—disease is disease regardless of type.

"Contagious." These words have been used in very diverse senses; but in general, contagious disease ("disease") has been considered as one which is caught from another by contact, by the breath, by bodily effluvia, etc., while an infectious disease supposes some entirely different cause acting by a hidden influence, like the miasma of prison ships, of marshes, etc., affecting the system with disease. This distinction, though not universally admitted by medical men, as to the literal meaning of the words, certainly applies to them in their figurative use. Thus we speak of the contagious influence of evil associates; the contagion of example; the contagion of fear, etc., when we refer to transmission by proximity or contact. On the other hand, we speak of infection by bad principles, etc., "when we consider anything as diffused abroad by some hidden influence."

It does not take long to step into the temples built upon superstitions and myths. We are, upon first investigation, thrust into the hands of "hidden" influence that abounds on all sides and to this unknown quantity our bodies are to be playthings. We are to be wafted through all the pleasures of fevers and finally landing, through the chariot of therapeutics, in heaven. What peaceful, absolute and unbiased confidence we must have in this "hidden" bliss to stand such a journey!

We next refer to "The Illustrated Dictionary of Medicine" by Gould, in which he says: "Contagion: The process by which a specific disease ("disease") is communicated between persons, either by direct contact or by means of an intermediate agent. Contagious diseases are communicable or transmissible by contagion, or by a specific agency, which, once present, may multiply and renew itself indefinitely and which always gives rise to the same disease." Dwell upon one feature. After all has been said and done and written about "Contagious and Infectious Diseases," we are yet in mystery as to what "the process" is. We would like to see a chain of reasoning, started from some practical working basis and carried through to completion, clearly depicting each and every stage by which the "contagious" or "infectious" materials would induce the "specific diseases" that we have been told much about, the cause of which "may multiply and renew itself indefinitely."

"Webster" is a literal standard and "Gould" a medical authority. So far, neither has given a scientific working basis for the providing of that "process," the lack of which leaves every question unanswered.

Dunglison says of "Contagion": "Transmission of a disease from one person to another by direct or indirect contact. Also at one time applied to action of miasmata rising from dead animal or vegetable matter bogs, pens, etc. Contagious diseases are produced either by a virus, capable of causing them by inoculation, as in small-pox, or by miasmata proceeding from a sick individual, as in plague, etc." The theory of "miasmata" had its day "at one time," but it is now going the way of all unreasonable fashions—to the rear. The name "contagion" is applied "to action" that the "miasmata" has. This is the first time that we ever knew a "hidden influence" had "action" until it came in contact with something which resisted it. He probably meant to convey the idea that when it came in "contact" with a man, that man resisted it with forces and the "responsive action," produced by the intelligence of man, he placed to the "inherent" credit of the gas or poison. This is the trick of "Now you have done it and now you have not." Man is to repel something that remains "hidden." Fighting echoes. Without this explanation we would not know just what this "action" was, where it came from, how it was produced and, step by step, we are still begging for a basis.

"Infection: Process by which disease is communicated to an individual by disease germs from the external atmosphere." Germs can be conveyed from one person to another, for this is a "process" of Innate Intelligence, her mediums are the air, food, water and other materials such as induce transmission through these three. The "process" of conveyance of "disease germs" is not what we are given to understand is going on, it is the process by which disease is communicated through "disease germs." Disease is a something which is not at ease and that "not ease" is confined to one body. How that "process" of uneasiness can be transported from one body to another, by germs, is the embarrassment to be faced. Thus the guilt of the transportation of such herculean, mammoth, gigantic diseases are proposed to be laid at the feet of these insignificant microbes.

"The Dictionary of Medicine" by Quain says: "Contagion is applied, in pathology, to the property and process by which, in certain sorts of diseases, the affected body or part causes a disease like its own to arise in other parts; and the Latin word contagium is conveniently used to denote in such cases the specific material shown or presumed, in which the infective power ultimately resides. The property of contagiousness belongs to a very large number of the diseases which affect the human body. The rationale of the word contagion as now used is that the property is understood to attach itself essentially to a material contact; not necessarily that, when infection is spread from individual to individual, the contact of all individuals must have been immediate, but that in all cases there must have been such passage of material from the one to the other as was in itself at least a mediate contact between them." Quain again throws us on the "process," even going so far as to "cause" a like disease in others. It is material whether "shown or presumed." He tells plainly, that if they cannot find the microbe they will and do "presume" that he is there and if they can't find him, then he "must have been." Upon "presumption," the M.D.'s would be free to "presume" anything and it would still be correct. That word "ultimately" leads us to know that he has battled this opposition. In therapeutics it is not necessary to prove your theory. Say "there must have been"; have the laws to defend you, right, wrong or indifferent, and you can and will force the public acceptance of such mythical opinions.

He further states that "the various specific matters which effect contagion in the living body, the respective contagia of the given diseases, seem all to have in common this one characteristic; that in appropriate media, among which must evidently be counted any living bodily texture or fluid which they can infect, they show themselves capable of self multiplication; and it is in virtue of this property that although at the moment of their entering the body they in general do not attract notice, either as objects of sense or of bodily change, they gradually get to be recognizable in both of these respects." B.J. calls Dr. Quain's attention to the tuberculosis bacilli, which are examined for in many cases of well defined, characteristic tuberculosis and are not found. The disease which they are supposed to cause is so marked that there can be no question of its identity, but the cause producer (?) remains so secreted, sometimes unto death, that he cannot be found.

He further continues: "Now the faculty of self multiplication is eminently one of the characters which we call vital; and when it is said that all contagia are self-multiplying things, that is at least very strongly to suggest that perhaps all contagia are things endowed with life.

"In order to give any general consideration of the question thus suggested, a contagion may conveniently, even if but provisionally, be distinguished as of two main classes, differing or at present seeming to differ from each other in the mode of action on the organism which they affect one class, namely, that of parasites; and the other class that of the true or metabolic contagia. On this separation, so far as present knowledge seems to justify it, the assumed grounds are that each true contagium, in proportion as it multiplies in the body, transforms in a way which is a specific in itself."

Dr. Quain is confused to know why these scavengers "self multiply." Is not this the law of self-preservation? Is it not the expression of that universal law of self-adaptation of all things alive? Is not man in the same category? Is it unreasonable that once these fellows have found rare "pickings" they are going to increase in quantity? Is it not equivalent to the law of cause and effect that as refuse increases so does the number of gleaners? Are you to blame garbage removers for the cause of the presence of the offal or for its creation? Suppose germs do "self multiply," is not that all the more evident fact that waste matter, in increasing quantities, is there and that there is a direct cause somewhere for it? Why say "So far as present knowledge seems to justify it," when he could look to anything that breeds and find a duplicate proven example? Must you have "assumed grounds" for such a subject?

If he would tell us what is transformed, from what to what and what does it, then we would be in a shape to agree or disagree more intelligently. But he hints at some "hidden influence" and leaves us groping for it with him.

This book spends some nineteen columns upon the subject of contagion and infection. Having studied it carefully, B.J. found that the basis of contagion is briefly that a certain microbe "infects" a certain body (whatever the "process" is we have not as yet learned) and then, by a "process" of "self-multiplication," they increase in such proportions that they kill the tissues that they contact with, locally or generally, and a specific disease exists according to whether they tear, pull, strain or stretch the tissues. For instance, if they cut it loose in the abdominal region, then that is typhoid; the same process in the nose would be simple fever of the head, etc. If they do any of the above and in addition parboil the vivisected portions and spit them out, then that is tuberculosis, etc. This is but an attempt to present the only definite hypothesis that B.J. can conceive to explain what this "process" is. As they do not say, B.J. must offer his own explanation.

These little fellers are there and because they are there is sufficient circumstantial evidence on which to "assume" that, inasmuch as they have no other known reason for being there, they are a cause producer of that disease with which the one in whom they dwell is affected. This is justifiable "as far as present knowledge seems to justify it."

Everything breeds after its own kind; therefore, the product is just what these men have the legal authority to "assume" they shall be. The assumptions along this line of illogical educated foolishness could be spread indefinitely.

B.J. wishes to give medical men much credit for proving that the microbe is there; that they are built differently to accommodate each kind of scavenger matter; but those are things that we daily observe without microscopes, on any farm, in any city or home. It does not require much education nor a better optical instrument than the eye to know that. Look back sixty or seventy years; there was no questioning then that horses lived a different life than cows, gave a different product; the chemical relations of secretions and excretions differed. Man does not dispute that he lives a life apart from that of the ape; that the cat was not a dog and did not live upon exactly the same things. Birds did not act like animals nor fishes like birds. This was a fact that no one disputed. Did the microbe exist? Surely, then and today. Did he not produce the same disease fifty years ago that he does now? Suppose he did, is this not another phase of their careless unobservance in not finding the cause of disease earlier? If they know it, what about people then that did not have this knowledge? Did they not get along as well, or even better, than now? Does not Dunglison's "at one time" show a changing for something else? Surely the microbe is not a recent production of God, coined to keep the medical men busy chasing phantoms. Was not the flea mentioned in the Bible? Therefore, he must have had smaller than himself to live upon—the flea is a germ. What was done to kill these disease-producing germs when he was unknown? What treatments were given to diseases then that modern medicine has improved upon? Are more lives being saved now than then?

Is not typhoid fever the product of a specific germ? So says our "assumed" thinkers. Yet what does modern specific medicine do with it? Leaves it entirely to the nurse with a little medicine now and then so that the physician has reason for a monthly statement.

Scientific knowledge, based upon physics, gets into unreasonable grounds. Most any phase can be "assumed" when it loses its basic elementary origin. Matter, to the physicist, is as too much clock work that could not help going and doing things. Intelligence, that he cannot see, does not exist, although B.J finds in every division of physics, they revert to something "vital"; it is the study of this they lack. It is their union that Chiropractic has and teaches; it is this consolidation that makes Chiropractic a practical Philosophy.

That you may enjoy the facts that B.J. shall present, we will engage a tally-ho and make an imaginary trip through the city and into the country to observe social relations and economics.

We get started through the country and all goes well until some observing fellow looks off in a field and sees a flock of crows circling in the air. Somebody says: "I wonder what those crows are doing there." Somebody who is a practical sort of a fellow, one raised on a farm says: "There is a dead horse, quite likely, and those crows have been eating the carcass, or going to, or will eat it." We are satisfied, we agree that this is reasonable. We wish to know, so we go to investigate. We find a dead horse that the crows have been eating. We immediately conclude that the crows killed the horse. Do we? We do not. Says the physician with his strabismic squint and a microscope that sets him straight: "I have found the crows that killed the horse."

We go a little farther. Off in the distance we see buzzards doing the same thing the crows were. We go to where they are, see a dead sheep, lying on the ground, half-eaten by the buzzards. Says the physician, "Again we have found the buzzards that killed the sheep."

Farther down the road, one of the ladies says: "Isn't it too bad he is dead?" pointing to a cat lying along the roadside. Some boy, of an inquiring mind (another of those practical fellows), turns the dead body over. Somebody says: "Look at the maggots." Somebody else proclaims that the maggots killed the cat, and "I wonder what kind of a maggot it is." A scientific fellow takes out his microscope, picks up one of the maggots, examines him under the glass, and says: "It is an elongated squirmus." The result is proclaimed scientifically that the "elongated squirmus" kills felines. It goes down in history that we have discovered something not "heretofore known."

Farther along, we come to a stagnant pool. The water is green and slimy, vile and filthy, and quite a stench comes up from it. We examine the water in the pool and find wigglers in it. We look further and find a fungus growth on the side of the pool and we decide that the wigglers caused the fungus, the wigglers caused the stench, and we henceforth pronounce the edict that "wigglers shall be killed to stop stagnation of water." We are put down in history as great men. We have discovered something.

You say, perhaps, B.J.'s illustrations are far-fetched. We think you will admit, though, without a question of doubt, that because there are crows that there is an argument "the crows did not kill the sheep," but they were there because it was dead.

You will further admit it was because there was so much decayed matter in the stagnant pool that these pollywogs, hair worms, etc., could live upon, that they were there and in such quantities.

In all things there is some form of life expression. It is this condition against which man now begins a systematic fight. The advertisements of remedial springs state the mineral ingredients but they dare not advertise the "animal" contents, for if they did, fear would enter as good judgment left and the spring would go begging for drinkers, bathers and soakers. Germs were there in the capacity of scavengers, because the beef was dead. You would not rush to the aid of science by arguing that the maggots killed the cat. They did not show up until its life was extinct. The same argument would hold with a rat.

Let us track our land researchers and visit the lakes. The seagulls are protected by law because of their adaptative faculties in removing all superficial floating scavenger matter. The oceans have their flying scavengers. Regardless of where you observe, you will notice that it is universal. It has been remarked what a wonderful power of vision sea-gulls and crows have. As high as they fly they will observe small objects and know whether they are dead or not and pounce on them very rapidly. It is not uncommon to see hundreds of birds following large fishing tugs waiting to grasp the refuse that is thrown from them. Will you offer the therapeutical line of reasoning that the dead fish attract the birds or that the birds attracted the dead fish, or that somewhere between the two was a bond of mutual "contact," the "process" of which you did not know as it was "caused" by some "hidden influence"? Where does the contagion come in? Or were the birds the "disease" that the entrails had "caused"? Which is which? Ridiculous! We agree, but it is as logical as the therapeutical assumptions that are laid for us.

You could not get the lake perch to follow the Mississippi scavenger boat. It takes the carp and buffalo to consume that kind of refuse matter. The characteristic of all cleaners of the lake could not live in the lakes; each has a place unto itself and depends upon certain quantities and kinds of matter for its livelihood. Are you going to defend the ridiculous statement that because we find crows flying around sheep that that is why the condition of death is contagious? Sheep are dead and scavengers are present. The "process" that brought them together was death. Is death contagious or infectious? It would be a hard matter for these crows to enter the living sheep and pull and tear at his vitals until he died to gain freedom from them. Are the sheep contagious to crows or vice versa? If so, why, have we not found the two together more often, or in the fields where all are alive? It is necessary to get death and the scavenger follows. Dead matter is what will induce the gleaner to appear. They will not hover over live sheep; that does not interest them.

Is the pond contagious to the wigglers or vice versa? Did death induce the animalculae to begin a habitation therein to restore coordination with that universal law of self preservation? Does not death induce life? Is not life dependent upon death matter, and vice versa? Are you to admit that maggots were contagious to the cat or the cat became an infectious magnet and drew these maggots? If it is a center of attraction now why was it not so during partial life, you answer that it was, yet to a form of scavengers known as fleas. Death took place in the cat and then maggots are ready for work.

Under hair of cattle, dogs, cats and in the wool of sheep will be found burrowing insects of many breeds and families. In the meat of hogs are the well-known trichinae. On dogs and cats are fleas. Many of these are so small that the microscope is necessary to find them. The chicken has a louse and even down to man we find that he has the pest known as the bed bug, which tortures some people and never condescends to look upon others. Particularly do such insectivora bother those who are dirty or have decomposed matter upon the surfaces of the skin due to disease. Why? Because they have little animalculae that are burrowing under the dead skin scales hunting for further food. In any form of skin disease, microbes are found. In dandruff it is not uncommon to have a characteristic scalp gleaner. He is also "assumed" to be the cause of that disease. Which came first and which followed as a consequence?

Although the following article is satirical and ironical, yet between the lines are many facts which substantiate the position that this chapter of B.J.'s has tried to bring forth.

22

————◆————

DISEASE? WHAT IT IS AND

ITS CAUSE

IN THE SYNOPSIS, dealt with in this chapter, B.J. compares man and his subdivisions, to those of a perfect manufacturing establishment.

A "system" in the sense as used, means not only the physical properties, but all the immaterial processes as well. Thus, the urinary system, nervous system, osseous system, digestive or circulatory system, is to include all the tissues as well as currents, both in creation, transmission and expression. A "corpse" is the remains of a man. Dust is not a man, For when man dies retrogression back to that stage begins.

Man is a system of systems. Each is the aggregation of units, and every link, an organization of cells. Man is the factory's superior in more than one respect; principally, he has an intelligence which lives within the structure. He is (1) able to move his factory from place to place, and adapts to surrounding conditions and (2) has the capacity to maintain his factory in its entirety. Manufactured objects cannot do these things.

We could make comparison by saying that the product of fuel and water placed in the factory's boilers, steam power, would be wasted were it not for man, who, through further mechanical aid, directs it to do specialized work. In the human body we put in food and water and, from that moment, we (Innate Intelligence) forget it. Beyond the meager point of introduction, man has nothing further to do with it. In every comparison between man and factory, you will find a parallel.

The organs and tissues of the human body have a similarity to machines, and their component sections are arranged and placed according to their efficiency. Is not the same systematic plan followed in any well regulated factory?

Upon entering a manufacturing establishment B.J. was directed to witness process No. 1—the making of castings in the foundry and from there this cast goes to the filing machine; next to be bored; then shaped, drilled and planed in the rough. It still needs further polishing and proceeds through three various necessary stages or refining finishings (as regards the surface). Next it is transported to the turning lathe, where the bearings are accurately turned; to the nickel-plating and burnishing machines. From that time it is wrapped in protective tissue paper, boxed and ready for shipment or local storage sale. Step by step we have observed the entrance of smelted ore to a commodity ready for use.

Each machine is so located that its finished article is passed to the next, which is placed nearest it. Each consecutive machine is so placed that it is where it is needed next. The filing and nickel-plating machines would not be found together. The products pass from one machine to another, so that each article, as it progresses from the rough to the finished, goes grade by grade.

The piecework, mechanical process, is developed in the Rock Island Arsenal small arms factory. At one end of a room enters the rough, cast barrel, which leaves at the farther end, finished. The rough timber is admitted at another gallery and leaves as finished stocks for the polished rifle barrels. In the third locality all parts are assembled. One man affixes the rifle sight; carries it to the next; he does his little movement; thus the substances are passed. It was a pleasure indeed for B.J. to make a tour of this immense building. On one floor we see the rough materials introduced and, by walking from one end to the other, through three floors, see it leave, at last, boxed, ready for shipment to wherever there are any of Uncle Sam's warriors.

Throughout this process is reflected the pattern of purpose which we understand about the human body, whose reflexes (nervous system) are selective, discriminating and deciding, although conditioned by the character and type of stimuli. Should the first man spoil a piece of timber it is thrown out or passed on to be utilized as best it can by the next process. It cannot be, subsequently, made perfect because someone blundered over it when passing it through his instruments. Each process is complete, so far as it goes; the sum total being equivalent to the completed object. Factory work is unital piecework; in the human factory "sympathetic"—"by means unknown"—is the explanation offered. Man does not call nor ask for "sympathetic" assistance. This is but one inconsistency of the human intellect in trying to decipher the actions of Innate—looking at them through chemical glasses instead of assisting them through mechanical movements.

The human body is based upon both of these principles: The chemical is the product of the mechanical, and vice versa. Every movement is mechanical as directed, either voluntarily (culture), or involuntary (innate). There is still another type of movement employing both classifications of the nervous system, namely artistic expression which we have learned to define as a product of mental effort, reflecting creative ability, and possibly heredity. It is the mechanical ability of man with which we as Chiropractors are concerned primarily, because it is possible through effecting proper spinal balance to determine required blood chemistry. Reason dictates that man's intelligence can never reach the stage where he can even mathematically blend substances in the proportions necessary to determine, leaving alone the restoration of spinal balance.

The mechanical and its study, human or otherwise, is complete because it takes mechanical principles exemplified to make its product—chemical. In consideration of the chemical we must revert to the mechanical which made that combination. Mechanical can be studied alone without the knowledge of what it may make. Chemical is the product of movements. All "movements" are mechanical. The chemical must be investigated, in connection with mechanical, to know what and how it was created.

It is a necessity to properly place and locate each organ, tissue and cell, according to its work; to best save time and material. If doctors would investigate in a mechanical manner, and lay bare the what, where, how and why of Innate in running this model factory, he could and would learn valuable pointers for their business, regardless of what approach they use. Let us briefly review the physical symptoms B.J. has set forth and see how befittingly they will compare with that of the factory.

1. The Osteological plan is the framework; the legs, supports; feet, the foundation, the thoracic walls are lateral restrictors to the future unity.

2. The Articulating classification is, as it were, the glue or nails which fasten the joints of No. 1, only in the human factory such allow movability of all parts, whereas in the factory built by men it is and must be stationary.

3. The respiratory method is the intake, which prepares, sifts, filters and heats the air. In this stage it passes to the pulmonary circulation, from whence the oxygen is transmitted to all tissues to assist in combustion—heat.

4. The arterial and venous circulatory scheme. The former is the conveyor of oxygen to and the latter of carbon dioxide from all tissues. They carry the combustible materials to and from the blasting machines (cells) of the heating system which keep the factory warm. This system

conveys oxygen from lungs to each individual cell. The calorific mental impulse (spark) then sets the deposited gas (8/9ths of which is liquid) into action—the combustion is heat. After the explosion the gases are resorbed by the venous system, transported to lungs and expelled.

5. The Serous Circulatory order, including all glands in the body, is the circulating serous system, which subjugates friction, maintains liquid and conveys nutrition to all parts. It is the lubricator of the system, and from being a liquid, keeps together, in a solid mass, all that which would be as so much dust.

6. The Urinary arrangement is the drainage to all that which is liquid.

7. The alimentary regularity of organs is the various machines which receive the rough materials and put them thru the manifold processes, thus preparing them for the finished function. It has a refuse system of solid substances. The liquid and solid sewage orders must work hand in hand. The raw material enters at one end of this long tube, makes many successive progressive steps, each having its particular action to perform until it sums to, 1st, that which is utilizable as nutritive materials, and 2nd, that which is waste material, and shavings and scraps, as it were.

8. The muscular system is that series of belts, cogs, etc., which conveys mechanical motions to the various organs; bodily machines and skeleton, allowing an external framework locomotion which factory-made objects, like automatons, sometimes have, but minus intelligence. Muscular movements allow this organic factory to be transferred from place to place, expressing and allowing vent to the intelligence which lies behind.

9. A generative classification. This is composed of those machines which, while they are an integral part of the factory, are not directly connected with its maintenance. It duplicates those parts of like machines that make up other factories; it is a process of where factory makes factory. This process might be elaborated to where every machine molds a certain kind of piecework. Each organized machine has one initial, mechanical function to perform. When a certain standard of quality has been reached and finished it is inwardly transported to the next machine. The two halves of this future machine, spermatozoon of the male and ovum of the female, of the two sexes our future individual factory.

10. The sense system is that telephonic communication between every machine and its unit cells, in the factory, which connects it with each regional manager in the office. Every controller of that output, at his desk (brain lobe) in the general office (brain) is in contact with all kinds of work (function) in the factory (body) over which he has command, and by millions of wires (nerves) coming to (centering at) his desk he can at all times (night and day, from birth to death) know just what kind of work, as to quantity, speed and quality, it is turning out. Each sense nerve fibrilla is as an eye that sees only the action of that cell and

immediately informs the Innate all about it. Senses are those interpretations at the mind which convey knowledge from the machine to headquarters; keeping the intelligence in constant contact.

11. Brain lobes are those sections through which Innate sends forth impulses, which gives to each nerve fibre its mental stimulus. The brain receives power from Innate and doles out the necessaries to nerves.

12. The brain is the general manager, so to speak, of all organs, superior to each machine, and exceeding all; the creator of the offices and the supplier of mechanically trained officers to fill them (no political games or grafting are indulged in here) or, properly speaking, he is the director of the establishment. Behind him is the proprietor—Innate—who owns every stick in its makeup and the earth upon which it was grown and stands.

The human body contains viscera, the latter arranged to its use. Every machine of a factory is similarly placed. For example, take a Miehle press or Linotype. Each part is slightly different, or has a great deal of resemblance, but every one has its niche where it must fit. It acts as one cog and must be in the best possible condition to deliver perfect work.

Each organ in the body is composed of various cells. Each tissue has individual characteristics, a special type of work to perform; and every cell must be in proper place and capable of putting into execution its model of action to have complete harmony throughout every detail. This chain can be reversed from cell to tissue, tissue to organ, organ to system of Viscera, and the complete systems of the latter to make one body. This body, the complete unit, has the ability to start materials, in the rough, execute them step by step, and produce the finished product, the highest type of personification.

Suppose the finishing machines were "operated upon"—removed. The expert foreman would not take the rough product from the saw to the varnishing room to be turned out as finished as in the past, when each machine was present. Neither must the physician try and compel the human factory to run in perfect, if not better harmony, with 1,2,3, or 4 organs minus; and if inharmony still exists, rip out some more. What folly when applied to the factory. Are not its mechanical principles as applicable to the human body? Is not such madness of every day occurrence with men ignorant of the first mechanical physical truth? The foreman would not dare to foist such nonsense, absurdities, or imbecility upon the proprietor of the factory. Why compel, by Medical Practice Acts, people to put up with such in their homes; with the beloved wife, daughter or son? Would it not be sense, wisdom, sanity and good judgment to apply the same mechanical principles to one machine as are applicable to another? Is it necessary to compel people to reason with good sense? No. It is only the inconsistencies that must be foisted and heaped upon the unwary by compulsory means. Demonstrate that which is practical, and health laws (there are none yet) external to the human body will be unknown.

Take for example, a sliding contact with oiled surfaces which are binding each other so closely that it is impossible to place oil between them. Through some accident the superior surface has become slightly displaced and thus approximates upon each other so close that there is friction where formerly was freedom. Attrition produces too much heat. In short, the machine will wabble from inability to run smoothly; sooner or later this excessive heat will "cut the metal," that is, wear it off in grooves or edges. Let us philosophize, M.D. fashion. "Continue to try and hypodermically and forcibly inject various oils, lubricants, etc., etc. For the excessive heat we will apply something which will draw from it the surplus heat, pour on cold water, aim to reduce the heat that exists." After an extended period of experienced guessing "as a last resort" they will, after an extended consultation, offer to and do (once, twice or thrice, or as long as the affection still exists) remove portions of the superficial runners, or remove all of those parts that rub, then they cannot rub. The practical mechanic would have done away with these imprudences and have adjusted that superior or inferior portion, according to which was subluxated, to its right position. The report, from the machine to Innate, would then be, "Tell the engineer to go ahead; put on steam; all is O.K." Which is practical? Which determines results before the details of the abnormalities are known?

B.J. says, man is a machine builded around such principles. Why not reason with him as intelligently as with any other piece of ingenuity?

Suppose we have ten machines and one, by an operation, was removed. It was necessity when everything was all right, but through some accident that machine's function was made idle. The howl is over the damaged machine. Man would use good judgment and adjust that which made it idle, although it may be in the center shaft, ten feet away, as soon as this was done, harmony would again prevail.

In the human body we must expect as much or more, for each has its machines which no factory can reproduce. Reason that if an external injury so smashes an organ, limb, etc., etc., that it cannot be replaced or expected to heal (which occasionally occurs), then it must be removed by surgery; but the majority of operations today are those where derangements are caused by some slight internal mechanical disability. Its location and what it is; its correction and how, is unknown to "regular" practitioners; therefore, for the want of better knowledge, it is removed; an irreparable damage. That part, of specific character, cannot be replaced. Life is taken and cannot be restored. Remove the indicted whether he was guilty or no. Kill the innocent for fear that they might commit murder. Remove the appendix, ovaries and womb for fear they may have future use and trouble the individual.

A large percentage of deaths, by operations, today, are human butchery. The person who performs these acts is more guilty of murder than he who commits a deed for justifiable cause.

When accident occurs and tissues are injured, symptoms direct the diagnosis and the doctor determines the prognosis. Is it logical to accept as final a diagnosis and prognosis that "nothing can be done" without consulting other proven systems which are notoriously being suppressed, as is the case of Chiropractic?

Why not use as good sense here as in the factory? They, on the reverse, take it out, and leave the body minus. You cannot do this in a factory; why attempt it in man? Suppose a pulley becomes bent; the line shaft, twisted; one or more of its boxings are slightly awry and produce friction; power is slackened and you have a hot-box. What is to be done? A mechanic (and by this I mean physicians are not) would adjust what was wrong. The physician treats the diseased chemical product with chemical compounds and applications of endless quantities and various qualities; the surgeon removes the chemically affected area, expecting better harmony to exist. Such folly is incomprehensible to a factory proprietor. Is not the body the best machine yet invented, conceived or patented?

It is founded upon all the mechanical principles that are known and many that are unknown. Many mechanical movements, executed in the human body if man could but decipher and use them, would make him many times the world's wisest sage.

Must it not be accepted as reasonable, if an arm is broken, that Innate, having unbroken connection between source of power and internal physical divisions, will run the machine properly? Is it unreasonable to propose the mechanical proposition that a broken energy connection would but express itself in the mechanical idleness of an organ? Should we not speak to a machine in mechanical quantitative terms to convey such ideas? Is it insane or unintelligent to believe that a machine ought to be put to rights in preference to giving to that divisional atom-organ in the human or factory a dose or treatment to the effects, and if good results are not manifest cut it out?

Suppose every machine has its mechanical function and every part of it is in exactly its normal place and its connection with Innate is perfect; consequently the transmission of Innate mental power is unceasing. We must conclude that positive action must follow plus normal quantity of power. It has direct connection with every head office. Every machine now is perfect; there can be nothing wrong, for each works as it ought to, in accordance with the lines, as it was built to do. A healthy factory is the result.

In the human body, with the Intelligence-Innate as general manager, his brain system of nerves, the viscera as the machines and skeletons as the framework, sense system for intercommunication; must we not deduct that if every structural bone is in its proper place, all power unrestricted, that machine cannot be otherwise than exactly normal?

Vertebral subluxations are common occurrences, hindering the quantity and quality of mental power. The muscles become inactive; they cease to act; the stomach is unable to digest food; there is partial or entire lack of motion at a specific locality. If that be the case, what is the result—incoordination; inharmony between mental and physical. If the functional machine cannot work, the Chiropractor's mechanically trained mind should observe and palpate for abnormal mechanical principles; find them!

The concentration should be on mechanical cause, not chemical effects. It ran all right yesterday, why not now? If your present knowledge be so meager as to not fit the case; your every hour and day to study should be conducted along and in accordance with the mechanical principles incorporated in this enterprise; if none of the known ones fit, study Innate and how she performs, so that you can work in and with her.

Instead of looking within the machine for its troubles, the M.D. looks outside, to see how much, what kind, how does it look under the microscope, what are its chemical properties and affinities, and to what family or specie does the microbe belong. The Chiropractor finds the cause of every disease to be one or more mechanical principles that are obviously wrong, therefore he investigates the machine itself, studies its every possible place where there is interference, where a hard substance is interposing with the soft, finding what is wrong with the mechanical that is interfering with the chemical. Anything external to that is but the effect acting upon what was previously wrong.

That is why a person trained and drilled to believe that excesses or lack of certain chemicals are the cause of disease, cannot grasp Chiropractic. He reiterates past teachings. The mechanic, on the other hand, progresses fast because Chiropractic is in accordance with his practical, result giving experience. To study Chiropractic Philosophy means to lay aside past conceptions. They serve to a point, but cannot work hand in hand, entirely with this scientific study.

B.J. states that each body is a movable factory unto itself. If you supply what is needed, fuel and water, good mechanics—nerve powers that are and always have been, will keep it to the highest pinnacle; it then can make its existence a reality.

The human mechanism performs best when in good adjustment. Like a watch, in order to keep time, each wheel, cog, bearing must be free of friction. The human machine requires little adjusting to perform, but that "little" factor is not found in the use of pills and hypodermics.

It is strange that men, who are very shrewd in other matters, should be so shortsighted, so ignorant, so utterly foolish in regard to the importance of keeping their marvelous, intricate and delicate physical machinery every day in perfect adjustment; for inharmony means inefficiency, lack of power. Many a businessman drags himself wearily through a discordant day and find himself completely exhausted at night, who would have accomplished a great deal more, with infinitely less effort, and have gone home in a much fresher condition if he had taken time to have his vertebrae tuned before going to his office.

The man who goes to his work in the morning feeling out of sorts with everybody is in an antagonistic attitude of mind toward life, especially toward those with whom he has to deal, is in no condition to bring the maximum of his power to his task. A large percentage of his mental forces will not be available.

When will he learn that it is not the number of hours we work, but ability that counts? Many of us would accomplish much more in two or three hours of vigorous, effective work, when the mind is fresh and resourceful, than we could accomplish in an entire day with the system run down. It is the worst possible kind of economy to try to force good work out of a discordant instrument—machine out of order.

Forcing the physical to work when it is out of plumb is a very shortsighted policy. It takes too much out of the human instrument. Multitudes commit suicide on many years of their lives by not keeping themselves properly adjusted.

B.J.'s description of the word "disease" is "not-ease"; lack of being comfortable, uneasy, restless; that condition of being physically not right. This in a factory may be one of a thousand characters. Perhaps there are uneasy mental faculties or uncomfortableness in the stomach, spleen, bladder, lungs, or bowels, etc. The uneasiness might be in the foot or hands. The combination of the where, what and how of disease and its symptoms is always indefinite. This is readily observed by the variance of opinions of many reputable physicians in disagreeing as to what to name them. If they debate in diagnosing the chemical disease, which is the outward condition; the symptoms, effects, that which the patient feels or sees; what must be their position as regards to its internal cause?

Quite frequently M.D.'s are very uncertain as to whether it is this or that; cannot definitely locate it; they are at sea until the chemical constituents of the disease have developed more prominently; he must know what that is before he can begin treatment. The Chiropractor usually has the ability of locating the cause, regardless of the combinations of symptoms, in the acute or chronic stages. The endless combinations of chemicals can be twisted, hatched and developed between the nine or more primary functions without end and can, on the whole, be interpreted according to the whims and fancies of the person studying them. It is a problem that thousands of lives have been lost for, "What was the disease?" and yet they seemingly are no wiser as to cause, today than then.

They know, as experts, what chemical disease is and how to chemically name and treat it, but their ability in trying to supply from the outside to the inside, that which cannot be manufactured by chemical means, proves that they have not reached rock bottom—the mechanical cause. Does their scientific chemical ability to guess at proportions, prove that this knowledge has reached deductive facts sufficient to remain stable? If so, where is it? Observe the past 300 years.

Chiropractors are not educated to study disease, its symptoms, and then name them. If their education has been chemically based on their precedents, there is slight question but that they would have followed the same ruts. B.J. as a teacher, fifty odd years ago, knew but little of what disease was. His study was devoted to propagate mechanical causes of this and the other combinations of abnormal mechanical proportions, which the M.D.'s had, chemically, down pat. Instead of progressing into the fundamental of this universe, mechanics—they have been working upon the products—chemicals—the knowledge of disease and its chemical proportions. Chiropractors are leaving behind them all chemical studies, all that pertains to working with effects; but they are progressing upon the philosophical study of the human body as a mechanical and electrical machine, in connection with his Innate. He is simplifying those conditions under direct heads and locating, specifically, and mechanically, correcting the cause of each.

When B.J. found a certain amalgamation of symptoms existing he didn't call or name them. His idea was "what is wrong mechanically." By keeping that and Innate before him B.J. solved the problem of this most complex machine. Chiropractic, mechanically speaking, is therefore "the science of (mechanical) cause of disease and art of adjusting (mechanically), by hand, all subluxations, for the purpose of freeing impinged nerves as they emanate through the intervertebral foramina, restoring normal currents, hence correcting abnormal (mechanical principles)—named functions, in excess or not enough—disease. (Science of Chiropractic, Vol. 1), written by B. J. Palmer, 1906. Chiropractic is not a knowledge of what disease is, but what causes it. This leads us back to this chapter's text—"Disease, What it is and its Cause," which is answered, "What disease is we care little, what its cause is and the art of correcting that, is B.J.'s lifework study."

Medicine has sacrificed millions of lives and countless dollars and effort needlessly, we feel, in their persistence of search for remedies which, at best, merely mask or suppress disease manifestations. Chiropractic, on the other hand, retains its original concept, and is nearer the solution of causes of physical and mental disorders, than Medicine ever can be. The major economic problem faced by Chiropractic today is how to better acquaint those in need of its application with its desirable effectiveness.

Urine can be analyzed, its quantities and qualities of each that are running from the machine can be deciphered. How does that chemical knowledge, which required months to learn, adjust the wrongly acting mechanical principle? Again, "biliousness" might be considered; it may also be given a chemical scrutiny, but when finished what have we? Nothing that is essential or of value to what caused or can adjust that condition.

In the study of causes then, it is necessary to reach cement foundation of this medicine. In factory, as well as body, we must study the methods of transporting power from the place made to where expressed. Expressed power must be considered. We need to investigate (every step upon a mechanical basis) the mechanical product of that machine, its normal mechanical action. When this we have, abnormal becomes readily apparent, just how or in what proportion the effects are, becomes an item of side issue. As to just how far, we as Chiropractors, wish to labor upon what kind of a chemical diseased condition is in the machine depends upon how much time we desire to waste or toady to the present day, superstitious, sympathetic, reflex action, that has been forced into our brains, whether we will or no. To cater to the present day whims is but to deceive yourself and patient as to that which is the truth. The Chiropractor, caught doing such practices, is as guilty as he who does believe it. It is easier to reiterate than to study new thoughts.

A Chiropractor, to B.J.'s way of thinking, who has a knowledge of Innate; the power that she makes; through what and how such is carried; the kind of machinery that expresses it; what kind of cells are necessary to make a certain pattern of action; how that machine carries on its work and what its products are and the mechanical principles involved from conception to action and birth to death, is intelligent. It is a study that appeals to every person who wishes facts that are incontestable. The instability of medical chemical principles are daily shown in every patient they have. They get better, worse, live or die, but never get well. How can they with a mechanical cause still existing; its entity being unknown to the attending chemical doctors; therefore the machine, slightly better or worse, continues to exist unadjusted.

Briefly, disease is the disturbance of mechanical power from Innate to organs. Death is cessation between the source of power and its expression. Health is the normal mechanical expression, throughout all machines of the human system, of impressions and their equal interpretation, the conception and expression, coordination between Innate (the power maker) and Physical (the mechanical expressor).

23

---◆---

IS THE GASOLINE ENGINE

A COUNTERFEIT?

WHAT IS a gasoline engine? One thing necessary is gasoline. Second, a storage battery. Third, somewhere between the gasoline and the engine, a carburetor. Gasoline is a liquid. So long as the liquid remains, nothing can burn it. Drop a lighted match in a barrel of gasoline and it won't explode so long as it remains a fluid, but so fast as that gasoline becomes a gas, so fast does it burn. It becomes necessary to transform the gasoline into gas. To do that we let the gasoline run from the gasoline tank to the carbureter through a pipe. There an intake pipe takes in oxygen, and by mixing oxygen with gasoline makes a gasoline gas. The gasoline gas goes by a pipe to the head of the engine in a gaseous form. On our right are storage batteries. It is immaterial whether you make it by the movements of an engine itself or by storage batteries, the fact is, you have electricity. We have two wires, one carrying electricity from the storage battery and the other carrying back the negative current, and they go to plugs at the head of your engine and there make a jump spark. The spark coming down the positive wire jumps over to the negative wire.

The process working simultaneously is this. Your gas is deposited. Along comes a spark of electricity and ignites the gas. The gas being enclosed within a receptacle, explosion takes place. Just below that engine is a cylinder head which is driven backward. Thus it is a process followed by series of explosions that produces motion which moves that axle and which consequently moves the wheels and your wheels run on the surface, or if you have not wheels like the automobile, you perhaps have a belt wheel and that belt moves machinery through your factory.

There is the simplicity of the principle. You notice primarily, then, several things in gasoline engines. One is a circulation of gasoline, the circulation of air, the circulation of electrical currents. Gasoline is converted into gas. Oxygen is converted to carbon dioxide and positive electricity is exchanged to negative current and your engine moves. We have in addition another circulation with this engine—water. The water keeps the engine cool, for by this process of moving regardless of how well oiled, friction takes place, and friction means heat, consequently it is necessary to have water circulating around this engine to keep it cool. There are four circulations. Gasoline, air, electricity and water. It is possible to have an air-cooled engine, but even then you cool your engine by the moisture of the water contained in air, so the principle remains the same.

What are the five circulations of man? Blood, serous, lymphatic, air, mental impulses. Man is a living, moving gasoline engine. Nothing else. A gasoline engine is nothing but a duplicature of things existing already in man. Man doesn't copy his existence from the automobile, the automobile is copied from man. Every mechanical movement was copied from man. There are only three hundred and ten movements in science, and they are all duplicatures of man. There isn't a patent at Washington, D.C., but what has its greater counterpart in man.

We will carry out the idea of man's gasoline engine and take a tissue cell as the fundamental. Serous fluid is gasoline. Blood circulation carries oxygen and carbon dioxide. Nervous system carries electricity through a positive and back through negative wires.

That tissue cell can't explode, cause movement, nor get a personification of heat without it gets certain equivalents. One of these is gasoline, and the gasoline goes down in the onward passage as serum, passes through that tissue cell, and passes out as urea. This circulation starts at your intestine and ends at the kidneys. Gasoline enters as serum and passes out as urea, showing that there has been a transformation, but before that serum gets into that tissue cell it must go through a carburetor. In the gasoline engine man makes the carburetor separate and apart from the tissue cell. Here we make it at the place we use it—the tissue cell. We will take the blood circulation, carry it through the tissue cell also. It is arterial blood on the outside of a tissue cell and venous blood on the other side, showing that there is a transformation from arterial blood to venous blood taking place within the walls of the tissue cell.

The process that took place is the exudation of serum first; the transformation of that serum or gasoline into gasoline gas; an explosion takes place; that gasoline goes as a liquid refuse called urea. That goes through the onward portion of the serous circulation. The arterial blood changes because the difference is, one has oxygen and the other has carbon dioxide.

There are still other things necessary. This process is simultaneous and is the only machine that can perform simultaneous actions. That is, at the same time the serum is being converted to gasoline gas, a spark or mental impulse reaches the tissue cell and causes an explosion. As a consequence we get several attributes known as motion, heat, etc.

As a result, we find there are three refuses, three excretions. One is urea. The other is carbon dioxide, and the other is the negative current. The beginning points of these circulations are: Your mental currents at the brain, ending at tissue cell. Serous circulation, intestines to cell; cell to kidneys. Blood circulation, lungs to heart; heart to cell; cell to heart and heart to lungs. So that the beginning and ending points of venous or arterial circulation arises at the lungs in contradistinction to the idea that the heart is the beginning. The heart is the pump and is between the tissue cell and lungs.

You ask, what about the circulation of air? The blood transports the air circulation just the same as a river transports boats; just as fish swim in the river. The boat swims on the river's surface; sometimes sinks into it; sometimes floats underneath. The same is true of the serous circulation, of the mental circulation wherein electricity is not a part of the nerve, but it goes through or over the surface, whichever argument you wish to advance.

You ask, granting this is a practical fact, what part does the lymphatic circulation play? The lymphatics have to do with the making of materials out of refuses which go to or help to make the chemicals which are to be a fluid as a by-product. For instance, bile. Bile is made by an action of the liver upon chemicals received by it. The serum which goes to the liver helps to nurture the liver itself and has nothing to do with the making of bile. The blood going to the liver has nothing to do with the nurturing of that liver, but carries to it the oxygen and takes away from it carbon dioxide, which is to help keep the liver warm and in motion. The mental current has nothing to do with the nurturing of the liver nor any cell in its structure. It carries currents which cause the action to take place. But the liver retains an internal function that it performs, which is the making of bile. The tissue cell structure of that liver is nurtured and receives sustenance and is held up to normal shape and form, by serous circulation. At the same time you have oxygen carried to and carbon taken away from it. Then you have mental currents going to it; but notwithstanding all those functions, which might be called external, it has a function distinctly internal—bile. Bile is carried from the inside of the gland to the intestines, and helps to perform the function of digestion. That bile in any other portion of the body would be a poison. Take that bile, put it in the mouth, the stomach, the arm, and it is poisonous. That is why jaundice is poison physically, because it is carried from one place where it was not a poison to another place where it is, in the same body. Bile is a poison made of poisons from other portions of the body. Man is a very intricate intercommunicating system. Don't understand B.J. to say that serum, after it has been utilized and known as a liver urea, goes directly to the kidneys and is thrown out. That goes to a lymphatic gland. The lymphatic gland takes something out of it, makes use of it; it then goes to another gland, which makes use of some of that material. So it is a process of another lymphatic gland working upon what was an excrescence to a gland higher up in the same system.

The lymphatics then are purely an intermediate system wherein the refuses from over the body are gathered and utilized to an end of taking from them some consistency which is of value in helping to sustain the glandular system in its work of internal function of secreting a fluid. Bile, splenic fluid, thyroid juice, are products of excrescences of other portions of the body. Man is the most economical machine made. What is excrescence in one place is utilized in another until finally, when it reaches the kidneys, there is no more use for it. Then, and not until then, does it become an excrescence, because various portions of the body have mauled over it until nothing more can be extracted. There is no nurturing value in urine. It would pay no one to drink his urine, from a nurturing standpoint. That is why, when M.D.'s want to get a person's kidneys to acting, they tell him to drink his own urine. It goes through rapidly. Innate realizes we have had this once before. That is the principle they work on, and in taking that it is supposed to take some of other with it. Thus you see its non-value.

To recapitulate: We have five circulations in man.

1. All blood circulation does is to carry oxygen from the lungs to the heart and from the heart pump it out through the arterial systems through all the portions of the body; to carry oxygen to oxygenate the tissue cells. The venous circulation has to do with the reception or receiving of carbon dioxide; carry it to the heart; from there to the lungs, and there expel it. The heart is but a pumping station divided into four parts; two parts pumping blood to the two parts of the lung and the two parts of the heart pull it back from the lungs.

2. The serous circulation begins at the small intestines. There it absorbs serum and ends at the kidneys, meanwhile going into and becoming a part of every structure of your body.

3. The lymphatic circulation is an intermediate, a discrimination takes place between what your serous circulation accepts and what the lymphatic circulation delivers. The lymphatic circulation accepts only that substance from glands which becomes a refuse to the serous circulation. The serous circulation accepts those substances from intestines that are nutritive. The lymphatic only such materials as would carry and produce

pigmented material or would carry and make glandular juices to wherever this circulation went.

4. Your mental impulse circulation is distinctly separate and apart from any other and has to do with the immaterial half which moves through the material half. That is, could we divide these five circulations into two halves we would say the blood, serous, lymphatic and air circulations was the material half and the mental impulses was the immaterial. In point of importance, one has the same bearing as the other four, because the four would do nothing without the one. In point of relationship, the two must be together to make one total. Some people see the doughnut and others see the hole.

In this relationship the serous circulation and mental impulse circulations are new. Harvey was noted for discovery of blood. B. J. Palmer is going to be noted for his discovery of serous and circulation of blood and lymphatic systems.

B.J. has now placed a new interpretation upon lymphatic circulation, because there is no one physiological function that so little is known about in physiology as that.

You can study page after page on lymphatic circulations and you will get no understanding of what B.J. has said or meant; he usually does not mean much because he didn't understand much himself. So in this relationship you are getting the essentials of the circulations of man.

If you would study these from relative viewpoints, you would comprehend better what they are and get essentials of value.

24

———— ❖ ————

A QUOTATION FROM
THE FLAMING SWORD

"THE PUBLIC has been stuffed for years, like Strassburg Pâté de foie gras, with harrowing tales of the danger from microbes, micro-organisms, bacilli, germs, streptococci, dislococci, micrococci, and so on for columns of learning—that it comes with a shock that a certain European found that life is possible under sterile condition. A sterile condition is one in which there are no cocci present. But the gentleman observes that while possible it is not normal. The whole of this modern excuse for medically ruling the people can be done away with by follow-ing Isaiah, when he commands the people to wash and be clean, to put away the evil of their doings. A simple plan that all can follow, much simpler, and, indeed, more effective than the free use of bichloride of mercury, formaldehyde, gas, burning sulphur and the other scientific substitutes for simple cleanliness which in the final analysis is the basis of health." (Homeopathis Envoy.)

In the language of the medical doctors, a germ, microbe, bacillus or bacterium is any micro-organism or disease germ which is claimed to be the cause of disease. Koreshan Science teaches positively that micro-scopic vegetable organisms, with their red-like jointed bodies or fil-aments, which are generally in constant movement, are not the cause of the disease but that they are scavengers or buzzards, which merely con-sume what is in a diseased and dead condition. Buzzards never attack what is alive. Thus the much-feared microscopical minute germs or bacilli are a blessing instead of something that must be feared.

Under the heading "The Germ Theory," the late Geo. Dutton, A.B., M.D., says: "The theory that germs or microbes are the cause of disease has set (almost) the whole medical world to studying the natural history of microscopic life. The advocates of this theory are evidently striving to turn all attention of the people from error, which is the real cause of all disease and which everybody ought to perceive, even with eyes, and to microscopic creatures that no one can see without the microscope, nor study without costly laboratories.

"The Germ Theory is a device that serves to keep the people in ignorance of what really does cause disease; is a scapegoat to carry their sins (errors) out of sight; is an excuse for taking deadly drugs and makes the task of avoiding disease, which is really easier than enduring the disease, apparently hopeless. The theory as an explanation of the cause of the disease is false and is productive of vast evil.

"Germs of disease (disease producing germs) of every description are a nuisance in every way and ought to be banished from good society. They are never the primal cause of disease. They may aggravate conditions already existing, but have no power to set up disease anew.

"Germs or bacteria are scavengers, some to remove and destroy waste matter that Nature and well-taught people cannot tolerate. Diseases producing (pathogenetic) germs are a disgrace to the medical profession; showing plainly that they have abandoned their sacred office of teaching, and left the sheep (the patient) to be devoured by the wolves. Healthful living is the remedy, and to that we must turn our attention."

All Allopathic Schools of Medicine administer strong and poisonous drugs, with the aim of killing germs or bacilli, but the poisonous drug, merely stops the fermenting of the waste substance. What is the result? The waste substance is no longer liquefied, and, as a consequence, it remains in the system to break out afresh at other times, for as long as there is waste substance in the body there will be germs, the scavengers.

The waste substance is the primary soil where the germs can be active, and the poisonous drug administered is the secondary soil. The two poisons, the waste substance and the drugs, are the immediate conditions of disease; the remote cause has a deeper origin, of which most all medical men are ignorant.